W9-BUM-724

Carcase Evaluation in Livestock Breeding, Production and Marketing

Carcase Evaluation in Livestock Breeding, Production and Marketing

Tony Kempster
Alastair Cuthbertson
Geoff Harrington

VON CANON LIBRARY
SOUTHERN SEMINARY
BUENA VISTA, VIRGINIA 24416

56169

WESTVIEW PRESS • BOULDER, COLORADO

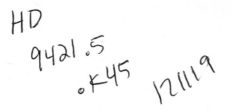

Granada Publishing Limited — Technical Books Division
Frogmore, St Albans, Herts AL2 2NF
and
36 Golden Square, London W1R 4AH
866 United Nations Plaza, New York, NY 10017, USA
117 York Street, Sydney, NSW 2000, Australia
100 Skyway Avenue, Rexdale, Ontario, Canada M9W 3A6
61 Beach Road, Auckland, New Zealand

Copyright © 1982 A.J. Kempster, A. Cuthbertson, G. Harrington

British Library Cataloguing in Publication Data
Kempster, Tony
Carcase evaluation in livestock breeding,
production and marketing.
1. Animal industry — Great Britain
I. Title   II. Cuthbertson, Alastair
III. Harrington, Geoff
338.1'76'00941   HD9427.G/

ISBN 0-246-11509-2

First published in Great Britain 1982 by Granada Publishing Ltd

Printed in Great Britain by Mackays of Chatham, Kent

All rights reserved. No part of this publication may be reproduced,
stored in a retrieval system, or transmitted in any form or by any
means, electronic, mechanical, photocopying, recording or otherwise,
without the prior consent of the publishers.

Granada ®
Granada Publishing ®

Published in 1982 in the United States of America by
Westview Press, Inc.
5500 Central Avenue
Boulder, Colorado 80301
Frederick A. Praeger, President and Publisher

Library of Congress Catalog Card Number: 82-50969
ISBN 0-86531-531-0 (U.S.)

Contents

Forewords by Professor Z. Carpenter and Dr H. de Boer   vii
Preface   xi

Section 1   General principles
1   Introduction   3
2   Carcase structure and composition   8
3   Growth and development   31
4   Prediction   47

Section 2   Methods of evaluation
5   Scale and cost   59
6   Live animal evaluation   60
7   Carcase evaluation   79
8   Relative precision of alternative methods   91
9   Carcase conformation   105

Section 3   Commercial grading and classification
10   Role of grading and classification in marketing   115
11   Pig carcase grading and classification   124
12   Sheep carcase grading and classification   146
13   Beef carcase grading and classification   163

**Section 4   Livestock improvement schemes, population
       studies and experiments**
14   Selection objectives   205
15   Pig improvement schemes   218
16   Beef improvement schemes   229
17   Sheep improvement schemes   235
18   Carcase evaluation in population studies and experiments   239

Section 5   Strategy
19   A strategy for carcase evaluation research   265

References   277
Index   300

Forewords

Having been involved in teaching and research involving carcase evaluation for some twenty-five years, it is particularly gratifying to know that this treatise is now available to those in the livestock and meat industry. It has been my good fortune to visit and observe the research and development activities of the Meat and Livestock Commission on a number of occasions. It is appropriate that the M.L.C. staff compile the vast array of data for such a book and use these data as a basis for an update on carcase evaluation techniques. No other organisation has made the long-term commitment to the extent of the Meat and Livestock Commission in obtaining detailed carcase composition on beef, pork and lamb carcases with a view to using these data for herd improvement programmes, for national classification systems and for developing a more clear understanding of meat animal growth and development.

The ultimate goal of the meat animal production enterprise is the eventual profitable production of meat for the consuming public. Realization of the economic impact of differences in carcase merit has dictated paramount changes in the industry. It is clear that carcases which meet the desired quality standards and have the highest yield of preferred cuts with the least amount of trimmable fat are of greatest ultimate value. Knowledge of production efficiencies and determination of growth potentials which coincide with desired carcase attributes have provided the impetus for improvements in genetic selection and management of meat animals. Early research indicated that carcase evaluation must not be separated from production efficiencies. For this to be accomplished, accurate methods for carcase evaluation are critically important. If production efficiency and carcase merit are to be utilised in selection programmes, the data should be accurate and precise over periods of time.

The authors of this book have provided the basis for important measurements for use in carcase evaluation and the rationale for the limitations associated with data collection, interpretation of data and the application of methods for breed improvement, production and management studies and for grading or classification systems. Provided that resources in terms of personnel, facilities and finances are available, the case is made for obtaining detailed dissection data which is, in many cases, superior to whole-body chemical composition determinations. The authors strongly argue for sophisticated, detailed dissection data to form the 'base-line' data set from which simpler predictors may be developed for many applications. Results from the vast data accumulated at the Meat and Livestock Commission indicate that a sample of the population to be predicted should best be utilised in the 'base-line data base'. The wealth of data included in this book is related to potential industrial applications for grading and classification of meat animals. Clearly, the compilation of the M.L.C. data into a single treatise along with discussion of the pertinent data will provide a valuable resource to research scientists and students of live animal and carcase evaluation, and the livestock and meat industries.

Fortunately, markets for meat animals are diverse and will in all probability continue to be so. Technological developments may have some dramatic impacts on desired carcase characteristics in the future that may not cause changes in breeding and production programmes, but successful producers, marketers and scientists must rely on sound procedures and techniques for carcase evaluation. This book will make lasting contributions to this necessary knowledge base. It is pertinent, that the market for products from meat animals is a world market. From this view, measures of carcase merit must become more universal. Applications of classification systems are becoming more similar among various countries. The various grading and classification systems of major meat-producing nations are discussed in this book.

This technical and philosophical evaluation of criteria for assessment of carcase merit will provide a 'base-line' for future studies. Congratulations to Tony Kempster, Alastair Cuthbertson and Geoff Harrington for this mammoth effort and tremendous contribution.

ZERLE L. CARPENTER
Head and Professor of Animal Science
Texas A & M University

There are various reasons for the growing interest in applied carcase evaluation in Europe. Major factors are the increased scale of operation in the meat chain and the common marketing policy in the E.E.C., both of which require greater understanding and technical cooperation at the interface of producers and users of carcases. The economic impact of carcase quality on production and breeding, makes carcase evaluation highly relevant to livestock improvement schemes and research.

However, the assessment of carcase merit is complex and no single approach, or set of criteria will ideally suit all objectives, populations or markets in the most cost-effective way. Moreover, research and development has been mainly national and/or fragmented, involving even more diversity of methodology and techniques. Many years of personal involvement in co-ordination at the European level have shown the consequent entanglements and laborious efforts required to achieve harmonisation.

Therefore this book fulfills the urgent need to synthesise carcase evaluation research work, and set out its practical applications and also indicate the direction of further research and development. The authors are extremely well placed to undertake this task by their position in the Meat and Livestock Commission, which represents both production and marketing interests, and whose applied research programme has focussed on the integral development of adequate techniques in successive phases of breeding, production and marketing.

Although drawing heavily on M.L.C. research and experience, however, the contents of this book are of real international interest because the main lines of thinking on methods of carcase evaluation and their use apply to situations in any country. The international applications are facilitated further by the authors who give adequate background information besides providing an appraisal of future developments and research requirements. The authors have also broadened the scope of their book by incorporating systems and developments from overseas. They have extensively reviewed the current systems of grading and classification in different countries and continents and discussed their principles and implications.

The book is undoubtedly unique and authoritative at the international level. The authors have performed a great service in making the subject of carcase evaluation more accessible, particularly to those dealing with carcase quality aspects as part of livestock improvement schemes.

The authors' efforts have resulted in a most valuable handbook. Not only will it achieve an improved understanding of carcase evaluation: it will also stimulate progress towards international standards of quality.

DR H. DE BOER
Editor of *Livestock Production Science*
Senior Research Worker in the Schoonoord
Research Institute for Animal Husbandry,
Zeist, Netherlands

Preface

Red meat production today is dominated by two elements. First, there are biological and agricultural considerations of resource use, in particular the efficiency with which feed is converted into lean meat. Secondly, there are marketing considerations, in particular the ability of farmers to adapt output to conform more closely to changing market demands.

Clearly progress in both elements is essential if red meat is to remain competitive with poultry and the ever increasing range of alternative animal and vegetable protein foods.

To this end, meat production continues to be the subject of much research, and even more applied science in the form of systematic selection programmes, breed comparisons and field trials. Development and extension work to encourage livestock farmers to become more market-orientated is also expanding.

The *carcase* is central to these various activities. Carcase quality provides the primary measure of output and is a key selection criterion. It is the focus of trade and of new marketing efforts by farmers. The carcase provides a convenient defined point of conversion of an animal to meat. It is handled in bulk at a relatively small number of slaughtering points, small that is in relation to the number of farms from which the animals come, and to the number of retail shops and other trading points through which the meat is sold.

The problem of evaluating carcase quality is, therefore, of concern to breeders and geneticists, to farmers and nutritionists, to traders and other marketing men, and frequently to agencies who regulate, serve or advise them.

But although the problems are common to all meat-producing countries, the solutions will vary because of the different breed mixes in the animal populations, the different production systems, and the variations in market structure and in consumer requirements.

Our particular interest in the problems of carcase evaluation springs from this very diversity of application. From the fact that one may be dealing on one day with a scientist specialising in the study of animal growth, on another with a meat wholesaler; with an E.E.C. economist trying to manage the Common Agricultural Policy or a pig breeder concerned that his new selection line should meet the needs of a foreign meat-processing industry; with a nutritionist employed by a commerical feed company or with an embryo farmers' marketing group. All, at some point, need advice from the carcase-evaluation specialist.

Despite the pivotal nature of the subject, much of the early research and commercial application was unsatisfactory. Investigations were frequently on too small a scale and objectives confused; data analysis and the interpretation of results left much to be desired.

One of the authors (G.H.), in a series of papers in the 1960s, sought to draw attention to these deficiencies, but it was not until the Meat and Livestock commission (M.L.C.) took over the work of the Pig Industry Development Authority and extended it to beef cattle and sheep that suitable data were generated, on a sufficient scale for all species, for us (in parallel with others with similar interests elsewhere) to begin to clarify some of the issues.

We have been actively involved in the practical application of carcase evaluation from breeding work through to the development of national and indeed international carcase classification schemes. The extensive M.L.C. data on carcase variations arose from development projects in these various areas. The data collection was meticulous within limits of costs and required precision (under the management of A.C.), and the design of trials (in collaboration with colleagues) and the exhaustive analysis of the data banks generated (led by A.J.K.), allowed a more thorough examination of alternative procedures than had been possible before.

Inevitably, therefore, we shall draw heavily on M.L.C. data accumulated over the last ten years.

All carcase work is a compromise. No panaceas exist and all things cannot be covered in all situations. Ultimately, choice of evaluation method depends on the balance of cost and accuracy. Those engaged in research, development or commercial application should think flexibly, consider all the options available to them, and seek the greatest value for money, avoiding in particular, the dangers of using methods which might lead to biased estimates of carcase value and incorrect decisions.

We aim this book at all those who require some knowledge of carcase evaluation; it is written in such a way as to be of help to a wide range of readers, including students of agriculture, agricultural marketing and meat science, and researchers in animal and meat science seeking guidance on the carcase evaluation methods most appropriate to their experiments. All those concerned to know more about carcase variations and their practical importance, be they farmers, meat traders or their advisers, will find something in this book of value to them. Full references will allow interested readers to pursue any particular topic in greater depth.

In writing this book we have sought to provide the reader with a sound basis for understanding the more practical aspects of the subject. Accordingly, there is a section covering the principles of carcase structure, growth and development, and another dealing with the statistical principles involved in the prediction of carcase composition. The various carcase-evaluation techniques available for use in livestock production, breeding and marketing are then reviewed critically in terms of their accuracy, cost-effectiveness and ease of application. The techniques available for making estimates of carcase composition in the living animal are also covered.

All the main meat-producing countries have developed, or are in the process of developing, national carcase grading or classification schemes. The progress of these schemes and their role in improving the marketing of livestock and meat in the individual countries are discussed.

The quality of meat, as distinct from its quantity and distribution, is an important subject deserving a separate book which would consider such attributes as colour, texture and flavour. While we have not attempted to cover this field in detail, it has proved impossible to disentangle it completely from certain aspects of carcase evaluation, particularly in relation to beef grading schemes and pig improvement programmes.

A further section of the book provides practical guidance on the methods likely to be most suitable in different circumstances in livestock improvement schemes, population comparisions and feeding and environmental studies.

We must acknowledge the pioneering work of the late Sir John Hammond and his co-workers in Cambridge, which inspired many, like us, to take an interest in this subject; also the Meat and Livestock Commission for its enlightened attitude to livestock improvement and its associated carcase evaluation, and for permission to quote from M.L.C. data. We thank Mr D.G. Evans for his helpful comments on the statistical text.

But we would like to dedicate this book to our colleagues in the M.L.C. Carcase Evaluation Units, whose hard work has provided the data upon which much of our thinking is now based.

SECTION 1
General principles

1 Introduction

The valuation of carcases is important at all stages of the meat marketing chain from farm through to retail sale. The processor or retailer has to meet his customer's requirements in terms of the size, attractiveness and composition of cuts or products offered for sale and has to estimate the amount of meat he will be able to sell from each carcase. Carcase quality is also of concern to the wholesaler and meat packer who buys from farmers and has to meet retailers' needs; and, not least, to the farmer who, consistent with farm constraints, should be concerned to match breeding stock and production systems to maximise his return from the market by providing the types of carcase in most demand by the meat trade.

The overall responsibility for improving or at least facilitating improvements in the efficiency of the marketing chain often lies with government organisations who operate national carcase classification or grading schemes and who are also concerned with price reporting and market support systems related to carcase quality.

Apart from its role in valuing carcases in day-to-day trading, carcase evaluation has other important related uses. Breeding programmes need it to identify the individual animals which are most valuable as parents for future generations, as do breed trials to establish which breeds and crosses are most suited to particular production and market situations. Carcase evaluation is also necessary in experiments to determine the relative efficiencies of different animals during various stages of growth and how these are affected by nutrition and other environmental factors. In many situations carcase merit has to be assessed in the live animal.

Carcase evaluation is above all a utilitarian subject. The practitioner is concerned with the selection and effective use of evaluation techniques in particular circumstances to predict carcase composition and commercial value. This generally means finding the best compromise between accuracy and cost and hence obtaining value for money.

Many of the techniques developed are detailed and costly, and unsuitable for practical application on farms or in meat plants. Although this book covers such procedures, we are more concerned with techniques for large-scale practical application where relatively inaccurate methods can be of considerable use and indeed may be relied on if they are cheap and convenient to use. Some form of visual assessment, the simplest form of evaluation, is nearly always possible and indeed may be the only feasible method under some conditions.

The relative accuracy of different techniques is likely to be similar, although not the same, for the range of carcases found in different countries. We have drawn particularly on experience in Europe, the U.S.A. and Australasia, but expect the conclusions to be relevant in other parts of the world.

The scientific and trade literature on carcase evaluation is vast and, as far as possible, we have identified and referred to the most recent and comprehensive reviews of individual topics. Those wishing to go into more detail will be able to use these key references as sources for further reading.

The first section of the book examines the general principles of carcase structure, growth and development, and the statistical analyses on which choice of evaluation technique is based. The second section examines the range of techniques available and the remaining sections consider their application in commercial classification and grading, in livestock improvement schemes and in experiments and population studies.

Historical review

Historically, carcase evaluation has been dominated by size and shape. For centuries, visual assessments (and to some extent handling methods) were the only means used to identify differences between animals, and indeed they still play a major role in animal breeding. In spite of their inherent subjectivity, such assessments have been used successfully in establishment of large numbers of defined breeds, differing widely in performance and specialisation.

Shape has been considered very important, its influence stemming from the aesthetic appeal of certain types of stock. For example, in the last century, the traditional British beef breeds, Hereford, Aberdeen Angus and Beef Shorthorn were all altered in shape to fit man's idea of what a 'good' beef animal should look like. In making this change to blocky, rectangular animals, breeders, producers and meat traders have come to believe that these shapes are associated with more meat and better quality meat. Any movement away from this ideal is seen by many in the beef industry as a step backwards.

Over the years, linear body measurements have been used to some extent but essentially to reinforce the visual shape assessment.

Detailed compositional studies involving tissue separation are relatively new phenomena. Only fifty years ago, Hammond and co-workers (306) at Cambridge began to examine the influence of stage of growth and plane of feeding on body tissue proportions, and twenty years ago, Butterfield (48) in Australia demonstrated that differences in shape between breeds are not reflected in important differences in the way total muscle weight is distributed between different regions of the carcase.

There are surprisingly few significant landmarks over these fifty years in the field of tissue growth and development. The classical work of Hammond set the stage for the continuing debate about the effects of nutrition on differential tissue growth. Although interesting in growth terms, this has done little to influence practical decision-making in the livestock and meat industries except for the regulation of fat growth in bacon pigs. If we know, for example, that low planes of nutrition produce commercially unimportant changes in the relative growth of muscle and bone, is it really worth arguing about whether the changes are statistically 'real' or not? Discussion among scientists of Butterfield's work and the studies which have followed it, has also revolved around whether the differences in tissue distribution are 'real' rather than whether they are of practical consequence.

The search for universal truth in anatomical growth studies has almost certainly influenced attitudes of research workers to carcase evaluation. Early workers used whatever carcases were available to them from their growth studies and then looked for the measurements which gave the best indication of overall composition. This was often done without regard to differences in breed, sex or the conditions under which the animals were grown. The rationale for this approach was apparently that prediction relationships, once established, could be used in many other circumstances. The approach has produced an extensive literature on carcase evaluation, much of which is of limited value when it comes to making the practical decision about which technique is best for a particular application, because we now know that the relative value of predictors is sensitive to the circumstances in which they are used.

There are a number of good reasons for the slow development of carcase evaluation research. Carcase work is expensive in terms of facilities, labour and carcase depreciation, and the scale of work has been limited for this reason. Research has also been centred in research institutes and universities remote from the intended applications in breeding programmes and marketing practice. Furthermore, the subject is not a glamorous one, and has not interested bright young people in the way that, for example, animal breeding has.

Pomeroy (313), reviewing carcase research up to the mid 1960s stated:

Generally speaking, research has been limited in extent, fragmentary and unimaginative, so much so that until recently few new ideas have emerged in a matter of thirty years. The examination of carcases has tended to be rather perfunctory and a lot of time has been wasted in looking for quick and easy ways of describing composition and value.

But realisation that the inadequacy of carcase evaluation techniques has been a limiting factor to the efficient operation of national breeding programmes and grading schemes is leading to a change of attitudes.

The area of pig carcase assessment has seen the earliest and most rapid developments in Europe. Techniques and attitudes to carcase evaluation in beef and sheep have slowly followed the pig example — in particular, that of the Wiltshire bacon pig. The dressing of carcases for Wiltshire cure involves the splitting of the carcase either by sawing through or chopping out the backbone, which exposes the backfat thickness and, indeed, much of the variation in fatness since backfat comprises some 70 per cent of the separable fat in pig carcases. The accessibility of this fat made it possible to grade carcases effectively on the slaughter line using a simple ruler. Denmark, the pioneer in pig breeding based on progeny testing, introduced the same mid-line measurements for carcase evaluation from the very beginning at progeny test stations in the early part of the century, and forged the link between objective selection measurements and objective commercial valuation.

Developments in the United States followed a rather different pattern closely related to the development of the United States Department of Agriculture (U.S.D.A.) beef grading scheme. In the early 1920s, there was much interest in the commercial valuation of cattle in terms of trimmed cuts and chemical composition following on from the studies of Moulton and co-workers (285). Similar work came later with pigs and then sheep. The Reciprocal Meat Conferences of 1952 and 1953 were major landmarks when methods of evaluation were defined clearly and standardised. Early developments in carcase and meat research in the U.S.A. have been reviewed by Bratzler (38).

Since then a range of equipment has been developed for measuring fat thickness in less accessible parts of the carcase and on live pigs. Such equipment is now being modified and applied to beef and sheep.

Stimulated by the work of Kielanowski in the 1960s, increased understanding of the relationships between growth rate, efficiency of feed utilisation and carcase composition, has led to a more effective use of growth performance characteristics as indicators of carcase composition in breeding schemes. The most sophisticated use has been in pig performance testing: controlling daily feed intake and overall maintenance requirements by comparing animals over a fixed time period, live-weight gain has been used as a direct indication of the partition of energy between lean and fat growth (228).

Pig carcase studies also provided the first significant information casting doubt on the universality of relationships between predicting measurements and overall composition. A number of workers in the 1950s and early 1960s showed that there were important differences in carcase composition between breeds and between sexes although they had the same fat thickness measurements. Early results on the subject were reviewed by Osinska (305).

Problems associated with such differences in prediction relationships are now becoming better understood for pigs as more information accumulates. Attention is also being focussed on their practical importance. One of the main recommendations following a recent co-ordinated study of carcase evaluation techniques for use in the common European Economic Community (E.E.C.) pig grading scheme, was that each country should estimate carcase lean content (which is the basis of the grades) using the methods that it finds most appropriate for its pig population, rather than to develop the scheme with common measurements and prediction relationships (77). In cattle and sheep too, the commercial value of some breeds can be under-estimated and that of others over-estimated by the assessments currently used in classification and grading schemes. We have argued that in the absence of better predictors, breed type should be included as a factor to overcome such bias (215).

Differences between breeds (or whatever groups are being compared) in carcase composition at the same fat thickness measurement (or with some other predicting measurement constant) will be caused by differences in tissue growth and development. The carcase is a complex entity and small differences in basic structure can easily throw prediction relationships out of line.

This brings us full circle and back to basic growth studies which must surely be the key to future developments in carcase evaluation techniques. Major breakthroughs in accuracy are more likely to emerge as a spin-off from detailed studies of the genetics and physiology of growth than from the empirical approach involving the studies of single predictors, or the comparisons of a range of predictors which have dominated the field up until now.

2 Carcase structure and composition

The commercial value of carcases depends ultimately on their size, structure and composition. The main structural characteristics of commercial importance are as follows:

(a) weight;
(b) proportions of the main tissues (muscle, fat and bone);
(c) distribution of these tissues through the carcase;
(d) muscle thickness;
(e) chemical composition;
(f) visual appearance of the tissues and meat quality.

WEIGHT

The weight and size of a carcase has a major influence, not only on the quantity of the various tissues, but also on the size of the muscles exposed on cutting and of the individual joints prepared from it. This is of importance particularly in relation to a retailer's ability to provide cuts of suitable size for customer requirements. Over generations, the meat industries in different countries and different regions of the same country have become accustomed to handle certain weight ranges of carcases; abattoir practices and cutting methods have been developed accordingly. Most wholesalers state desired weight ranges in buying schedules and apply discounts to carcases falling outside these ranges. In some cases these discounts are severe and are a constraint on the use of improved breeds and production systems.

In Britain, for example, the demand for small joints with the skin on leads to a high proportion of pigs being slaughtered at light weights. Some 25 per cent of the population is slaughtered at carcase weights below 50 kg, while we estimate that the optimum slaughter weight, in terms of the efficiency of meat production, is between 65 kg and 80 kg (63). This type of demand has also had a major effect on the production of New Zealand lambs for the British market, as will be discussed in chapter 12.

In terms of processing efficiency, heavier weights are an advantage because of reduced labour and other processing costs per unit weight of marketable product. Heavier animals also produce a greater weight, and hence value, of edible by-products.

PROPORTIONS OF THE TISSUES

Among carcases of similar weight, the percentage formed by each tissue varies considerably depending on breed type and growth rate. The proportion of lean meat in the carcase is of major importance since this is the prime determinant of yield and commercial value. Leanness is the criterion by which most consumers judge quality and value for money. Taken as a generalised ideal, the best carcases should have an optimum level of fatness and minimum bone.

Questions about the optimum level of fatness in beef cause much debate particularly in the English-speaking world (351). While there is resistance to changes in fatness levels by certain sectors of the meat industry and some people continue to lay great emphasis on the importance of visible intramuscular (marbling) fat in beef, there is growing evidence which fails to support the belief that fatness contributes significantly to improved eating quality of the lean meat once a minimum level is present. There is also increasing consumer demand for lean meat stimulated by the desire of many people to be slim and by fears about the possible link between saturated animal fats and blood circulatory problems.

Table 2.1 gives our estimate of the difference between production and consumption requirements for beef fat in Great Britain. This estimated consumer demand for fat, if matched by production, would still leave British beef fatter on average than in several other European countries. At the other extreme, the average level of fatness for 'current production' is substantially below that of the U.S.A.

The production of leaner carcases also makes sense in terms of the efficiency of production because four to five times as much energy is used to produce a given weight of fat as the same weight of lean. Increasing production costs and the need for greater efficiency is also contributing, therefore, to the trend towards leanness. The conflict between cost and assumed quality considerations is well illustrated by the history of the U.S.D.A. beef grading system (see chapter 13).

The over-fatness of carcases is a problem in many developed countries. Pigs are more amenable to genetic selection than the other species and major reductions in fatness levels have been achieved and are likely to continue in line with the trend of consumer demand. The pig industry has also had a clearer objective for improvement with leaner carcases being worth more.

DISTRIBUTION OF TISSUES

The distribution of tissues through the carcase is potentially important because there are wide differences between cuts in their retail value; for example, beef fillet steak is worth nearly three times as much as stewing steak at present in Britain. However, muscle weight distribution is a fairly constant characteristic and there is little variation to exploit commercially.

On the other hand, the distribution of fat between different depots in the carcase and in the body cavity does show important variation. The general distribution of fat is important because it influences the overall efficiency of meat production: fat in the body cavity or excess fat trimmed during retail

Table 2.1 Current production, estimated market demand and estimated consumer demand for beef carcases in Great Britain (164)

	Distribution of carcases between fat classes in the M.L.C. beef carcase classification scheme (%)*						Average separable lean in carcase (%)	Average separable fat in carcase (%)	Estimates of average fat trimmed (% of carcase weight)	
	1 (very lean)	2	3L	3H	4	5 (very fat)			in trade	by the consumer
Current production (1978)	2	20	42	27	8	1	60	22	10.0	6.0
Estimated market demand**	5	55	25	13	2	—	63	20	8.5	5.2
Estimated consumer demand	20	70	8	2	—	—	65	17	7.0	3.5

*Details of the scheme are given in chapter 13; this is the former terminology subsequently altered in 1981 (see Table 13.14).
**Our estimate of the distribution of carcases which the meat trade as a whole would have considered ideal in 1978.

preparation is of little commercial value in comparison with that sold as a part of retail cuts. The position of fat in the carcase is also important because sub-cutaneous fat can be trimmed more easily than intermuscular fat and is, there-fore, preferable in carcases containing fat in excess of consumer requirements. Indeed, excess intermuscular fat cannot be trimmed from some joints, especially from lamb carcases, without mutilating them. The evenness of fat distribution is also important because wedges or bulges of fat in some joints can lead to excessive trimming or devaluation.

MUSCLE THICKNESS

While this characteristic appears to vary considerably from carcase to carcase, much of this variation can be attributed to weight and fatness variations. Among carcases of similar weight and fatness, blockier carcases will tend to have thicker muscles, but this remaining variation has little impact on retail realisation values. Retailers tend to favour carcases with good meat thickness, however, as this is thought to be associated with a higher yield of saleable meat and to improve the appearance of joints. There may also be advantages in terms of tenderness (106) and reduced weight losses in the preparation and cooking of cuts, but the commercial significance of these advantages is not clear (24).

In some circumstances, thicker muscles may be a positive disadvantage. For example, the eye muscle (cross-section of the *M. longissimus*) may be too large and thick in bacon-weight pigs to achieve the number of slices per unit weight demanded by the consumer. However the economic significance of variation is much less important to the meat industry than variation in lean and fat content, which has a direct and usually measurable impact on realisation values. Thick-ness of muscle may also be manipulated more easily by simply raising or lower-ing carcase weight, or by shaping during the preparation of cuts.

CHEMICAL COMPOSITION

The chemical composition of carcases does not usually have a direct bearing on their commercial value (except insofar as it reflects physical composition) since, to a large extent, they are valued on the basis of the physical characteristics considered above. However, chemical composition may nevertheless be important in relation to a number of factors including the eating quality of the meat, the processing characteristics, the propensity to lose weight between slaughter and consumption, the keeping qualities and the nutritive value.

Meat texture (degree of toughness or tenderness) is the main factor in eating quality. Texture is influenced not only by the state of the contractile com-ponents of muscle, but by the quantity and chemical nature of the connective tissue. The quantity of connective tissue (the most important component of which is collagen) differs from muscle to muscle within a carcase. Further, as animals grow older the connective tissue within each muscle becomes tougher, primarily because the collagen is more cross-linked and does not dissolve so readily on cooking.

The chemical composition of fat may also have an influence on eating quality.

For example, the highly saturated nature of lamb fat leads to it solidifying quickly during cooling after cooking, making it less palatable than more unsaturated fats, but the latter type of fat, particularly in pigs, is more prone to rancidity. The degree of saturation also influences the appearance of meat. If pig fat is soft, the necessary rigidity to stand up well during cutting and subsequent packaging is lacking. This may lead to difficulties, for example, in presenting attractive, vacuum-packed slices of bacon. Such unsaturated fat can arise in the production of leaner animals where the subcutaneous fat present tends to be less saturated, and in pigs fed diets containing unsaturated fats. Unlike ruminants, pigs tend to deposit dietary fat in the form in which it is absorbed.

The processing characteristics of meat, such as its water-binding capacity, are affected by its chemical composition. On occasions the chemical composition of the product may be directly related to the chemical composition of the carcase. For example, in the U.S.A. some pig-slaughtering and processing plants strip the lean meat and fat from warm sow carcases and turn it immediately into sausage products, the so-called 'whole hog sausage'. In these circumstances, the choice of type of pig used may be such that the composition provides a close approximation to the required product formulation.

There are several useful reviews on the chemical composition of meat (for example 243, 320).

VISUAL APPEARANCE AND EATING QUALITY

These characteristics will not be considered in detail in this book except when they are related to the other carcase features in some way as, for example, the association between fatness and texture or flavour and its impact on grading methods, or the association between blockiness and pale soft exudative muscle in pigs and its impact on selection objectives.

Before examining the different methods available for evaluating the various characteristics outlined above, the structure of the carcase and its relationship with the live animal from which it comes, will be outlined. Reference will also be made to base-line techniques which provide the framework against which different carcase evaluation procedures can be assessed.

Anatomical structure

The chemical components of the body are combined to form the hard and soft tissues. Bone and to some degree cartilage form the hard tissues, while muscle, fat and connective tissue form the soft tissues.

BONE

Bone gives the soft tissues a supporting framework, providing rigidity to the living body as a whole; but the bones also form a series of mechanical levers operated by muscles and their tendons. In addition, bone protects such internal organs as the brain.

The process of slaughter conventionally involves hanging the body from the hind legs. Fig. 2.1 shows how the position of the skeletal parts changes in relation to the soft tissues as the live beef animal becomes a carcase. Unless the carcase is boned out while hot, muscles enter *rigor mortis* in a very different position from that assumed while the animal was alive. This affects the relationship between measurements taken on the live animal and those taken on the carcase; there are also implications for eating quality since the method of hanging will affect the extent to which particular muscles are stretched during *rigor*.

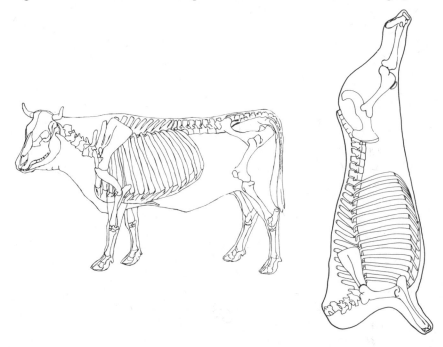

Fig. 2.1   Comparison of the bovine skeleton in the live animal and the hanging carcase

Pelvic hanging has been proposed as an alternative to conventional methods for beef carcases as it allows certain key muscles to go into *rigor* in a stretched condition with a net benefit to tenderness (186); inevitably the appearance of the carcase is substantially changed, affecting conformation assessments, and creating problems in the preparation of cuts.

There are obvious differences between species in their skeletal size and the proportions formed by the various components. Fig. 2.2 compares the skeletons of typical beef, sheep and pig carcases when adjusted to the same length. The head is nearly always excluded from the beef or sheep carcase, but in some countries it is conventionally included as a part of the pig carcase. This may affect definitions of carcase lean meat percentage.

There is also variation in the number of lumbar and thoracic vertebrae and associated ribs, both between and within species (fig. 2.3).

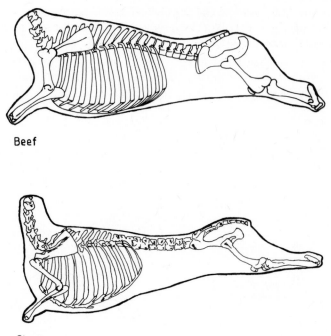

Beef

Sheep

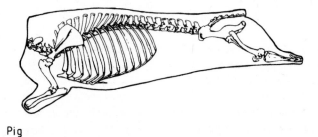

Pig

Fig. 2.2   Comparison of beef, sheep and pig skeletons in carcases dressed by the methods standard in Great Britain

Within a species, the number of cervical and sacral vertebrae is constant. In both sheep and pigs, the total number of thoracic and lumbar vertebrae is nearly always the same, but it is common for a carcase to have, for example, one extra thoracic vertebra and one less lumbar vertebra, or vice versa.

To identify a particular vertebra or rib, the convention is to count from the anterior end of each set of bones. So the first rib lies next to the seventh cervical vertebra and the last rib next to the first lumbar vertebra. The 'head' of a rib is the part next to the vertebra with which it articulates, whereas the 'tip' of a rib is the part furthest from the vertebral column where it joins the cartilage in the flank or breast. These definitions are important in locating positions for probing and cutting carcases.

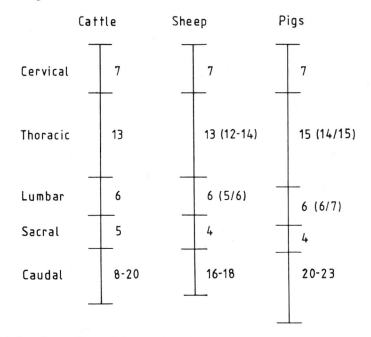

Fig. 2.3   Comparison of the number of vertebrae in cattle, sheep and pigs

MUSCLE

The largest component of the carcase is muscle. Excluding the head, there are over 100 different muscles which can be grouped in a variety of ways and in different degrees of detail. Grouping by anatomical function may be of value in studies of muscle growth (43). This detailed approach can be combined with one more commercially-based to determine, for example, the impact on commercial value of differences in muscle distribution. There are, of course, different approaches to commercial cutting in different countries. In many, particular joints are made by cutting across muscles, so pieces as sold will consist of a mixture of muscles differing markedly in expected eating quality. In other countries, notably France, commercial cutting is more anatomically based allowing cuts as sold to consist of more homogeneous grouping of muscles.

The location of individual muscles is described anatomically by Sisson and Grossman (344), but some more practical guides to the location of muscles in carcases have been published for pigs (192), sheep (191) and beef (43, 51, 367).

The thirty largest muscles, which make up some 70 per cent of the total weight of muscle of the beef carcase, are listed in table 2.2, together with an indication of their texture when cooked.

Table 2.2 The thirty largest muscles of the beef carcase, their anatomical location, their percentage contribution to total muscle weight (from 43) and a rating of their texture when cooked (based on 322)

Muscle	Anatomical location**	Percentage of total muscle	Texture rating*
M. gluteobiceps	PL	6.8	4
Mm. longissimus thoracis et lumborum	NT/LA	6.7	3
M. semimembranosus	PL	4.7	5
M. serratus ventralis	NT	4.0	4
M. gluteus medius	PL	3.7	3
M. pectoralis profundus	NT	3.7	7
Mm. intercostales externi et interni	NT	3.5	5
M. triceps brachii caput longum	TL	3.1	4
M. vastus lateralis	PL	2.6	5
M. obliquus externus abdominis	NT/LA	2.5	6
M. iliopsoas	LA	2.3	1–2
M. semitendinosus	PL	2.3	3
M. rectus abdominis	NT/LA	2.3	5
M. infraspinatus	TL	2.1	3
M. latissimus dorsi	NT	2.1	7
M. spinalis et semispinalis	NT	2.0	4
M. rectus femoris	PL	2.0	5
M. obliquus internus abdominis	LA	2.0	7
M. gastrocnemius	PL	1.9	4
M. cutaneus trunci	LA/NT	1.9	6–7
M. supraspinatus	TL	1.8	4
M. adductor	PL	1.6	6
M. transversus abdominis	NT/LA	1.5	7
M. semispinalis capitis	NT	1.5	6–7
Mm. pectorales superficialis	NT	1.5	7
Mm. vastus medialis et intermedius	PL	1.5	4–5
M. gracilis	PL	1.4	5
M. longus colli	NT	1.4	6
M. brachiocephalicus	NT	1.4	7
M. trapezius	NT	1.3	7

**PL = Pelvic limb; NT = Neck and thorax; LA = Lumbar abdominal; TL = Thoracic limb.
*1 = Very tender; 2 = Tender; 3 = Slightly tender; 4 = Medium; 5 = Slightly tough; 6 = Tough; 7 = Very tough.

For most practical purposes, muscle or lean consists of skeletal muscle fibres and fat contained within the epimysium, after removal of adherent fat, tendons taken at right angles at the limit of the muscle fibres (or red lean), and tendinous tissue sheets removed from the abdominal muscles. The latter applies particularly to the thick tendinous sheet on the *M. rectus abdominis* and to the peritoneum which covers some of the abdominal muscles. The terms 'muscle' and 'lean' are regarded as synonymous. The former is most commonly used when referring to specific muscles or anatomical groups of muscles, and where studies of muscle growth are involved. The term 'lean' or 'lean meat' is used in more commercially-orientated investigations. However, the term 'lean body mass' has scientific connotations, being the chemically fat-free part of the whole body.

Knowledge of muscle location can be of help when faced with practical commercial problems affecting the size, shape and fatness of cuts. Indeed, some understanding of muscle location is desirable for those involved in product quality control in meat plants. For example, the appearance of lamb loin cutlets or bacon slices can be affected by where they are cut in relation to *M. serratus dorsalis caudalis*. This muscle, adjacent to the important *M. longissimus*, consists of a series of small muscle blocks attached to the last few ribs. Because of the disposition of these muscle blocks, some transverse cuts across the loin in the rib area may fail to include a part of this muscle. If this happens, the cut surface looks fatter and may cause the rejection by quality controllers of individual packets, while another cut made only a few millimetres away may show the full thickness of this muscle and so appear a markedly leaner cut.

FAT

The third major component of the carcase is fat which is laid down in several physically separable depots. The fat deposited within the muscles themselves (the intramuscular or marbling fat) plays an active role in muscle metabolism and also acts as a storage depot for excess energy, especially during the later stages of fattening. Of the physically separable fat depots, the following are of particular importance:

(a) perinephric and retro-peritoneal (the kidney knob and channel or pelvic fat in beef and sheep carcases, and the flare fat in pigs);
(b) subcutaneous (external);
(c) intermuscular (seam).

In beef carcases, the cod or udder fat may also be of significance. While the udder is usually removed from older females during carcase dressing, the cod (scrotal) fat in males and the udder (mammary) fat in heifers is usually retained on the carcase in British practice. The cod or udder fat is similar to the sub-cutaneous fat and accurate anatomical differentation is difficult. However, in detailed carcase dissection work, they may be removed in a standardised manner by reference to the skeleton and the dorsal edge of *M. cutaneus trunci*.

The perinephric and retro-peritoneal depot lies in the body cavity and is now commonly removed on the slaughter line from beef carcases as part of the dressing operation. If necessary, the two parts of this depot can be separated by a line between the symphysis pubis and the sacrum.

Subcutaneous fat is all the fat (including the connective tissue framework) on the external surface of the side and beneath the *M. cutaneus*, which can be removed without excavating into the grooves between muscles. Intermuscular fat is the remaining physically separable tissue.

The other components of the carcase, such as tendons, lymph nodes, blood vessels and connective tissue sheaths from abdominal muscles can be grouped together and variously described as 'other tissues', 'remainder' or waste.

SALEABLE MEAT

In commercial practice, muscle or lean is usually sold with some adhering fat. This mixture of lean and fat is referred to as 'saleable meat' or 'trimmed deboned cuts', although depending on the species, cut, and country, saleable meat may contain some bone. For example, lamb cuts in the U.K. are commonly sold bone-in. (Where we use the term saleable meat, it is always referring to boneless trimmed lean meat).

The ratio of lean to fat in the meat sold depends on the fatness of the carcase from which the cuts are derived, the nature of the cut and the preferences of retailers and their customers. When customers self-select their purchases from retail display cabinets, there is a worldwide tendency for those cuts with high lean/fat ratios to be preferred, other things being equal; but in Britain, retailers still vary in the fatness of the carcases they select and in the amount of fat they trim in the preparation of retail cuts (see fig. 2.4).

Table 2.3 shows the composition of typical beef, sheep and pig carcases at three levels of fatness. There are marked differences between species in the proportion of the total fat which occurs in the different separable depots, and therefore in the ease of trimming fat for retail sale.

In later chapters, we shall discuss the prediction of carcase lean content by visual assessment or measurement of the subcutaneous fat; the results of many studies show the predictive value of measurements taken along the back in preference to those taken elsewhere. This superiority may reflect the fact that the main muscle, *M. longissimus*, is a regular, well-defined muscle and that skeletal reference points on rib or vertebra are easy to locate even on live animals. Fig. 2.5 illustrates the appearance of the *M. longissimus* and its surrounding fat in a typical beef carcase sectioned at several sites along the back. The location of some of the common measurements taken for carcase evaluation purposes is indicated.

DIRECTIONAL DEFINITIONS

In carcase evaluation work, identification of the location of measuring sites and the direction of cutting lines is helped by the use of topographical terms which indicate whether, for example, the measurements are being taken on the side of a vertebra towards the animal's head (cranial or anterior) or towards its tail (caudal or posterior). Fig. 2.6 illustrates directional terms for the standing animal and for its carcase.

AGE

The state of bone and cartilage development may be used as an indication of the maturity of a carcase and its meat. In cattle there is a fairly clear pattern of change in the colour of the bones and in the ossification of the cartilages. For example, in the young animal up to about two years of age, the pubic symphysis or 'aitch bone' can be split easily by cutting with a knife through the cartilage. Later in life, the cartilage becomes ossified and the resulting bone has to be sawn through.

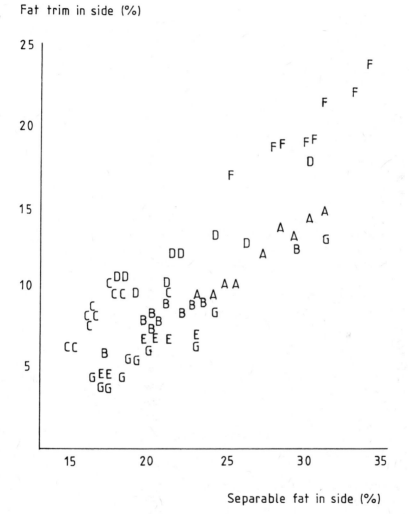

Fig. 2.4 Results of commerical cutting tests on sides of beef in comparison to full dissection of the opposite side. Fat trim percentage of sixty-four sides of beef, each cut by one of seven retailers (A to G), compared with percentage of separable fat (ex KKCF) (273)

The spines of the dorsal vertebrae (or chine bones) also show marked changes with age. In the young animal, the spines are largely white and cartilaginous but

Table 2.3 Composition of the average beef, sheep and pig carcases* in Britain and the typical range

	Beef			Sheep			Pigs		
	Lean	Average	Fat	Lean	Average	Fat	Lean	Average	Fat
Lean meat %	66	59	50	64	57	48	67	59	53
Total fat %	16	25	37	14	24	38	22	31	38
subcutaneous	3	8	15	5	11	20	15	22	28
intermuscular	10	13	17	7	10	13	5	6	7
KKCF/flare	3	4	5	2	3	5	2	3	3
Bone (including small waste component) %	18	16	13	22	19	14	11	10	9
Total	100	100	100	100	100	100	100	100	100
Subcutaneous/intermuscular fat ratio	0.3	0.6	0.9	0.7	1.1	1.5	3.0	3.7	4.0
Lean/bone ratio	3.7	3.7	3.8	2.9	3.0	3.4	6.1	5.9	5.9

*All carcases ex head, feet and skin.

they are gradually ossified and become redder; tips of cartilage become ossified last. Most cattle slaughtered at about two years of age or less have soft, red spines terminating in white soft cartilage.

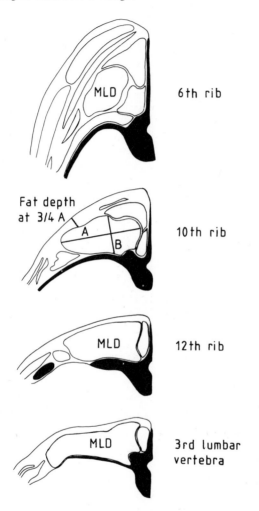

Fig. 2.5   Change on appearance of *M. longissimus* (MLD) and associated muscles at four positions along the back of a beef carcase. The locations of some of the common measurements taken for carcase evaluation purposes are indicated

In the live animal, and also if the head is available in the abattoir, an indication of the age is provided by the pattern of tooth development. Cattle lose their central calf incisors and start to produce permanent incisors at an average of about 22 months of age. However, there is considerable variation and the first permanent incisors may begin to erupt between eighteen and twenty-six months. When both central permanent incisors have erupted the animal becomes 'two-toothed'. Later in life it becomes four-toothed, six-toothed and then develops a full mouth of permanent incisors. Most commercial cattle (other than breeding cows) will be slaughtered with either calf teeth or two permanent incisors.

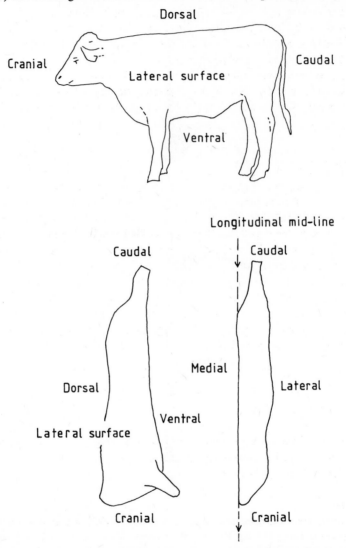

Fig. 2.6   Terms used in defining positions and directions on live animals and carcases. In addition to those illustrated, the following may also be found:

proximal — parts which are relatively nearer to the long axis of the carcase (e.g. the parts of limbs nearest the vertebral column);

distal — parts which are relatively distant from the long axis of the carcase (e.g. feet);

superficial — parts which are relatively close to the surface of the carcase.

deep — parts which are relatively far from the surface of the carcase.

In the past, the state of development of the molar teeth has tended to be ignored when assessing age, but recently these teeth have attracted more attention because they can be used to give a more precise guide (11). For example, the first pair of molars on the lower jaw start erupting at around five months of age and are fully up by one year, at which time the second pair of molars are emerging. Sheep lose their first lamb incisor teeth at about fifteen months of age and achieve a full mouth of permanent incisors by three and a half to four years of age. As with cattle, the molars can be used to provide an indication of development at a younger age. As an example, the first pair of molars start erupting at about three months of age for the lower jaw and five months of age for the upper jaw.

Live to carcase weight relationship

The relationship between the live animal immediately before slaughter and the weight of the carcase produced is important in many commercial situations. It influences the price paid for live animals and the time at which animals must be slaughtered so that their carcases fall into specified weight ranges. In breeding schemes, population studies and experiments, it is the link between growth performance and carcase characteristics.

The relationship is commonly expressed as the killing-out or dressing percentage (carcase weight as a percentage of live weight). Both weights can be obtained in many different ways and careful definitions are required for information on killing-out percentage to be interpreted correctly. Some of the weights that can be used are as follows:

Live weight
(a) Before leaving the farm:
    (i) starved for 24 hours,
    (ii) not starved,
    (iii) average of weights taken on each of two or three days before slaughter;
(b) At the auction market or other point of sale;
(c) In the lairage before slaughter.

Carcase weight
(a) Hot carcase weight within one hour of slaughter, with carcase dressed to a given specification;
(b) Estimated cold weight obtained by making a standard deduction from hot weight;
(c) Actual carcase weight after 24 hours' cooling;
(d) Actual carcase weight obtained from the sum of the parts after cutting and tissue separation.

Killing-out percentages are very sensitive to the conditions under which the live weights are taken, so commercial costing and price reporting must be based on the weights that are used in commercial practice. If this is not done, the relationships between live and dead weight prices can be distorted.

For breeding and experimental work, the standardisation of conditions is desirable to remove as much unwanted variation as possible by, for example, starving the animals for a day before slaughter or by taking the live weights on several occasions before slaughter. Single weighings can be notoriously inaccurate depending on the diurnal pattern of excretion of individual animals. In some experimental work, regular measurements of live weight may be taken over the period of the trial so that growth curves for individual animals can be constructed and weights calculated at any time, and most importantly on the day of slaughter. The problems involved in live weight measurement have been discussed by Geay (141).

Carcase weights are not so sensitive to the time of weighing but are highly dependent on the dressing procedures used. The precise definition of what constitutes the carcase and under what conditions the weights are recorded, is essential in selling on a carcase-weight basis and associated classification and grading schemes. Particular considerations are as follows:

(a) whether the head, feet and tail constitute part of the carcase and, if not, how the cutting lines dividing them from the carcase are defined;
(b) whether internal fat depots, kidney, perinephric and retroperitoneal fat (KKCF) are considered part of the carcase;
(c) whether any trimming of subcutaneous fat or intermuscular fat is permitted from the carcase before weighing;
(d) whether the carcases are weighed hot immediately after slaughter or when cold.

Most national classification and grading schemes relate to carcases dressed in a standard manner. However, there are some important differences in definitions between countries which can cause confusion in carcase evaluation work and the development of common classification and grading schemes. Most schemes, for example, specify that no external fat shall be removed before weighing. In France, however, the beef dressing procedure stipulated by the Office National Interprofessionnel du Bétail et des Viandes (O.N.I.B.E.V.) does allow trimming of some external fat (émoussage) causing some problems in fat classification.

There are also differences between countries in whether hot carcase weights, actual cold carcase weights, or cold weights estimated from hot weights are used as the basis of payment to the producer. It is not critical which is used because market prices will adjust to any definition, since by convention the whole animal, carcase plus various by-products, is valued by price per unit weight multiplied by that weight. Whatever the basis chosen, the critical factor is standardisation. Hot weight payment is generally simpler to operate, because carcases are weighed hot and no adjustment is necessary; a number of countries are now adopting this procedure.

Weight losses during cooling are sensitive to individual abattoir circumstances (to factors such as speed of chilling and the extent to which water sprays have been used). It is important, therefore, when changing the basis of payment or checking existing rebates, to carry out a large-scale survey covering many abattoirs to obtain a valid national result. In a survey of pig carcases carried out in Britain and involving forty-eight abattoirs, the overall average carcase weight loss to 24 hours post mortem was 2.25 per cent with a range of 0.6 percentage units between individual abattoirs handling pigs of similar weight (219).

Table 2.4 Components of the live animal as a percentage of live body weight (typical figures for average pigs, cattle and sheep in Great Britain, based on M.L.C. information)

	Pigs (%)	Cattle (%)	Sheep (%)
Gut fill	10	17	12
Skin (hide/fleece)	–	7	13.5
Empty gut	3	4.5	6.5
Intestinal and caul fat	1.5	4.5	3.5
Heart, lungs and trachea	1.5	1.5	1.5
Liver, gall bladder, pancreas and spleen	2.5	1.5	1.5
Head	–	3	4
Feet	–	2	2
Blood	4	3	4
Other components	1	1	1.5
Hot carcase inc. KKCF	76.5	55	50
Total	100	100	100
Weight loss on cooling	1.5	1	1.5
Cold carcase inc. KKCF	75	54	48.5
KKCF	–	2	–
Cold carcase ex. KKCF	–	52	–
Weight loss during dissection	1	1	1.5
Sum of dissected parts*	74	51	47

*Inc. KKCF for pigs and sheep; ex. KKCF for beef.

Typical weights of the components of live cattle, sheep and pigs are shown in table 2.4 together with killing-out percentages defined in various ways.

FACTORS INFLUENCING KILLING-OUT PERCENTAGE

As the animal grows, killing-out percentage normally increases steadily due to a higher rate of muscle and fat growth in the carcase than growth of components in the body cavity. Changes from the normal pattern occur if there is a significant alteration in diet as, for example, when cattle and sheep change from milk feeding to roughage diets, which increases both the weight of the digestive tract and gut contents.

Higher levels of feeding are usually associated with more concentrated diets and increased rates of fattening, so that animals on higher levels of feeding tend to kill-out better. *Ad libitum*-fed animals also usually kill-out better than animals fed the same diet to a restricted scale.

There are important genetic differences in killing-out percentages associated with differences in rate of fattening and appetite. In addition it is now becoming clear that killing-out is associated with body conformation (blockiness) both within and between breeds (194). Breed types with better conformation at the same level of fatness tend to kill-out better. This association appears to be due to differences in the size of the body cavity and weight of internal organs. Genetic differences in hide and head weights also influence killing-out percentages but these are largely independent of conformation.

Sexes are rarely compared at the same level of fatness and there is little evidence on whether differences exist in killing-out percentages independent of fatness. However, where there is a difference in reproductive organs, this will influence the weights achieved; for example, everything else being equal, entire males will kill-out worse than castrated males if the testicles are not included as part of the carcase.

The length of the fasting period before slaughter can also influence the killing-out percentage. Carcase weight decreases as the time between the last feed and slaughter increases. Of particular importance in this context is the effect on producer returns of the length of transport and lairage time between farm and slaughter, and whether the animals are fed after leaving the farm. Although of considerable economic importance, there is little sound information with which to determine optimum procedures between farm and slaughter.

Definition of base-line for carcase evaluation

Most carcase evaluation work is carried out with an economic objective ultimately in mind and is concentrated on those characteristics which have the greatest effect on carcase retail value. Setting aside carcase weight, the description of carcase leanness or saleable meat yield is of most importance. This raises the question of how this should be defined. On what definition of overall carcase leanness should we decide, for example, that one breed of pig or one individual sire should be used in preference to others, or that one protein supplement is preferable to another?

The distinction between the base-line and carcase measurements used to predict it should be clearly understood. The base-line is the 'ideal evaluation' which would be applied to all animals if cost were no obstacle. When we estimate carcase composition from simpler measurements we are trying to get as close as possible to the results which would have been obtained had the base-line itself been used on all animals.

A range of techniques is available from fat trimming and de-boning as used in commercial practice, through more standardised cutting and tissue separation, to whole body chemical analysis.

For most purposes, a base-line in terms of cutting seems preferable to chemical analysis since value judgments by consumers are made on the basis of the appearance or physical composition of the carcase or joint. Chemical analysis is relevant mainly to processors but is expensive to operate as a base-line technique if accuracy is to be achieved.

The next question, then, is how detailed should the cutting be? Commercial cutting procedures, providing data on saleable meat yield and bone and fat trim, are cheap, and results are immediately relevant to meat traders. But, commercial practice differs from place to place and over time as livestock populations and production and marketing methods change. Such procedures are also difficult to standardise and often do not provide the precision necessary in breeding programmes and experimental work. Tissue separation, on the other hand, although more expensive is suitable for a range of applications and considered by the authors to be a more suitable general base-line technique for carcase evaluation work.

If resources allow, the most comprehensive procedure is to apply tissue separation after dividing the carcase into cuts followed by chemical analysis of the resulting tissues. Such an approach would be particularly valuable in growth and nutritional studies when it is important to determine the extent to which specific nutrients are retained in the carcase. It was one of the recommendations made by an E.E.C. group of experts considering carcase evaluation procedures for beef (94). Apart from providing information on the chemical composition of tissues, such a procedure also enables the standard of physical separation to be monitored.

The tissue separation techniques used to determine the base-line may involve careful separation, with scalpels and scissors, of individual muscles from bone attachments and surrounding fat (for example, 315) as opposed to methods involving separation by butcher's knife into lean meat, the physically separable fat depots and bone within major commercial joints (for example, 88, 89) which takes half the time. We consider that the separation by butcher's knife is adequate for nearly all purposes and that more detailed techniques are rarely cost-effective.

A realistic approach to the degree of detail in the base-line is necessary. There is a danger that the importance of precision will be over-estimated and only the most detailed technique chosen. The expense of such techniques will inevitably limit the extent and effectiveness of their use. Just as it is necessary to find a compromise between the precision of alternative predicting measurements and their cost, so it is important to find a compromise between the cost of a base-line technique and its precision. The most efficient ways of using base-line techniques are discussed later in chapter 18 on population studies and experiments.

Less detailed techniques widely used in the U.S.A. involve the separation of carcases using commercial but standardised de-boning and fat trimming methods. We have used such techniques in population studies but consider them to be predicting rather than base-line techniques and they are referred to as such in a later section. An alternative technique sometimes used is to separate the soft tissues from the bones followed by a rough separation of the muscle or fat tissues, with the fat content of the muscle mass then determined chemically to allow calculation of the fat-free muscle mass.

The range of separation procedures used for beef research in Europe has been summarised by the European Association of Animal Production (E.A.A.P.) (114) and those used for pig carcase evaluation in the European Economic Community by the C.E.C. (77). Base-lines in the U.S.A. have generally been either commercial trimming techniques or chemical analyses, although the American Meat Science Association set up a working party in 1981 to consider alternatives.

Considering the various techniques available, we would recommend the division of the carcase into standardised commercial joints and their separation into component tissues and different fat depots using a butcher's knife. This has provided a satisfactory base-line in a whole range of M.L.C. studies and is also used effectively in a number of other countries. Cutting sides into joints before subsequent separation of the tissues provides information on joint proportions and on the distribution and thickness of tissues in these joints. It can also be linked easily to chemical analysis when more comprehensive information is required, or simplified to sample joint separation or the separation of subcutaneous fat only without introducing new procedures.

Furthermore, for those interested in the grouping of muscles anatomically rather than by commercial joints, information can be obtained on an approximate anatomical basis by adding together the weight of muscle portions which occur in different commercial joints. In view of the relative constancy of muscle weight distribution, more detailed separation procedures seem difficult to justify especially where the separation and weighing of individual muscles is involved, unless of course individual muscles are separated in commercial practice, as they are for example in France and Belgium.

Information on the chemical composition of carcases is necessary when assessing the response of animals to various environmental influences, especially nutritional. For example, the efficiency of transforming the nutrients in the diet into body protein and energy can be evaluated and, used in association with physical separation, a deeper understanding of the growth of tissues can be achieved. It is also of value when examining factors associated with the appearance and eating quality of meat.

Chemical analysis of the whole carcase or of the tissues is expensive mainly because it depends on producing a fully representative homogeneous sample from variable carcase material. A high labour cost is involved as well as carcase depreciation due to comminution of muscle. Various approaches have been adopted for preparing carcases for chemical analysis. Most involve mincing and homogenising, but autoclaving the whole carcase has also been used (239). A range of procedures is available for analysing major components of the carcase.

The International Standards Organisation (I.S.O.) (for example, 182) and the Association of Official Analytical Chemists (18), define the procedures which are most widely applied for bench-type approaches. However, the high cost of labour in carrying out analyses has encouraged the development of automated procedures, some of which can provide similar precision to more conventional techniques.

The dissection of one side of the carcase only is adequate for most base-line work. Significant differences have been recorded between sides in tissue percentages but it is generally accepted that the improvement in precision obtained from dissecting both sides does not justify the considerable increase in costs involved. The money is usually better spent on the evaluation of more carcases.

Most side to side differences occur in bone content because of inaccuracies in centre splitting. If there is a problem, the vertebral column can be removed from both sides to obtain vertebral bone weight for the dissected side. Real biological bilateral asymmetry in carcases is of negligible importance.

HOW SHOULD THE BASE-LINE COMPOSITION BE EXPRESSED?
Having decided on the base-line technique, consideration has to be given to the way it is used. For example, when comparing different predictive measurements, is it better to predict the weight of lean in carcase or the weight of lean in carcase expressed as a percentage of carcase weight?

Much of the debate about this has been unfruitful, including claims that it is statistically better to use the weight rather than the percentage (102). However, workers are best advised to use the technique with which they are most comfortable and which meets their requirements, rather than to use weight of lean automatically. Certainly percentage lean in carcase has much to commend it because the number of independent variables in prediction equations can be reduced. Further, many practical applications are framed in terms of percentage lean in carcase, particularly in classification schemes.

STANDARDISATION OF BASE-LINE TISSUE SEPARATION
Throughout the world, research workers in the field of animal production use a variety of methods in their experiments. Some describe their methods in detail and in such cases others can understand the results and compare them with their own without difficulty. Unfortunately, however, many research workers do not provide such a detailed description and their results may not be given the attention they deserve because of difficulties in understanding.

These problems can be avoided if standard base-line techniques are used as they are in other fields of research. Standard techniques for chemical analysis are, for example, widely used in fundamental research. However, applied science inevitably relates to the practical conditions in a country, and standardised methods are more difficult to use. Indeed the record of standardisation of carcase evaluation techniques over the years has not been good; much lip service has been paid to the ideal, but little progress achieved. More concerted efforts in the U.S.A. and Europe have been seen in the 1980s.

Efforts to standardise methods in Europe were begun in the 1950s by the E.A.A.P., which collected information on pig progeny testing and carcase evaluation in European countries. The result of its work was published by F.A.O. (127).

The collection of information was started in response to interest in the possibility of standardising the methods of pig testing and selection in Europe. Discussions on the problems of standardisation went on until the 1960s but were then given up. Today one can hardly find two countries in Europe using the same system for the testing of pigs or for carcase evaluation. This may be expected in pig breeding which is carried out essentially within controlled environmental circumstances, where the evaluation technique applied is just another environmental factor to control.

Efforts are now being made in Europe to standardise beef carcase evaluation methods and to improve the awareness of techniques used in different countries. A recommended standard E.E.C. method for beef anatomical jointing, tissue separation and weight recording has been published (384).

The need for standardisation of techniques is most important in the application of commercial classification and grading schemes across different countries. The common E.E.C. pig grading scheme has grades defined by fixed ranges of carcase lean percentage and a co-ordinated exercise has been carried out to compare the techniques used in different countries for determining carcase lean content against a standard method (77). This exercise bears examination by anyone contemplating the wider standardisation of techniques. It was closely related to a practical application with clear economic objectives and an international base-line for carcase lean content was used to relate national methods. Countries were not expected to change their national methods except possibly where these were shown to be poorly related to the international base-line. The proposal is that lean percentages for grades will be defined by the international method and that the national methods would link this with the grading measurements currently taken in the individual countries.

3 Growth and development

The body composition of an animal changes as it grows and matures. The skeleton is relatively well developed at birth and grows fairly steadily thereafter. Muscle grows faster than bone after birth resulting in a progressive increase in the muscle to bone ratio. Fat tissue grows at a slow rate initially but during the fattening period its growth increases dramatically.

The relative growth of the different fat depots changes as fattening proceeds. The classical view of their order of development was intra-abdominal (internal body fat), intermuscular fat, subcutaneous fat and then intramuscular fat, but there is now evidence to suggest that intra-abdominal fat has a period of rapid growth later (201).

As the animal grows and the overall proportions of tissues change, the body develops to meet functional needs and the proportions of each tissue in different regions of the carcase change accordingly. The pattern of development is similar for bone, muscle and fat: development occurs earliest in the distal limbs with gradients of increasing growth moving inwards towards the back and loin. There is also a further gradient moving from the head towards the loin. Details of the pattern of development have been given by Berg and Butterfield (31).

The age and degree of maturity (i.e. the degree of progress made towards mature weight and composition) at which animals are slaughtered and compared will influence the variation found in carcase composition and the suitability of different measurements and techniques of carcase evaluation. Some knowledge of the factors influencing differences in carcase composition is, therefore, required when selecting evaluation techniques for different practical circumstances.

Growth curves

The rate at which an animal matures has a major influence on its composition at a given weight or age. The effect of differences in rate of maturity can be considered most simply in relation to adult body weight. The principles are the same for cattle, sheep and pigs and information for cattle will be used as an illustration.

All cattle have a target adult body weight which they are expected to reach by a certain age. When food is freely available those with heavier target body weights normally eat more and grow faster. So Charolais cattle grow faster than Hereford cattle and bulls grow faster than heifers. There has been much research interest in the relationship between growth rate to maturity and mature weight (*W*); it is established that growth rate to maturity is proportional to *W* raised to some power between 0.75 and 1.0, so cattle with heavier mature weights take longer to mature. (Reference 41 is especially useful on this topic.)

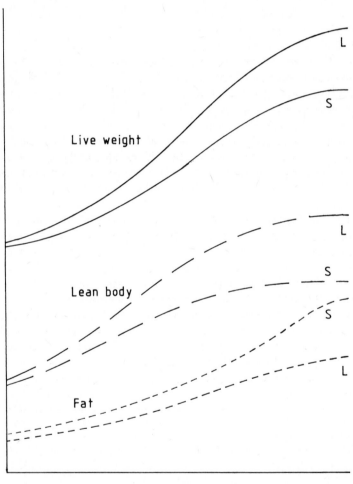

Fig. 3.1 Growth curves for a late-maturing animal of large adult body size (L) and for an early-maturing animal of small adult size (S)

As growth proceeds towards the target weight, there is a shift in the use of nutrients from bone and muscle growth to fat deposition, with animals of lower target weight generally using more of their nutrients for fat growth at a given age (i.e. they are earlier maturing). Some people refer to a sharp increase in fattening at a given age but it is not clear whether such a point exists or whether there is a gradual change in the pattern of tissue deposition as growth proceeds. Typical growth curves for a late-maturing animal of high target weight and an early-maturing animal of low target weight are shown in fig. 3.1, assuming a fairly gradual change in the pattern of tissue growth.

There are also important sex differences in rate of maturity. Heifers mature at lighter weights than steers and bulls, and fatten earlier. Provided that the fatten-ing phase has been reached, and under similar feeding conditions, heifers will be fatter than steers at a given weight and steers fatter than bulls.

Although this clear inverse relationship between growth rate and rate of maturity exists between the extremes of target body weight (breeds with heavier target weights growing faster and maturing later), there are differences in growth curves among breeds of more similar target weights which can disturb the rela-tionship. The Friesian, for example, grows relatively slowly and fattens later than would be expected from its target weight in comparison with the Hereford. Examples of these different types of growth curve are shown in fig. 3.2.

Differences observed between breeds in carcase composition are related there-fore to differences in target adult body weight and rate of maturity. But breeds also differ in muscle to bone ratio which is reflected in carcase lean content differences at the same level of fatness. Muscle to bone ratio is affected little by differences in degree of maturity and breeds have characteristic values over quite wide ranges of fatness. Breeds selected for body thickness or for draft usage generally have higher muscle to bone ratios than those selected for dairy characteristics. Limousin and Blonde d'Aquitaine cattle have the combination of thick muscula-ture and light bone structure which gives them outstandingly high ratios, whereas at the other extreme, the Canadian Holstein has an extremely low ratio reflect-ing much thinner musculature and heavier bones. Typical meat to bone ratios of crosses out of British Friesian dams by the main sire breeds are shown in fig. 3.3.

Given these basic relationships, the influence of the point at which different breeds are compared on the carcase composition of breeds grown contem-poraneously can be assessed. (Differences in tissue weights are considered as a percentage of carcase weight).

Comparison at:	Variation among breeds differing in target body weights
Equal live weight	Important variation in carcase composition: fast growing, later-maturing breeds will be leaner than slower growing, earlier-maturing breeds
Equal age	Variation in carcase weight: some variation in carcase composition depending on range of target weights and differences in growth curves
Equal fatness	Limited variation in carcase composition reflecting differences in muscle to bone ratio but substantial variation in weight

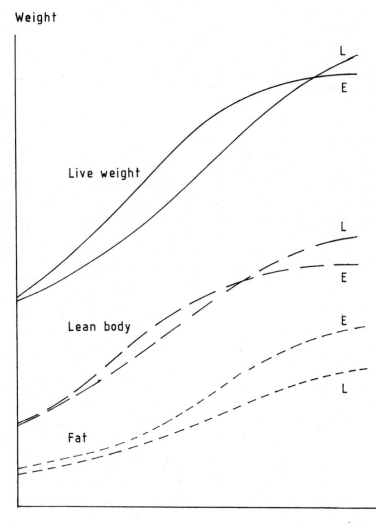

Fig. 3.2   Growth curves for early- (E) and late-maturing types (L) of cattle of similar mature size

The variation is illustrated in fig. 3.4 using results from the major U.S.D.A. breed evaluation programme carried out at Clay Center, Nebraska. The cattle were serially slaughtered and comparison is possible on different bases. Equal chemical fat in the *M. longissimus* was chosen as the definition of 'equal fatness' but this left considerable variation between breeds in the dissectable fat content of carcases as judged by the fat trim percentages. We have attempted to adjust for these differences in the final column and also show results for comparable cattle from M.L.C.'s beef breed evaluation programme, in which breeds were compared at equal carcase subcutaneous fat content assessed by visual appraisal of external fat cover. This figure shows the reduction in meat yield between breeds which occurs as the basis of comparison changes from weight to age and then to 'fatness'. It also illustrates how the definition of fatness can influence the results. This point is important in many areas of carcase evaluation and will be returned to in a later section.

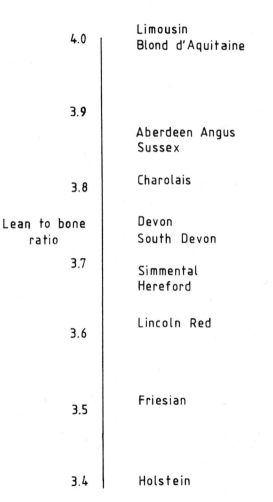

Fig. 3.3 Typical lean to bone ratios for crossbred cattle by different sire breeds. Based on various reports (29, 210, 211, 235)

Differences between sexes in muscle to bone ratio are influenced by the criterion on which they are compared. At an equal level of fatness, bulls will be superior to steers in muscle to bone ratio because they are less mature. There seems to be little difference between steers and heifers in a similar comparison.

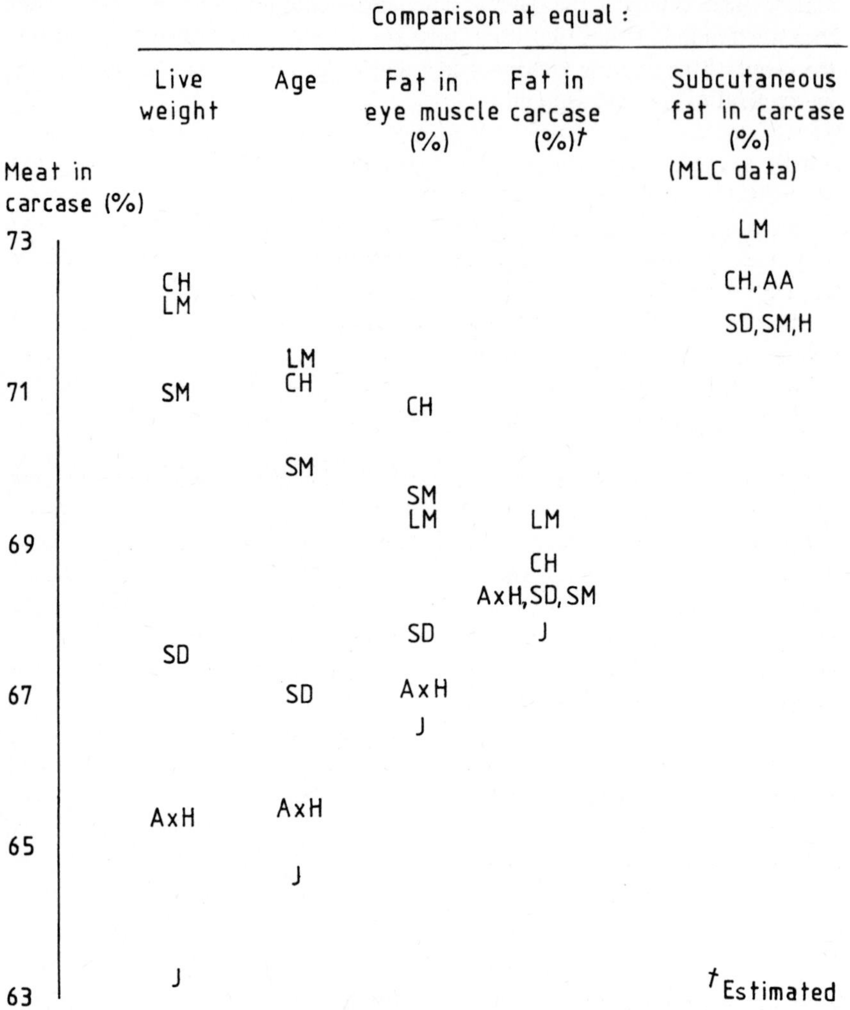

Comparison at equal :

Meat in carcase (%)	Live weight	Age	Fat in eye muscle (%)	Fat in carcase (%)†	Subcutaneous fat in carcase (%) (MLC data)
73					LM
	CH				CH, AA
	LM				SD, SM, H
		LM			
71	SM	CH	CH		
		SM			
			SM		
			LM	LM	
69				CH	
				AxH, SD, SM	
			SD	J	
	SD				
67		SD	AxH		
			J		
	AxH	AxH			
65					
		J			
63	J				†Estimated

Fig. 3.4 Meat yields from carcases of crossbred cattle by different sire breeds: Clay Centre data (236) with M.L.C. data (209) for comparison

Key: AA Aberdeen Angus; A × H Aberdeen Angus × Hereford; CH Charolais; J Jersey; LM Limousin; SM Simmental; SD South Devon

Influence of level of nutrition

These effects of differences in target body weight apply when the animals have free access to food. Carcase composition at equal weight or age is also influenced by level of nutrition.

While the interpretation of nutritional effects on growth has differed between research workers for many years, lean body mass and fat are now seen to be affected quite differently by changes in nutrition. The growth of lean body mass, comprising muscle, bone and other essential tissues, is relatively independent of temporary changes in level of feeding, with the exception of a small labile component which is more quickly drawn on during periods of under-nutrition (130). Most of the fat, on the other hand, is used to buffer the essential tissues from changes in energy intake. At high levels of feed intake, excess energy is stored as fat; when feed is limited in supply, energy stored as fat is used for maintenance and growth so that there is only a small reduction in the energy retention of lean body mass. Significant changes occur in lean body mass only when nutrition is severely restricted.

An important factor in commercial beef production is to match breeds to systems of feeding to achieve optimum levels of fatness and weight for different markets. Earlier-maturing sire breeds are normally best suited to extensive forage-based systems and later-maturing breeds to intensive cereal-based systems (fig. 3.5).

From the point of view of choosing methods of carcase evaluation, differences in nutrition complicate the relationship between weight and fatness for animals of the same breed. Consequently, weight provides less information about carcase fatness for a group of animals from different feeding systems than for a group of animals from the same feeding system. On the other hand, since muscle and bone and their interrelationship are fairly resilient to changes in feeding, measurements based on these characteristics remain useful predictors of carcase composition in groups of cattle from different feeding systems.

At a given live weight, the percentage of fat in the carcase is closely related negatively to the percentage of lean. It follows, therefore, that these characteristics are largely interchangeable from the carcase evelution point of view, and this explains the emphasis given to fat measurements as predictors of carcase lean percentage. However, this interchangeability should not obscure the fact that these characteristics are influenced in quite a different manner by nutrition and genetics.

Variation in muscle and bone weight distribution

Muscle weight distribution (the proportion of the total muscle which is found in different parts of the carcase) has received considerable attention from research workers, particularly for cattle, and it is now generally accepted that this is a relatively stable characteristic both genetically and environmentally. Bone weight distribution has also been shown to be relatively stable (the subject has been reviewed by Berg and Butterfield, 31).

Nevertheless, differences have been found between breeds in muscle weight distribution (results from some of the main trials are summarised in fig. 3.6). These are due to some extent to differences in rate of maturity if comparisons are made at the same weight or age, when later-maturing animals would be expected to have more muscle and bone in the earlier developing parts of the carcase (particularly the limbs). Differences also exist independently of rate of maturity. For example, the muscular continental breeds have a small advantage over other breeds, when compared at the same level of fatness, in the proportion of muscle in the more valuable parts of the hindquarters. Somewhat larger differences can exist between double-muscled and normal cattle at the same degree of maturity. Published information on the differences between double-muscled and normal cattle has been summarised by Johnson (187).

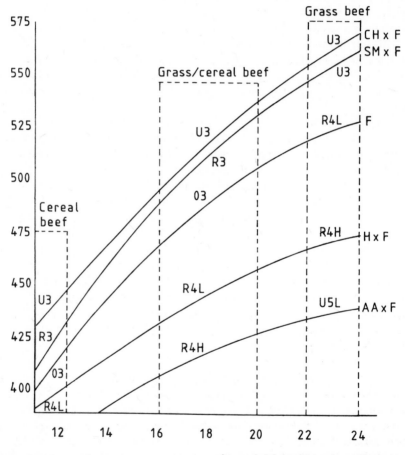

Fig. 3.5   Average live weight and age at slaughter for steers of several breeds and crosses on different production systems. Typical classification for fatness and conformation (using the terminology of the E.E.C beef carcase classification scheme − see table 13.14)

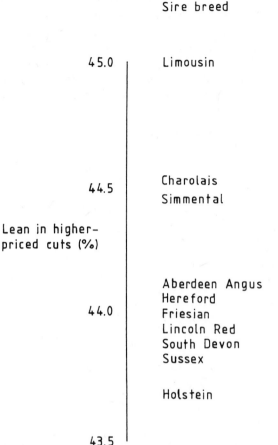

Fig. 3.6 Typical percentages of total lean which occurs in the higher-priced cuts: top piece (ex leg), loin, rump and fore rib. Based on various reports (29, 210, 211, 235)

The sexes also differ in muscle weight distribution, the differences becoming more obvious as cattle mature. In older bulls there is a pronounced development of muscles in the neck region (the crest) and a reduced proportion in the higher-priced cuts; steers often show a partial crest whereas in heifers there is no such development (31).

Variation in lean and bone weight distribution in populations of cattle differing, for example, in breed or sex has implications for the estimation of overall carcase composition, particularly when the weight of individual muscles or the dissection of a small part of the carcase or sample joint provides the basis of estimation. If there is on average relatively less lean in a particular joint for one breed than for another, the use of this joint may lead to biased estimates of the differences between the breeds in overall carcase lean content. This point will be returned to later when the choice of carcase evaluation techniques for use in population studies and experiments is considered.

Muscle and bone weight distributions are stable to changes in nutrition in the same way as muscle to bone ratios and weights. Body weight loss can alter relative muscle development (342). However, to induce small changes, extreme differences in plane of feeding have been required, suggesting that the possibilities of altering tissue distribution using commercial feeding levels are small.

Variation in fat partition and distribution

The partition of fat between different depots (subcutaneous, intermuscular, intramuscular and intra-abdominal) and their distribution between different regions of the carcase, have commanded less attention from research workers than most other aspects of growth and development. Difficulties are created by the fact that there are few clear-cut anatomical boundaries in adipose tissue.

The pattern of fat deposition changes as fattening progresses so it is important to identify and remove the effects of differences in the overall level of fatness when comparing breeds or other factors.

Published information on breed differences in the fat partition of cattle, sheep and pigs was reviewed by Kempster (201). Results available from breed trials indicate that there is important genetic variation for all three species in the partitioning of fat between depots, at the same overall level of fatness. For example, extreme dairy-type breeds of cattle deposit a higher proportion of their total fat internally (as KKCF) and a lower proportion subcutaneously than native British breeds such as the Hereford and Aberdeen Angus; mountain breeds of sheep also tend to have more KKCF than British down breeds, such as the Suffolk and Hampshire, which have been developed as terminal sires for meat production. The ranges of differences between breeds of cattle and sheep are shown in tables 3.1 and 3.2. There is however less variation in the way a given weight of subcutaneous fat or intermuscular fat is distributed between different parts of the carcase.

Differences have also been recorded between sexes in fat partition at equal total fat, but these are small and relatively unimportant. Information on the environmental effects on fat partition and distribution is particularly limited. An important question in this context, from the point of view of carcase evaluation techniques, is whether fat patterns are capable of being modified at a given level of overall fatness, or whether they are controlled too closely by fatness within the breed. A redistribution from the internal fat depots and intermuscular fat towards subcutaneous fat and intramuscular fat would be particularly useful in terms of improving the efficiency of carcase saleable meat production. There is little evidence to indicate that such a change is possible within breeds.

Fat partition and distribution are important from the point of view of carcase evaluation for several reasons.

Table 3.1 Summary of results of differences between breeds of cattle in fat partition: weights of KKCF and intermuscular fat (IMF) expressed on various bases, relative to Hereford or Hereford cross

Trial	(1)		(2)		(3) cereal-fed		(3) grass/cereal-fed		(4)	(5)	
	KKCF	IMF	KKCF	IMF	KKCF	IMF	KKCF	IMF	KKCF	KKCF	IMF
Base breed											
Hereford	100	100	100	100	100	100	100	100	100	100	100
Hereford x	119	103									
Dairy breed											
Ayrshire					157	103					
Friesian			159	105	132	107	128	102		119	104
Friesian x	119	103									
Friesian* x with:											
Aberdeen Angus	119	100					123	99		90	100
Charolais	107	107			116	110				125	106
Devon										108	102
Limousin					149	95				106	100
Simmental					130	104	116	106		106	98
South Devon					149	95					
Sussex										108	101

Table 3.1 (contd.)

Trial	(1) KKCF	(1) IMF	(2) KKCF	(2) IMF	(3) cereal-fed KKCF	(3) cereal-fed IMF	(3) grass/cereal-fed KKCF	(3) grass/cereal-fed IMF	(4) KKCF	(5) KKCF	(5) IMF
Pure beef breed or beef breed cross											
Aberdeen Angus			138	103	108	104				100	100
Charolais			176	104					148	119	106
Devon										104	103
Limousin									148	111	100
Lincoln Red										104	107
Luing										131	108
Simmental									144	115	110
South Devon									133	115	108
Sussex										104	97
Welsh Black							123	92		112	106
Jersey x beef breed									162		

*or Swedish Red and White

(1) Lindhé and Henningsson (252): fat depot weights as percentages of total chemical fat, with comparison at approximately equal fat percentage in carcase.

(2) Charles and Johnson (69): fat depot weights as a percentage of total dissected carcase fat, adjusted to equal total dissected fat in carcase.

(3) Kempster, Cuthbertson and Harrington (214): fat depot weights adjusted to equal total fat weight in carcase.

(4) Koch et al (236): KKCF weights at equal fat trim weight in carcase.

(5) Kempster, Charles and Cook (205): fat depot weights as a percentage of carcase weight, adjusted to equal percentage of subcutaneous fat in carcase.

Table 3.2 Summary of results of differences between breeds of sheep in fat partition: fat depot weights as percentages of carcase weight, relative to the purebred Suffolk or Suffolk cross

Trial	(1)		(2)		(3)	
	KKCF	IMF	KKCF	IMF	KKCF	IMF
Base breed						
Suffolk or Suffolk x	100	100	100	100	100	100
Purebred						
Blackfaced Mountain	121	90				
British Longwool	150	93				
Welsh Mountain	160	98				
Crossbred with sires						
Border Leicester			90	103		
British Longwool	118	87				
Dorset Down			98	103	99	102
Hampshire Down			93	104		
Ile de France			98	101	100	99
Intermediate*	114	94				
North Country Cheviot			103	98		
Oldenburg					94	99
Oxford Down			98	103	95	97
Southdown	132	98	95	105		
Texel					107	89
Wensleydale			103	95		

*Intermediate-type lambs by Dorset Down or Hampshire Down sires.
(1) Kempster and Cuthbertson (213): national survey of breed types.
(2) Croston, Jones and Kempster (83): M.L.C.'s ram breed trial.
(3) Unpublished results from a breed comparison trial carried out at A.B.R.O. Edinburgh. The trial was described by Wolf, Smith and Sales (393).

(a) Many of the simple predictors of overall carcase composition used in breeding programmes and classification schemes involve the measurement of subcutaneous fat thicknesses or areas. The precision achieved with such measurements depends on the variability of fat partition and distribution between different animals. If breeds, or whatever factor is being compared, differ significantly in the ratio of subcutaneous fat to total fat, bias will exist in the estimated differences between them in overall carcase composition.

(b) Variations in fat partition have a similar implication for breeding schemes. If there is a poor genetic relationship between the growth of different depots, selection against overall fatness based on one depot will not achieve an effective reduction in other fat depots.

(c) Fat partition is also involved in beliefs about eating quality. Intramuscular fat (marbling) has traditionally been an indicator of beef quality and since it is a later developing depot, high levels of fatness have been necessary to achieve what was considered the desired level of marbling. This point finds expression in the U.S.D.A. beef grading system, and indeed marbling has been proposed as a predictor of carcase meat yield.

(d) More recently, fat partition has been seen as an expression of different physiological types of cattle, sheep and pigs which have characteristic differences in stress susceptibility, metabolic efficiency and meat quality (253). Although there is little evidence, other than with pigs, to indicate a strong relationship between these factors, research in this area may lead to the development of new methods for identifying breeding stock which produce lean meat most efficiently.

To improve the estimation of carcase composition, it is important to know why fat deposition follows a particular pattern. Berg and Butterfield (31) suggested that differences in fat distribution could be explained in terms of the line of least resistance. They considered that the muscles and body shape create variable pressures and fat is deposited where easiest. Such a hypothesis may explain the distribution of fat within individual depots and why relatively little variation exists. However, fat partition between depots presents a different problem. The results indicate that certain forms of activity, such as high levels of milk production and possibly the ability to survive in hill environments, are associated with greater fat deposition in the internal fat depots.

If a simple explanation, such as line of least resistance, were to explain most of the variation in fat partition and distribution, much of the bias involved in the use of simpler predictions could probably be explained by live weight, level of feeding and degree of maturity. However, the existence of important differences in fat partition at constant degree of maturity, due it seems to differences in genetic history, suggests that bias due to fat partition will remain a problem in carcase evaluation work so long as the best way of predicting carcase lean content in commercial applications is through measures of external fat cover.

Link between growth, feed efficiency and carcase composition

The main determinants of feed efficiency (unit output per unit input) are level of food intake and the partition of metabolisable food products between maintenance, protein deposition and fat deposition. The energy costs for maintenance are related to the active body mass, and normally taken as being proportional to live weight to the power 0.75. The metabolisable energy costs above maintenance are similar at about 54 MJ/kg for the deposition of fat and protein (364). However, since muscle is 75-80 per cent water and adipose tissue is normally less than 15 per cent water, the energy requirement to deposit a unit weight of muscle is substantially less than that required to deposit a unit of weight of fatty tissue. The ratio is between 1:4 and 1:5.

Given this relationship, measures of efficiency can be used as an indication of carcase composition under a number of circumstances. Measures of efficiency will contribute an important part of the prediction of carcase lean content in pig breeding programmes based on selection indexes incorporating growth and carcase characteristics. Indeed, the prediction can be refined by careful control of feed intake and the length of the test period (and thus the maintenance requirement) so that differences in efficiency depend essentially on the partition of energy between fat and muscle growth (228).

Selection based on growth rate has been used extensively in cattle breeding to improve the efficiency of feed utilisation, on the assumption that faster growing genotypes are heavier and, therefore, more efficient. However, this relationship has been the subject of much debate because unfortunately growth rate is generally positively associated with adult body weight (234). Animals of large body size have higher maintenance requirements and it is argued that the cost of maintaining breeding stock should be included in the overall calculation of efficiency, and growth rate corrected for body size in breeding schemes. This problem has not generated such debate in pigs because they are multiparous and breeding stock costs are shared over a considerably larger output.

Choice of carcase evaluation technique

Since animals of different types grow and develop at different rates and have basic differences in muscle to bone ratio and fat partition at the same degree of maturity, the choice of which carcase evaluation technique to use will depend on the types of animals involved and the basis on which they are to be compared.

Consider, for example, a progeny test in which pigs are slaughtered and compared at the same live weight, and a breed comparison trial in which cattle are slaughtered at the same level of fatness.

In the former case, live weight will obviously be of little value as an indication of carcase composition, whereas age or measures of fatness are likely to be important because they identify the late-maturing progeny groups which are leaner at a fixed live weight.

In the latter case it is necessary to consider on what basis the breeds are judged to be equal in fatness. If they have equal external fat cover, measures of subcutaneous fat are not likely to be of value as predictors, but there might still be value in measuring other fat depots if variation in overall carcase fatness is thought to exist.

In both cases, measurements related to the muscle to bone ratio might be valuable in predicting carcase composition.

Fig. 3.7, from M.L.C.'s beef breed evaluation programme, illustrates the relative contributions of bone and fat trim to meat yield when breeds are compared at equal carcase subcutaneous fat percentage.

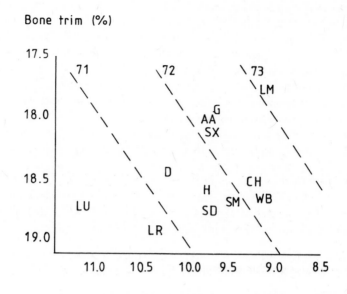

Fig. 3.7 Comparison of breeds in bone trim and fat trim at the same external fatness (fat class 3L in the M.L.C. classification scheme*) with bands of equal saleable meat yield (%) indicated (210)

Carcases were from purebred Galloway (G), Luing (LU) and Welsh Black (WB) or out of Blue-Grey and Hereford x Friesian dams by the sire breeds indicated:

AA Aberdeen Angus; CH Charolais; D Devon; H Hereford; LM Limousin; LR Lincoln Red; SM Simmental; SD South Devon; SX Sussex
*This is the former terminology subsequently altered in 1981 (see table 13.14).

4 Prediction

An understanding of statistical principles is essential for the interpretation of carcase evaluation results and, in particular, for the comparison of alternative predictors. The following is a brief guide to these principles, indicating some pitfalls in the use or misuse of the most common method of analysis — namely regression.

Methods for calculating basic statistical parameters from raw data are not described. These are covered adequately in a number of simple statistical textbooks.

The mechanics of such calculations are now straightforward. A range of cheap calculators is available, programmed to perform basic regression analyses directly. In addition, a further range of programmable calculators and mini-computers, capable of complex calculations, can meet most users' requirements. Access to more powerful computers is necessary when large quantities of data with many variables are being analysed and more flexible data handling is required.

Simple regression line, correlation coefficient and residual standard deviation

The statistical problems of prediction will be illustrated by the example of estimating carcase lean percentage in pigs (that is y, the dependent variate) from a fat thickness measurement such as P_2 taken over the *M. longissimus* by probe (that is x, the independent variate). Fig. 4.1 shows the results of plotting the measurements of these two characteristics made on a sample of pigs.

The average values of x and y in the sample ($\bar{x}$ and $\bar{y}$) are shown, together with a hand-drawn line that subjectively fits the data as closely as possible. Such plots are, in fact, a simple and useful way of carrying out a preliminary examination of data, and often provide a better starting point than the calculation of statistical parameters. One can see, for example, whether the data from the sample are grouped in any way, or if certain values are extreme. Such grouping or extreme points may significantly alter the parameters obtained, particularly when small numbers of carcases are involved.

This line is of the form:

$$y = a + bx$$

Lean in carcase (%)

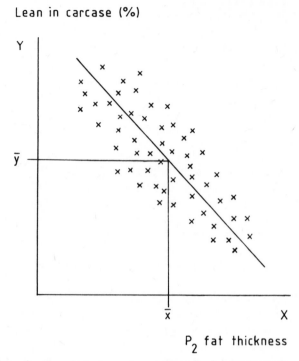

P$_2$ fat thickness

Fig. 4.1 Plot of carcase lean percentage against P$_2$ fat thickness for a sample of pig carcases. Hand-drawn line which subjectively fits the data is shown

where a is the intercept on the vertical axis (the value of y when $x = 0$) and b is the slope of the line (that is the change which occurs in y for a given change in x). In the example, b is negative because leanness decreases as fat thickness increases.

Subjective fitting of regression lines by eye is unsatisfactory for a proper examination of data, and statistical procedures are available to determine the line of best fit. This gives values of a and b which minimise the sums of squares of deviations of the observations of y from the fitted line (fig. 4.2). This minimum sum of squared deviations leads to a measure of closeness of fit — the residual standard deviation (residual s.d.). The regression line once fitted can be used to predict a value of y from any additional observation of x (made on the same population of carcases) and it is possible to calculate from the residual s.d. how accurate these predictions will be.

In general, the closer the scatter of points about the line, the more precise the prediction. However, precision in this sense is a function of variability in the chosen sample.

The statistical parameter which describes the scatter of points about the regression line is the correlation coefficient (r), which is also used to measure the percentage of variation in y explained by x (calculated as $100r^2$). The correlation coefficient is influenced by the range of values in the sample on which it is based. Although satisfactory for comparing predictors in the same sample of carcases, the correlation coefficient is not in itself suitable for comparing the precision obtained in different samples.

Lean in carcase (%)

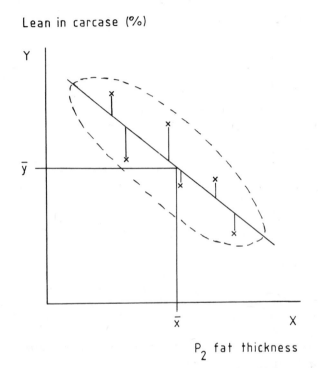

P$_2$ fat thickness

Fig. 4.2 Plot of carcase lean percentage against P_2 fat thickness showing the line of best fit which minimises the sums of squares of the deviations of y observations from the line

When making such comparisons, the residual s.d. is a much better criterion. It is related to the correlation, but takes account of the variation in y:

$$\text{Residual s.d.} = \text{s.d.} y \sqrt{[(1 - r^2)\frac{n-1}{n-2}]}$$

where s.d.y is the standard deviation of y and n is the number of carcases in the sample.

Considered in terms of the example, r^2 is the fraction of the variation in carcase lean percentage which can be explained by P_2 while $(1 - r^2)$ is the part which cannot be explained (the residual variation).

The dangers of relying on the correlation coefficient can be shown by reference to the two samples of pigs illustrated in fig. 4.3. The relationship between the various parameters in these two samples is as follows:

	Sample I	Sample II
Variation in x (s.d.)	5.10	2.99
Variation in y (s.d.)	4.10	2.29
$100r^2$	75	21
Residual s.d.	2.05	2.05

The results indicate that carcase lean percentage shows more variation in sample I and that P_2 as judged by the correlation coefficient (r) appears to be a good predictor. In sample II, however, there is less variation in carcase lean percentage and a lower correlation. But there would be no more error in the prediction of carcase lean percentage in sample II since the spread of points about the regression line is the same as shown by the residual s.d.

Advertisements for new measuring equipment commonly incorporate results drawn from very variable samples to provide a high correlation and impress prospective buyers. Such claims should always be viewed with caution and an assessment made of how the variation differs from that of the circumstances in which the equipment might be used. By the same token, if one piece of equipment is compared with another, this should be done using samples of carcases with the same variation; or better still, they should be compared on the same sample of carcases.

A residual s.d. can be considered much in the same way as any standard deviation. If the prediction equation were to be used on 100 animals, about two-thirds of the predicted values will be within ± 1 residual s.d. of the actual values and 95 of the predicted values will be within ± 2 residual s.d. of the actual values.

Besides being a more useful indication of comparative precision, the residual s.d. is generally easier to interpret than the correlation coefficient when selecting characteristics to use in classification and grading schemes, or for use in population studies and experiments. The correlation coefficient is more commonly relied on in breeding scheme design and analysis, but in that case the variation in dependent variates is taken into account separately when selection indexes are computed.

The convention adopted for the presentation of results in later sections of this book is to report the sample variation of the characteristic being predicted, and the residual s.d. when a particular predictor is used.

The regression line determined from a sample is, of course, itself an estimate of the relationship between y and x in the whole population. The parameters a and b are themselves estimates of 'true' underlying population values. An implication of this is that each estimate of y determined from a regression equation has attached to it a standard error of estimate which is a function not only of the residual s.d. but also of the sample size used to estimate the equation, and the distance of the appropriate observed x from the mean of the sample. The error of an estimated value of y is smallest when the regression is based on a

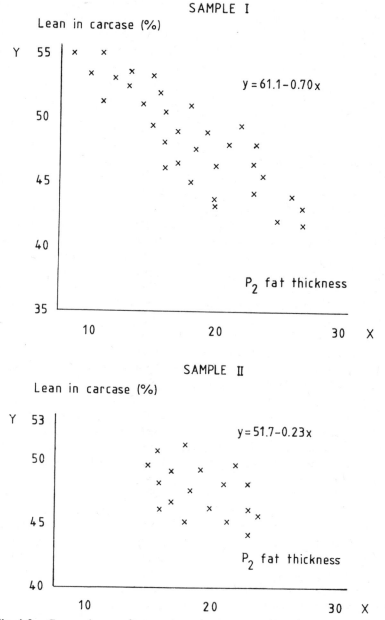

Fig. 4.3 Comparisons of regressions in two samples of carcases differing in variation

large sample, when the animals on which the determination of the line is based are concentrated at the extremes, and when the carcases to be estimated are at or near the mean of the dissected sample. These considerations indicate that the sample of carcases requires careful consideration when setting up regression equations.

But there is a big gap between theory and practice in the use of regression equations. Even if a regression equation is determined with high precision by using what was considered at the time as a large, perfectly representative, carefully selected sample, further errors are easily introduced by small changes in measuring technique or procedure when the equation is applied. In the case of measurements like P_2, they may have to be taken by a different person, or there may be a change in slaughtering procedure so that the carcases are warmer when they are measured.

More serious error, which we shall term *bias*, can result if the equation is applied in quite different circumstances from those for which it was constructed. This is all too frequent as resources are often not available to carry out base-line evaluations and establish purpose-built equations. The equation may have to be used on a different breed of pig or applied when the P_2 measurements are taken on the live pig by ultrasonics instead of by probe on the carcase.

The only way of eliminating such bias with certainty is to determine regression equations in the same circumstances as those in which they will be used, although judicious choice of predicting measurements can help in some circumstances. Statistical procedures for handling the problem of bias will be considered later in the section on population studies and experiments.

Comparison of regression equations

There may be an advantage in combining regression equations computed from different groups of animals. If the equations in the groups do not differ more than would be expected by chance (bearing in mind that each is based on a sample), the increase in numbers provides an improved estimate of the regression parameters. A regression equation demonstrated to hold over a range of groups of animals will also lead to much greater confidence for its application in new circumstances.

The statistical procedures for testing differences between equations examine intercepts (the a) and slopes (the b) separately. Intercepts frequently differ, but significant differences in slope rarely occur unless there is a very wide range in variation among the animals examined. Among animals slaughtered at the same weight, age or fatness, there are usually few slope differences between regression equations relating measurements or other simple predictors to elements of carcase composition.

Data with a common slope may therefore be pooled, while retaining different intercepts for different groups. The residual s.d. so obtained effectively measures the average precision achieved within the groups and is commonly referred to as the pooled within-group residual s.d.

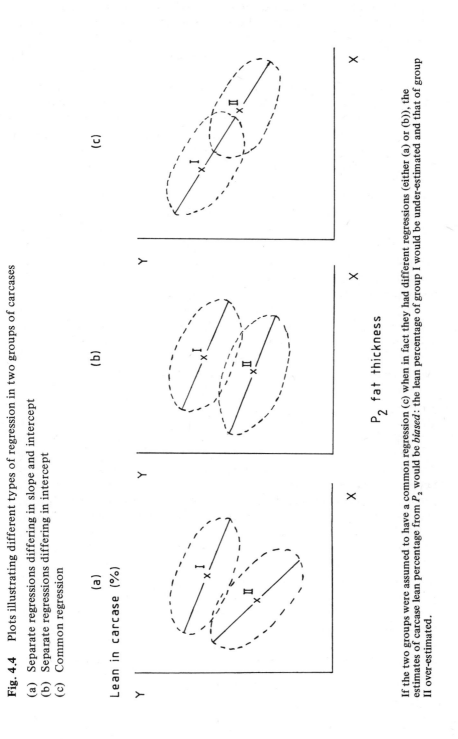

Fig. 4.4 Plots illustrating different types of regression in two groups of carcases

(a) Separate regressions differing in slope and intercept
(b) Separate regressions differing in intercept
(c) Common regression

If the two groups were assumed to have a common regression (c) when in fact they had different regressions (either (a) or (b)), the estimates of carcase lean percentage from P_2 would be *biased*: the lean percentage of group I would be under-estimated and that of group II over-estimated.

If neither intercept nor slope differs significantly between groups, the groups can be considered as part of a larger single group with an overall regression equation.

The three situations — separate regressions for each group, common slopes in each group but different intercepts, and common regression lines — are illustrated in fig. 4.4 (a), (b) and (c) for the regression of carcase lean percentage on P_2.

Fig. 4.4 (b) also provides an illustration of prediction bias. If an overall regression line were used to estimate the average lean percentage of the two groups, it would over-estimate one and under-estimate the other.

Multiple regression

Carcase composition may be predicted from more than one independent variate. The multiple regression equation with two independent variates is of the form:

$$y = a + b_1 x_1 + b_2 x_2$$

where b_1 and b_2 are called the partial regression coefficients for independent variates x_1 and x_2. Further independent variates introduce further partial regression coefficients.

In principle, calculation of correlations and residual s.d. and of differences between groups, are similar to but more complex than those for simple regressions.

Consider the prediction of carcase lean percentage from P_2 fat thickness when there is also variation in carcase weight. Carcase weight is easily obtained, so when evaluating the usefulness of the P_2 fat thickness measurement as a predictor, it is sensible to ask: how valuable would P_2 be as a predictor of carcase lean percentage among pigs of the same weight? If P_2 were only useful when there was variation in weight, there would be no point in probing — we could simply weigh the carcases. P_2 is shown to be of 'real' value when its addition to an equation, already including carcase weight, leads to a significant reduction in residual standard deviation.

The correlation between carcase lean percentage (y) and P_2 (x) when variation due to carcase weight has been removed is known as the partial correlation with carcase weight (w) constant $(r_{xy.w})$. This can be calculated from knowledge of the correlations between each of the pairs of characteristics as follows:

$$r_{xy.w} = \frac{r_{xy} - r_{xw} r_{yw}}{\sqrt{[(1 - r^2 xw)(1 - r^2 yw)]}}$$

A common problem is to choose those of a number of measurements which contribute usefully to the predictive accuracy when combined together in a multiple regression equation. There are statistical computer programs which test all combinations and add variates in order of their additional contribution to the precision with which y is predicted.

Having selected the first variate, the next most precise variate which adds most to the equation is then added and so on. When each of the measurements has the same cost, this approach is acceptable but when measurements differ in cost, a more logical approach is to use first the measurements which give the most precise prediction for their cost. This may lead to a different conclusion when only a small number of variates can be used.

Curvilinear regression

Although the simple linear regression between x and y is adequate for many purposes, there are situations where a more complicated relationship exists and it is necessary to fit a curve. Several types of curve can be used but one based on the linear regression with the square of x added often fits the data adequately:

$$y = a + bx + cx^2$$

If curvilinearity does occur in the data, fitting of the appropriate curve will improve the precision of prediction.

Methods of evaluation

5 Scale and cost

There have been numerous studies to examine the value of different live animal and carcase characteristics for predicting overall carcase composition. However, most of the early work was carried out on a small scale using data collected as part of feeding and breeding studies. The samples of carcases were rarely ideal for examining the suitability of predictors for a range of practical applications and, all too often, only a single measuring technique was examined, making it difficult or impossible to compare its precision with other techniques.

Thus a major deficiency in early carcase research was that so much of it was non-comparative in nature: all that could be said at the conclusion of such studies was that a particular method looked 'promising', this comment being based on a subjective appraisal of the variation found. The position is improving since a number of centres around the world are now carrying out detailed evaluation of a range of techniques in carcase work, associated directly with large-scale breeding schemes and population studies.

In this section, we have drawn on these large-scale experiments, bringing the information together in a final chapter which covers each species separately and compares the precision of the more important measuring techniques.

The question of cost also needs to be considered. There are difficulties since the costs of dissection and carcase-cutting depend to a great extent on the facilities available in the individual laboratory or carcase evaluation unit, on the labour content, and on the ability of the meat trade in the area to use the output. Costs of carcase evaluation can, for example, be much reduced if the output is in a form which can be sold as conventional cuts at normal prices. Where costs are quoted for cutting and dissection, we have used information from the M.L.C. Carcase Evaluation Unit, expressing the costs as a percentage of the cost of dissection of a complete carcase side.

6 Live animal evaluation

Prediction of body composition on the live animal is necessary in a whole range of circumstances, from the producer selecting animals from his stock that are ready for slaughter, through the selection of superior sires on the basis of performance tests, to the scientist monitoring changes in body composition during growth.

Despite the commercial importance of accurate predictive techniques, efforts to develop them have been relatively unsuccessful. The precision achieved with the most sophisticated equipment has been little better than that obtained by simple fat and muscle measurements taken on the carcase. To some extent this has been due to a lack of clear objectives but it is also important to recognise that there are significant problems associated with the development of accurate predictors for use on live animals. The animal is anatomically and structurally complex and is rarely as conveniently unmoving as the carcase.

The lack of clear objectives is particularly noticeable in the measurements taken by live animal probes or ultrasonic machines where workers have correlated live animal measurements with the corresponding measurements made subsequently on the carcase. As Berg and Butterfield (31) point out: 'If a live back fat measure is to be of any use it must predict carcase composition not another back fat measurement. How useful is 0.6 correlation of ultrasonic loin eye measurement to carcase loin eye area when the latter has only 0.2 correlation with per cent carcase muscle?'

Live weight

As animals grow their carcase composition changes: the proportion of fat increases at the expense of muscle and bone. For animals of similar type grown contemporaneously, live weight will, therefore, normally show a high positive correlation with the proportion of fat in the carcase and, because of the close relationship between muscle and bone, a high negative correlation with the proportion of lean in the carcase.

Even in mixed-breed populations with animals coming from different production systems, there is often an association between weight and fatness although the degree of correlation will be variable. This variation is not always recognised by those who point to high correlations between weight and fatness derived from animals varying widely in weight. One can imagine circumstances where the assumption of a positive relationship will be misleading. Consider, for example, Aberdeen Angus and Charolais cattle grown in the same production system and slaughtered at the same age, or cereal-fed and grass-fed cattle of the same breeds slaughtered at market weights. In both cases across breeds, the lighter carcases may well be fatter.

Another aspect of the relationship between live weight and fatness is that it will be sensitive to the way animals are fed, the environment in which they are grown and any sub-clinical disease which may alter their growth rate. Live weight, and its relationship with composition, is also very dependent on the contents of the digestive tract which can vary from 10 per cent to 20 per cent of live weight in cattle, depending on the type of diet fed. An equation developed to predict fatness from live weight in one set of circumstances is therefore unlikely to apply with acceptable accuracy in other circumstances.

One instance where live weight can be of value is as an approximate guide to the weight at which lambs of different breeds should be slaughtered to achieve a given level of fatness. This is used in Britain as a basis for advising farmers when their lambs are likely to be ready for slaughter. A crossbred lamb's potential adult live weight lies midway between the adult weights of its parent breeds. Well-grown lambs slaughtered at half their potential adult body weight will normally kill out to produce carcases weighing just below 50 per cent of live weight and with a level of fatness close to the national average in Britain. Carcase weights for some of the main crosses are shown in table 6.1. The usefulness of this simple technique around the world would be improved considerably if reports of results of research and testing programmes with sheep routinely included mature weights of breeding animals.

How then should live weight be handled as a predictor in other circumstances, since it is normally associated with carcase composition and is sensitive to the environment? Weight is a predictor with negligible cost and it is normally available in all practical circumstances where predictors are used. Since the choice of predictors depends on finding the best compromise between precision and cost, measurements of negligible cost which are likely to be valuable predictors should automatically be included in prediction equations. The answer, therefore, is always to include live weight as the first independent variable in the equations, and to determine the value of other predictors as further independent variables, that is determine how valuable the others would be as predictors among live animals of the same weight.

Had this simple policy been adopted by all those examining the relative value of different live animal evaluation techniques, there would be much less confusion in the published literature. Unless live weight has been included in prediction equations, one cannot be sure whether the precision ascribed to more costly predictors could not, in fact, have been achieved at negligible cost by using live weight alone.

This point is, of course, not limited to live weight. In circumstances where other simple growth performance characteristics are available, these should also

Table 6.1 Carcase weights of lambs by different sire breeds when compared at the same level of fatness* (based on M.L.C.'s ram breed trial, 83), and comparable carcase weights estimated from adult body size.

| Sire breed | *Trial results* | | Estimated |
	No. of carcases	Carcase weight (kg)	carcase weight (kg)
Southdown	423	16.5	16
Dorset Down	550	17.4	17.5
Hampshire Down	417	17.8	18
Ile de France	298	18.5	18.5
North Country Cheviot	394	18.7	18
Texel	404	19.3	18.5
Suffolk	530	19.4	19
Border Leicester	412	19.9	20
Oxford Down	397	20.1	21
Wensleydale	302	20.5	21.5

* 12 per cent subcutaneous fat in carcase; on the borderline of fat classes 3L and 3H in M.L.C.'s sheep carcase classification scheme (198).

The trial involved three dam types: Scottish Blackface, Scotch Halfbred (Border Leicester X North Country Cheviot) and Mule (Blue-faced Leicester X Swaledale). The sire breed results are for lambs out of an average of the three dam types.

be handled in the same way as live weight if they contribute usefully to prediction. For example, in breeding schemes, live weight for age (or daily live-weight gain) will almost certainly be available. The value of other predictors should then be examined with weight-for-age constant.

In the discussion following, where the precision of different predictors is quoted, live weight at evaluation is constant unless otherwise stated.

Body dimensions

There has long been interest in the use of external body measurements of the live animal to predict carcase composition. While there are a number of reports of their use in experiments to record changes in growth and shape, they have not been used widely.

The early results appeared promising but were often obtained within groups of animals showing wide variation in size and shape, and interpreted only by correlation coefficients. High correlations with tissue weights were obtained reflecting variation in live weight and its association with body dimensions.

Some relationships can be established between external body measurements and skeletal characteristics (such as the weights and dimensions of bones) particularly where there is little interference from overlaying fat and muscle. But accurate estimates of soft tissues are more difficult to obtain. Little is known about the effect of variation in each tissue independently on body dimensions, and distinguishing the effects of fat and muscle on shape is difficult: animals can be blocky because they have thick well-developed muscles or because they are fat.

A further problem concerns the accuracy with which the measurements can be taken. There are many reports to indicate that the accuracy is inadequate to discriminate between members of relatively homogenous groups of animals. Estimates of skeletal structure tend to have the highest repeatabilities, followed by measures of bone and flesh (for example, width of the shoulders) where the skeletal structures involved help to stabilise the relationships. Estimates of soft tissue only (for example circumference of hind leg) are least repeatable. Taylor and Craig (362) outlined some of the problems of obtaining reliable live animal measurements and the subject has been reviewed more recently by Fisher (124).

Once the important effect of a large range in weight was appreciated, the results examined in this new light were disappointing. Only with a large number of measurements do dimensions add significantly to the information provided by live weight in estimating carcase composition (see 144). But even then the advantage is small.

Techniques are available to provide an integrated measure of width over the entire length of beef carcases which could be used for live animal measurement (123). Profile areas can be obtained from photographic negatives of dorsal views with adjustment for length differences. However, such techniques have not been fully evaluated for live animal assessment.

More detailed shape measurements can now be made using the stereophotogrammetry method. The earliest experiments involved expensive equipment, but a relatively cheap type of stereophotogrammetry known as the Moiré method has been used to record live animal shape successfully (283). The animal is photographed under a grating and when the transparency is superimposed on a photographic print of the animal, contours of shape are produced. However, again there is little objective information on how well such techniques predict composition or how they compare with other more commonly used techniques such as ultrasonics.

There has recently been a resurgence of interest in the U.S.A. in the use of measurement systems for determining the genetic merit of cattle. These systems, which include growth characteristics as well as body measurements, use advances in computer and video-technology (for example, Genetic Profiles, Arlington, Texas), and have been heavily promoted to cattlemen.

Visual assessment and handling

Visual and handling assessments of the live animal have the considerable advantage of not requiring the transport or use of special equipment. They are useful in commercial practice to select animals for slaughter and when evaluating animals in the market, but they are not sufficiently accurate for most experimental purposes.

A major problem in visual assessment as with linear measurements is to distinguish between muscling and fatness, both of which can improve the appearance. Fatness has the effect of filling in the indentations between muscles and where they insert, giving the rounded appearance of more muscular animals. Visual assessments of conformation are, therefore, likely to be more effective as indicators of muscling within a narrow range of fatness and particularly when levels of fatness are low.

Results in the experimental literature on the precision achieved with these techniques are very variable indeed, influenced particularly by the range in fatness and conformation in the group of animals examined. Picking out the very fat and lean animals is relatively easy especially when there are differences in breed and sex in the groups. But with the limited variation which is found within breeds in improvement schemes when animals are compared at the same weight or age, the difficulties are greater. Useful reviews on the value of live animal visual assessment were published by Barton (22) and Kallweit (190).

Handling the animal to assess fatness can add usefully to the accuracy achieved both with visual scoring and linear body measurements, particularly if the assessor is experienced and knows what he is feeling for.

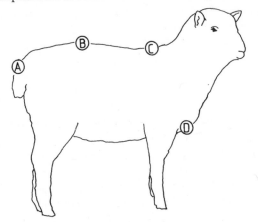

Fig. 6.1 Recommended positions for handling lambs to assess fatness (276).

A Around the tail root (dock); B Along the spinous processes of the back bone and over the eye muscle and the tips of the transverse processes in the lumbar region; C Along the spinous processes of the back bone over the shoulder; D Along the breast bone (sternum)

There are several points where lambs can be handled to assess the level of fatness. The two most important are A and B on fig. 6.1, but if in doubt, C and D can be used as an additional guide. The level of fatness at A is assessed by handling the tail root to see how much fat is covering the individual bones of the tail. (As lambs become fatter, it is more difficult to detect individual bones).

Fatness at B is assessed by placing the hand over the spinous transverse processes of the loin to assess their prominence. (The less prominent the processes, the fatter the lamb). Such a handling technique can be used to assess the fatness of all breeds, but allowance must be made for differences in thickness of wool. Minimum finger pressure is essential to avoid bruising which can seriously depreciate the value of carcases.

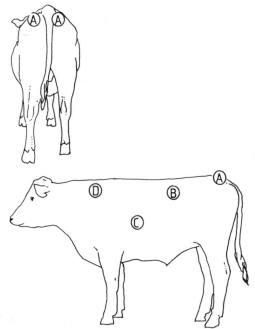

Fig. 6.2 Recommended positions for handling beef cattle to assess fatness (274).

A Over the pin bones and on either side of the tail head; B The transverse processes of the loin; C Over the ribs; D The chine and the shoulder blade ridge

Fatness in beef cattle can be assessed (fig. 6.2), by varying finger pressure at four key points. The condition of the flank is also commonly used but, although useful as a guide to cattle of extreme fatness, it is less reliable in helping to assess cattle in the middle of the range. The brisket is not recommended because it is impractical to use when handling cattle under farm conditions. The cod fat may be deceptive as size and fullness are affected by the method of castration. The presence of considerable quantities of kidney fat may interfere with the assessment of the fat cover over the loin. Differences between the positions of the left and right kidney affect handling, therefore the left side of the animal, as seen from behind, should be used rather than the right.

A number of standardised systems have been developed to obtain a more precise description of live animals by a visual method. Most of the standardised systems depend on graphic or photographic standards as exemplified, for example, by the East of Scotland College of Agriculture condition scoring for cattle (110) or the U.S.D.A. feeder cattle grades (370). The value of these standards is that they cause the judge to concentrate his attention only on the key points. An additional advantage is that different judges in different places and at different times will give similar scores to similar animals. This allows more confidence to be placed in comparisons from place to place and generation to generation.

Charles (67) examined the measurements of the 'anal fold' of fat using callipers as a means of estimating carcase composition in live cattle. He found that the precision of carcase lean prediction was comparable with that achieved with fat thickness measurements taken over the *M. longissimus* on the cut surface of the carcase. There was quite a range of fatness in these data and several breed types were involved, but the technique certainly merits further study because of its simplicity.

Ultrasonic techniques

Ultrasonic techniques have the greatest practical value of various objective methods presently available for predicting carcase composition in live animals. They are used extensively in pig breeding and increasingly in cattle breeding and research.

TYPES OF EQUIPMENT AVAILABLE

The ultrasonic equipment available ranges from simple machines giving a reading of fat thickness to complex scanning machines capable of producing two dimensional pictures of cross-sections through the animal body. Advances in scanning equipment have been reviewed by Miles (282). Briefly the principles are as follows.

A basic ultrasonic machine consists of a pulse generator, a transducer, receiving circuits and a display. Electrical pulses derived from the generator are applied to the transducer, which converts them to very short pulses of ultrasound and directs them into the animal. Each acoustic pulse travels through the body at a velocity characteristic of the tissues through which it passes. When an interface between two tissues is reached (adipose tissue and muscle for example), the pulse is partly reflected and partly transmitted. The reflected pulse returns to the transducer which reconverts it to an electrical pulse. Small electrical signals, representing echoes, are then superimposed on the transducer line and fed to an amplifier, rectifier and shaping circuits for display.

A display of echo amplitude against time is called A-mode display. Here the output from the video amplifier is fed to an oscilloscope and the echoes appear on the screen as spikes, spaced at intervals on the time base line (plate 1). This arrangement is used in several of the simple ultrasonic machines (such as the Sonatest, manufactured by Balteau-Sonatest, Wolverton, U.K.) which are used effectively in many pig breeding schemes. In some types, for example the Medata (manufactured by Medata Systems Ltd, Pagham, West Sussex, U.K.), the position of the spikes is converted to a direct digital reading of fat thickness.

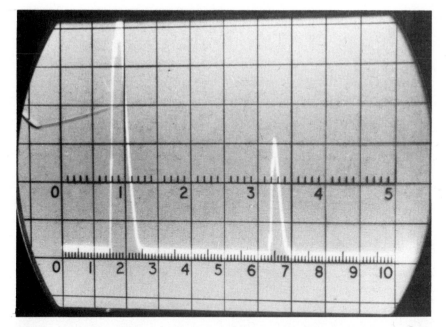

Plate 1 'A' mode ultrasonic display of a live pig showing the thickness of *M. longissimus* and fat over it. The trace on the lower scale of the oscilloscope shows a fat depth of 15 mm and a fat + muscle depth of 64 mm

Alternatively, in B-mode display, reflections are applied as negative pulses to the cathode of a cathode ray tube so that they modulate the brightness of the time base line and so appear as bright spots on the screen. B-mode displays are used in two-dimensional scanners.

Until the 1980s, most scanners employed a single ultrasonic transducer to progressively build up a scan over a period of time. Three types of machines were purpose built for animals using different methods of action and coupling, as described below.

Simple scanner using mechanical coupling
An example of this type is the 'Scanogram' developed by Professor J.R. Stouffer in the U.S.A. This machine (manufactured by Ithaca Inc., 735 West Clinton St, Ithaca, New York) has been widely used for the evaluation of cattle, pigs and sheep (plate 2). Its transducer is motor driven along a special track, shaped to fit the animal's back, while by means of a system of cams and gears the movement of the probe is mimicked by a camera photographing a linear B-mode display on an oscilloscope. A two dimensional scan is built up by holding the shutter of the Polaroid camera open as the transducer travels the length of the track (358).

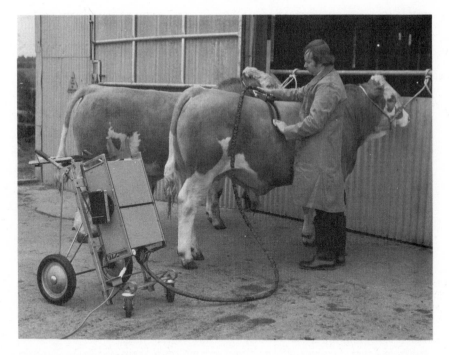

Plate 2 The Scanogram being used to measure fat thickness and area on bulls at an M.L.C. Performance Testing Station

Simple scanner using electrical coupling
An example of this type is the 'Ilis Observer', developed in the U.S.A. and marketed by International Livestock Improvement Services Corporation, Ames, Iowa. The transducer of this scanner is housed in an oil bath and moves along a straight rail on turning a handle. Its position on the rail is synchronised electrically with the display. Coupling to the animal's back is made through a flexible membrane.

A compound scanner with electrical coupling
An example of this type is the S.V.C. Scanner (26). This machine was developed in Denmark but has since been superseded by a more sophisticated real-time scanner.

Real-time scanning was originally developed for use in hospitals to enable the physician to see rapid internal physiological movements such as the beating of the heart. Horst (178) was the first to use a real-time scanner, the Siemens 'Vidoson' to scan livestock. This uses a single transducer mounted in a coupling medium at the focus of, and facing, a parabolic reflector. The transducer rotates so that the tissue is rapidly and repetitively scanned with a parallel beam.

Later the Danscanner was specially designed for use on animals by the National

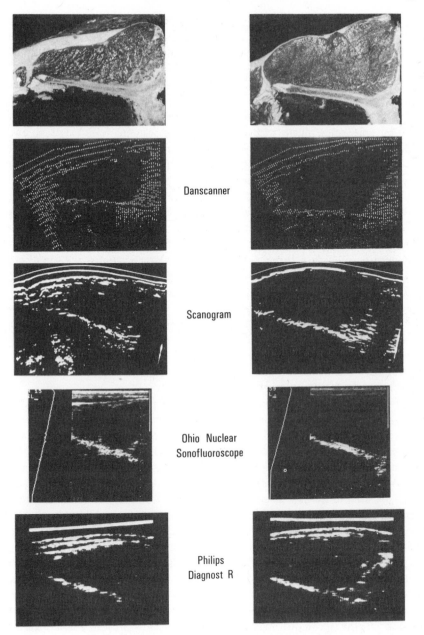

Danscanner

Scanogram

Ohio Nuclear
Sonofluoroscope

Philips
Diagnost R

Plate 3 Comparison of ultrasonic scans produced by four types of scanner on live cattle of contrasting fatness (left fat; right lean). Scans were taken at the third/fourth lumbar vertebra and the corresponding cross-sectional carcase picture is shown at the top. (The photographs are taken from the Commission of the European Communities report 'Ultrasonic techniques for describing carcase characteristics in live cattle' (27))

Institute of Animal Science and the Institute of Bio-Medical Engineering in Denmark. The machine uses an array of very small transducers and produces a practically instantaneous picture by rapid electronic switching from element to element.

Several companies have produced array scanners for hospital use, for example Diagnostic Sonar's 'System 85', Ohio Nuclear's 'Sonofluoroscope' and Philips 'Diagnost R'. These machines are small, reasonably robust and several built for medical application might with care be used for scanning farm livestock. Such machines are also relatively cheap because unlike the purpose-built animal machines, they have a mass market in hospitals. Examples of the ultrasonic scans produced by four types of scanner on live cattle are shown in plate 3.

Ultrasonic scanning of animals has been directed primarily at imaging the strong echoes derived from major tissue interfaces, for example interfaces between adipose tissue layers, muscle and bone, etc. The relatively weak echoes generated within the tissues by scattering of the ultrasound at points where the composition of a given tissue changes have been largely ignored and suppressed. However, modern medical scanners widely use a grey-scale or coloured image to indicate the relative levels of echoes arising from within the major tissues, thereby rendering visible their consistency as well as their outline. Although the technique has been available for several years, and is standard in modern human diagnostic instruments, no instrument built specially for use on animals incorporates the feature, so it has yet to be exploited in animal evaluation studies.

PRECISION ACHIEVED

Research on the use of ultrasonics began with pigs in the mid-1950s (172). Early work concentrated almost exclusively on the measurements of subcutaneous fat thickness as an indicator of fatness and on the depth of the cross-sectional area of the *M. longissimus* as an indicator of muscling. In this region, the musculature consists mainly of the *M. longissimus dorsi* which is a regular and well-defined muscle, relatively easy to measure. Further, the skeletal features are easy to locate, thereby making it easier to reproduce the measurement positions on each animal. Results with the simple A-mode and B-mode machines were shown to provide a useful indication of fat thickness in relation to their cost (183, 359) and were quickly adopted in pig performance testing schemes.

While fat thickness measurements are closely related to carcase composition for pigs, the same cannot be said for cattle. Yet most of the ultrasonic studies with cattle, summarised by Gillis *et al.* (142), have correlated ultrasonic measurements with those taken subsequently on the carcase — when the ultimate usefulness of the technique must be assessed by how well it predicts carcase composition in terms of actual tissue proportions. Another limiting feature of many experiments is, as indicated earlier for other techniques, that variation in live weight has not been taken into account in the analysis. This consideration is particularly important when relatively expensive techniques such as ultrasonics are being evaluated; no variation which could be explained by live weight must be ascribed to the ultrasonic technique.

A further inadequacy in some studies is that the potential of the scanning machines for measuring fat and muscle areas has not been utilised. Some, when evaluating the different machines, have gone to the trouble of taking cross-sectional pictures but have only measured fat depths on them, rather than areas to aim at a more precise prediction of carcase composition. Results from different trials are difficult to amalgamate since they vary in the samples of animals evaluated, the regions of the body measured and the way the different measurements have been used. However, an attempt has been made in tables 6.2 to 6.4 to bring together the results from the main trials using the Scanogram as a control. Some general points can be drawn from this summary.

Table 6.2. Residual s.d. for the prediction of carcase lean percentage of live pigs from measurements with different ultrasonic machines

Trial	(1a)		(1b)		(2)		
	SC	SN	SC	IL	SC	SN	DN
Standard deviation of carcase lean percentage	3.94	3.94	4.12	4.12	1.63	1.63	1.63
Residual s.d. for							
Live weight (W)	3.73	3.73	3.67	3.67	1.62	1.62	1.62
W + best fat thickness	2.56	2.72	2.26	2.61	1.35	1.29	1.33
W + best fat area*	2.78		2.61	2.72	1.44		1.45
W + M. longissimus area	3.37		3.38	3.40	1.62		1.62
W + best combination of measurements examined	2.29	2.69	2.25	2.36	1.35	1.29	1.33

SC = Scanogram; SN = Sonatest (A-mode); IL = Ilis Observer; DN = Danscanner
* Fat area over the M. longissimus at the last rib.
(1a) Kempster et al. (218): 143 pigs from different companies in M.L.C.'s commercial pig evaluation. Data were pooled within sex and company.
(1b) As above but 38 pigs only.
(2) Alliston et al. (6): 39 pigs of two selection lines. Data were pooled within line.

Results for pigs (table 6.2) indicate that fat thickness measurements taken in the rib region by simple A-mode machines like the Sonatest can provide a reasonable level of precision in carcase lean prediction. With a base standard deviation of 3.0 for carcase lean percentage, a residual s.d. of around 2.0 is easily achieved.

There is no improvement if the areas of fat on cross-sections are measured by scanning machines, but a small improvement if M. longissimus areas are measured. The improvement in precision is unlikely to justify the additional cost of scanning equipment, such as the Scanogram. The more complex Danscanner does not appear to provide a more precise carcase lean prediction than the Scanogram. Little information is available on the precision of the simpler digital machines. Preliminary work from our own studies suggests that they are rather less precise than the simple A-mode machines with an oscilloscope display, provided the latter is interpreted by a skilled operator.

Table 6.3 Residual s.d. for the prediction of carcase lean percentage of live beef cattle from measurements with different ultrasonic machines

Trial	(1) SC	(2a) SC	(2a) SN	(2b) SC	(2b) SN	(3) SC	(3) DN*	(3) PH*	(3) OH*
Standard deviation of carcase lean percentage	2.87	4.95	4.95	3.77	3.77	3.9	3.9	3.9	3.9
Residual s.d. for									
Live weight (W)	2.55	4.95	4.95	3.04	3.04	3.4	3.4	3.4	3.4
W + best fat thickness	1.65	2.97	3.88	2.38	2.68	2.9	3.0	3.0	2.7
W + best fat area**		2.91		2.08		2.8	2.9	3.0	2.5
W + M. longissimus area	2.38	4.74		2.85		3.3	3.2	3.4	3.3
W + best combination of two measurements	1.60	2.60	3.73	1.90	2.56	2.5	2.4	2.5	2.1

SC = Scanogram; SN = Sonatest (A-mode); DN = Danscanner; PH = Philips Diagnost R; OH = Ohio Nuclear Sonofluoroscope
* Real-time scanning machines
** Fat area over M. longissimus
(1) Tulloh, Truscott and Lang (368): 29 Aberdeen Angus and Friesian cattle.
(2a) Kempster et al. (217): 46 cattle of mixed breeds.
(2b) As above but with 50 Hereford × Friesian steers.
(3) Bech Andersen et al. (27): Summary of results from a co-ordinated trial carried out in Denmark on 23 young bulls of Danish Black and White and Danish Red breeds, and in Britain on 30 cattle of mixed breeds.

The simple A-mode machines are less successful with cattle (table 6.3) and scanning machines bring significant advantages. Residual s.d.s. for simple machines are in the region of 2.5 per cent carcase lean with a base s.d. of 3.0 per cent. With the Scanogram the residual s.d. may be reduced below 2.0, the same degree of precision as achieved in similar circumstances with pigs. The limited information available indicates that the real-time scanners examined have been no more precise than the Scanogram (27).

In general the measurement of M. longissimus area in cattle has contributed little to the prediction of carcase lean content, although there is an indication that the more complex machines offer a better result in this respect than the Scanogram. Bech Andersen (26) reported results with the Danish S.V.C. equipment (based on a complex B-scanning principle) which also suggested that M. longissimus measured with this equipment contributed more to prediction than it did with the Scanogram in the trials shown in table 6.3.

Ultrasonics have not been as successful with sheep as with the other two species, although there have been fewer attempts to refine techniques. The

Table 6.4 Residual s.d. for prediction of carcase lean percentage (defined in various ways) of live sheep from measurements with different ultrasonic machines

Trial	(1)	(2a)	(2b)*		(3)		
	SC	SC	SC	DN	SC	KR	SP
Standard deviation of carcase lean percentage	4.00	2.92	4.14	4.14	2.00	2.00	2.00
Residual s.d. for							
Live weight (W)	3.25	2.89	3.85	3.85	2.00	2.00	2.00
W + best fat thickness	3.05	2.62	3.29	3.65	1.98	1.96	1.96
W + best fat area**		2.49	3.20	3.58			
W + M. longissimus area	3.20	2.89	3.85	3.85			
W + best combination of measurements	3.00	2.40	3.20	3.58			

SC = Scanogram; DN = Danscanner; KR = Krautkrämer U.S.M. 2 (A-mode); SP = Scano-probe (direct reading A-mode).
* All measurements were taken at the twelfth rib
** Fat area over the M. longissimus
(1) Shelton, Smith and Orts (343): 102 Rambouillet rams. Prediction of percentage of trimmed primal cuts.
(2a) Kempster et al. (203): 147 crossbred lambs by six different sire breeds. Analysis was pooled within sire breed.
(2b) As above but with 254 crossbred lambs by nine sire breeds.
(3) Fortin (128): 33 lambs of a meat sire breed. Prediction of percentage of trimmed primal cuts.

order of precision is reflected in residual s.d.s of 2.5-3.0 per cent carcase lean against a base s.d. of 3.0 per cent, with fat areas taken over the M. longissimus at the twelfth rib using the Scanogram on lambs of the same breed (table 6.4). The reason for this poorer result is not clear, but both the smaller fat thicknesses and the greater mobility of the skin may be contributory factors. The need to clip wool from lambs can also be a problem and the recent development of an ultrasonic machine with a pencil-sized transducer may be an important step forward (143). This transducer is small enough to operate on the skin exposed when the fleece is parted. The first published estimates of its precision for predicting carcase fat content are relatively good; the precision achieved with a fat thickness measurement over the M. longissimus between the twelfth and thirteenth ribs was slightly poorer than that obtained with the corresponding measurement taken on the cut surface of the carcase.

The results of individual studies in particular experimental circumstances can give no more than an indication of how the machines will perform in practice. The precision achieved will depend on the particular population studied, the precise details of the scanning technique used, and the skill and experience of the operator. Indeed, any comparison of machines is, in reality, a comparison of machine-operator combinations. Anyone considering a particular application of ultrasonics should not, therefore, rely entirely on reports in the scientific literature. His work should incorporate a trial involving carcase dissection to establish directly the precision and cost-effectiveness before heavy investment in equipment is made.

We have examined the precision achieved with different measurements in the loin and rib region taken by Scanogram in different samples of cattle (217). The positions giving the most precise prediction of carcase lean percentage varied with the sample of cattle, no one position being consistently good across the different samples. In view of this, the practical approach when selecting predicting measurements for use on a new untested group of cattle would be to combine fat areas from two or three positions along the body.

The only consistent finding with regard to position was that the highest correlation found between percentage lean and ultrasonically measured *M. longissimus* area was at the third lumbar vertebra which was not the position where the highest correlations were recorded between ultrasonic *M. longissimus* areas and the comparable measurements taken on the carcase. This was at the thirteenth rib position where, as indicated in chapter 2, the muscle is more clearly defined. This finding underlines that it is incorrect to assume that the ultrasonic measurements which have the highest correlation with comparable carcase measurements will be those which give the most precise prediction of carcase tissue percentages.

Although a useful practical tool, ultrasonics have serious limitations because they depend for their accuracy on the relationship between small sections of the animal body and overall carcase composition. Most studies of ultrasonic measurements have been limited to the rib region; in future the pursuit of techniques which involve other areas of the animal body is likely to be more rewarding. Stouffer and co-workers (377) suggested, on the basis of their results with carcase measurements, that if ultrasound could more accurately estimate shoulder fat thickness, yield might be more precisely predicted in live animals; however the suggestion does not appear to have been followed up.

A variation of the ultrasound technique, which measures the velocity with which ultrasound passes through tissues, may be valuable because it can be used where there are less clear-cut tissue interfaces, for example in the hind leg (395). In addition it provides a direct reading avoiding the need for visual interpretation of tissue interfaces from photographs.

Back fat probes

Probes have been used, primarily on live pigs, to measure the thickness of subcutaneous back fat. A small incision is made in the skin and the instrument pushed through until the resistance of the muscle surface is felt. A simple steel rule with a knife edge was the first probe used for this purpose (171). But Andrews and Whaley (12) developed the Leanmeter probe which works on the difference in electrical conductivity between fat and lean.

These instruments appear to provide a level of precision in lean prediction similar to that achieved with mid-line carcase fat thickness measurements. However their use is not permitted in several European countries on animal welfare grounds.

Dilution techniques

These involve the measurement of body water by dilution of a tracer, and estimation of the chemical composition of the body from the close inverse relationship between body water and chemical fat. A known amount of tracer is introduced to become distributed uniformly through the body water. The concentration of the tracer at equilibrium is then measured by taking a sample of body fluid, usually blood.

Numerous tracers have been tried: urea, thiourea, sulfanamid, antipyrene, N-acetyl-4-aminoantipyrene, heavy water (D_2O), and tritiated water (TOH). Early work was reviewed by Dumont (104).

The consensus among users is that labelled water (TOH or D_2O) is the most promising tracer for estimating total body water. Its use has been discussed in detail by Robelin (328) who came to the following conclusions:

(a) The two tracers (TOH or D_2O) are not significantly different.
(b) Standardisation of feeding is essential for accurate determination because gut water is included in the assessment. Variation in the amount of ingesta can cause major inaccuracies in estimated composition.
(c) Since the relationship between body water and fat can be influenced by age and nutritional history, breed, sex and plane of feeding must be controlled or used as predictors along with the tracer results.
(d) Reasonable accuracy can be obtained in comparisons, but absolute measurements are not generally of sufficient accuracy for practical application.

A factor influencing the choice of tracer may be the extent to which the value of the carcases of treated animals are depreciated. Tritiated water, for example, is radioactive and has a long half-life, so the meat from treated animals would be unfit for human consumption.

Gaseous methods can also be used. The animal is enclosed in a chamber and a known amount of gas introduced, some of which is absorbed and dissolves in the fat. When equilibrium has been reached, the amount of gas absorbed can be calculated by difference. Several gases have been tried including krypton (180), but there are problems in their application.

Dilution techniques are time consuming and detailed. This effectively relegates them to experimental use, for example, in long-term feeding trials with different levels of feeding in different periods. But for accurate measurement of body composition in such experiments, slaughter and full side tissue separation followed by chemical analysis remains the most comprehensive method.

K^{40} technique

The development of whole-body counters has made it possible to estimate gamma radiation arising from the naturally occurring radioactive isotope of potassium (K^{40}) (132). As with dilution techniques, the basis of the estimation is that the indicator is in constant proportion to major body components.

While this technique has been used widely in some parts of the U.S.A., the expense of whole-body counting chambers must create doubts about its cost-effectiveness. Technical problems involved in the use of the K^{40} technique are associated with equipment calibration and the elimination of background interference. Accurate estimates of body composition are possible (132), but Carr, Walters and Whiteman (60) found that K^{40} provided little increase in the precision of lean prediction in pigs when added to live weight.

Electronic meat measuring equipment

This is the equipment, manufactured by the E.M.M.E. Corporation, Phoenix, Arizona under the trade name E.M.M.E., which consists of a fibreglass tunnel surrounded by an energised copper winding to create an electromagnetic field. An animal inside this tunnel becomes, in essence, the magnetic core of a solenoid and changes in the characteristics of the magnetic field will occur according to the core conductivity. Lean tissue has greater electrical conductivity than fat and affects the magnetic field differentially. The changes in conductivity are monitored electronically and displayed as a digital read-out.

Machine operation can be initiated and terminated by photoelectric cells at the entrance and exit of the tunnel and the E.M.M.E. compensates automatically for the speed of passage and size of the animal. Gut-fill can be an important source of variation in live animal measurement and the manufacturers recommend that the animal is starved for 18-24 hours before measurement.

Initial Canadian work with pigs suggested a considerable potential for this technique, which was found to be better than fat thickness measurements taken by probe. Combining E.M.M.E. readings with the live probe measurements of fatness improved the prediction of carcase lean percentage in the live animal. However, after more detailed evaluation, Fredeen, Martin and Sather (136) concluded that the technique did not have the degree of reliability necessary for use in pig breeding programmes.

The E.M.M.E. SA 60 model, a smaller version designed to measure the lean-fat ratio in boxed beef, has proved successful and is an integral part of the quality control systems in a number of large U.S. processing plants. It is also used in Canada to estimate the content of meat during canning, and automatic adjustment of the composition of the meat to within pre-set limits can be achieved by computer control. This success has led the manufacturers to put their main thrust of development and promotion into this area, rather than into live animal evaluation.

X-ray techniques

The value of X-rays for fat estimation has been studied (for example, 108). Problems occur in taking satisfactory X-ray pictures of the living animal and of obtaining tissue measurements from the pictures. However, the technique could provide estimates of overall carcase composition and of the thickness and distribution of the tissues.

In the late 1970s, E.M.I. Medical Limited developed, primarily for diagnostic work in humans, a body scanner using a non-conventional X-ray system. The technique, known as computed tomography (C.T.), involves the presentation of anatomical information by computer synthesis of an image from X-ray transmission data obtained in many different directions through the plane of the body under consideration. Preliminary results from the evaluation of the technique with pigs were published by Skjervold *et al.* (345).

This will almost certainly prove to be an accurate tool for assessing the composition of the animal body. But again, very high cost is likely to work against the use of such a technique, in addition to the need to bring animals to a central point of measurement.

N.M.R. imaging

The use of nuclear magnetic resonance (N.M.R.) to provide images of biological material is a recent development. The basis of this approach and its potential has been described by Andrew (10). The technique is being developed for use in human medicine with encouraging results, but it remains to be seen how far this very expensive approach could be applied to farm livestock.

Physiological predictors

While there is increasing interest in the use of hormone assays to assess potential growth rate and carcase quality, to the best of our knowledge there are no routine practical applications as yet. The optimism sometimes expressed in the value of such techniques seems unjustified by their performance.

Lister (254) claimed in 1976:

The identification of future breeding stock to meet new production criteria can only be achieved by the use of test procedures which make use of the physiological principles governing growth, development and metabolism which are now emerging. The animal breeder's rule of thumb can no longer suffice.

Yet the animal breeder's 'rule of thumb', which now is in fact a battery of indirect methods of carcase evaluation, will have to suffice for some years because physiological techniques are still in their infancy.

Which kind of measurement of endocrine state will give most information on differences in growth potential? Simple serum levels for most hormones are unlikely to be of use because they are sensitive to so many factors. While a number of investigations of particular lines or breeds have been reported, there is little to indicate that they give useful information. In the large selection experiment at Beltsville in the U.S.A., with Duroc and Yorkshire pigs selected in two directions for back fat thickness, serum levels of cholesterol and glucose were higher in the fat lines (357), but the selected lines did not exhibit atypical levels. The results from the two-trait selection experiment in growth rate and fat thickness in Norway (374) also did not indicate dramatic differences between lines.

Much of the work on endocrine differences between breeds has been done in connection with studies of the porcine stress syndrome and sensitivity to the halothane test (referred to in chapter 15). Differences in thyroxine levels and delayed insulin response have been found between halothane-sensitive pigs (characterised by the Belgium Pietrain) and non-halothane-sensitive pigs (characterised by the British Large White and Yorkshire) (255).

Standal (355) suggested that some of the differences observed in the low growth, low back fat line in the Norwegian experiment were due to selection for Pietrain-like characteristics, i.e. selection for muscularity and the halothane gene. He drew a distinction between selection for these characteristics and selection for low fatness *per se* which was associated with high growth rates in the other line. This is an important distinction because endocrine differences associated with the frequency of the halothane gene may not be particularly valuable as indicators of growth and carcase composition in breeding schemes. The halothane test is available anyway to identify pigs which carry the gene and often selection may be necessary in halothane-free breeds or lines. It would be wrong, therefore, to over-emphasise the value of physiological predictors associated with the halothane gene.

Nevertheless, physiological predictors have major potential advantages over most other live animal evaluation techniques because they are likely to be suitable for use early in life to predict subsequent growth performance and carcase composition. The physiology of growth must, therefore, be an important area for continued research. After all, there would have been advantages in detecting 'halothane-sensitive pigs' using physiological means had the halothane test not conveniently become available.

7 Carcase evaluation

Visual assessments of fatness

Visual assessment of fat cover is a cheap and convenient method of predicting the fat content of beef and sheep carcases. In the absence of more precise predictors suitable for use in commercial abattoirs, this has become a principal component of the classification and grading schemes in many countries.

When applied by trained assessors, the precision can be comparable with that achieved with the best fat thickness measurements taken on the cut surface of the carcase. However, such assessments suffer from a number of disadvantages inherent in most systems of subjective judgement. The standardisation of assessments made by different people is particularly difficult.

Important factors influencing accuracy and consistency are:

(a) the experience of the assessors;
(b) the nature and extent of the definitions of the differences between steps on the scoring scale;
(c) whether or not value judgements have to be made, for example when the highest score is given for an optimum level of fatness;
(d) the range and average level in the carcases being assessed;
(e) how much the environmental conditions in which the assessments are made vary. The level of lighting and the angle from which the carcases are viewed can, for example, influence the judgements made.

The number of steps in the scoring scale is also important. A scale of 1 to 5 is usually too narrow for adequate discrimination between carcases, while a scale greater than 1 to 10 is too wide for most people to operate successfully. Williams (383) proposed that a seven-point scale is optimum for application in carcase work. When scales with more than ten classes are used, they should be divided into a number of main classes which are then subdivided. In the E.A.A.P. fatness scale, for example, there are fifteen classes, made up of five main classes each with three subdivisions (98).

Provision of a photographic reference scale is essential. These are particularly helpful when assessors are regularly exposed only to carcases representing a narrow part of the whole range of the scales (140). This batch effect can be a problem for national classification schemes where there is wide variation in breed types and where particular breeds are dominant locally. The use of photographic scales also helps to overcome the idiosyncrasies and subconscious prejudices of assessors. The reliability and use of visual assessment have been considered by Harries and co-workers (152).

Reference scales do not solve all the problems because interpretations will vary. The standardisation of visual scores is best approached by having each class defined in terms of dissected composition, as has been done in the M.L.C. beef and sheep carcase classification schemes. Here each class was defined by a range of carcase subcutaneous fat percentage. In the beef scheme for example, fat class 1 was less than 4.5 per cent, fat class 2 was 4.5-7.4 per cent, and so on (90). For standardisation checks at a national level, a number of carcases are dissected to check the application of the scales and to remedy the situation if there is any movement in the standards applied.

Despite all such procedures for standardising visual scores, uneasiness about the use of subjective judgements remains and there are clear advantages in making the predictors of carcase composition as objective as possible. Objective measurements place borderline carcases more definitely with less dispute.

However, it is equally important to recognise that many so-called objective measurements have some subjectivity associated with them. For example, in measuring the thickness of fat over the *M. longissimus* in pig carcases by intrascope, the actual measurement is influenced by the care taken in inserting the instrument at the correct position and by the pressure applied in taking it.

Visual scoring techniques are useful for assessing carcases under commercial conditions, providing their inherent limitations are recognised, and providing adequate training and supervision backed by photographic standards is given to those undertaking the assessment. As long as visual assessment is used as a basis for carcase payment, such assessments should not be neglected in beef production research in view of the economic implications.

Carcase measurements

Many carcase measurements have been examined as predictors of carcase composition. Some have found extensive use in practical applications, particularly in classification and grading schemes. In view of this, specific measurements and their practical use will be considered in the section on carcase classification and grading. Here, we shall consider the different types of measurements and their relative precision.

Although many different measuring positions have been defined and tested, they may be grouped as follows:

On intact carcases
(a) carcase weight;
(b) carcase dimensions, for example width, length and depth;
(c) fat thickness measurements taken by probe;
(d) muscle thickness measurements taken by probe;

(e) total tissue depth measurements taken by probe;
(f) weights of perinephric and retroperitoneal fat which can be removed and weighed without cutting the carcase.

On centre-split carcases
The thickness of fat at various points can be measured conveniently in the dorsal mid-line on the split pig carcase. In addition, there have been attempts to measure muscle thickness on this surface.

On quartered carcases
(a) fat thickness measurements;
(b) areas of fat;
(c) muscle thickness measurements;
(d) areas of the cross-section of muscle;
(e) the ratio of fat to lean areas on exposed cross-sections.

Such measurements can be taken on any exposed surface although they have generally been restricted to the rib and loin regions, and to measurements of the *M. longissimus* and overlying fat.

CARCASE WEIGHT
Carcase weight can be handled in precisely the same way as is live weight in the prediction of carcase composition in live animals. This potentially valuable predictor is normally available in practical circumstances at negligible cost. Carcase weight should always be included as the first independent variable when different predictors are being compared.

This simple policy, if adopted by all research workers, would have overcome much of the confusion which occurs when predicting measurements are credited with precision which could be obtained more simply by using carcase weight.

Most prediction equations which have been set up for use in grading schemes include carcase weight. But in some of these — the Danish equation for pig carcase grading, for example, and the U.S.D.A. yield grade for beef — it appears low (third or fourth) in the list of independent variables. This suggests that these equations have been developed with precision rather than with the ratio of precision to cost in mind. On the latter criterion, weight would be the first independent variable. If carcase weight is constrained to be the first independent variable, then it is possible to assess the additional precision achieved by incorporating more expensive measurements.

LINEAR CARCASE MEASUREMENTS
There has been interest from time to time in the use of linear carcase measurements, in particular during the 1950s (155, 173), but again much of this work failed to identify the advantage of such measurements over and above weight and simple measures of fatness. The limited extent to which such measurements have been taken up and used in practical applications reflects their low value.

Carcase length has little value as a predictor of carcase composition, but it has come to be important in the Wiltshire bacon industry in Denmark and Great Britain as a means of discriminating against short carcases which are considered unsuitable for whole side cure. Length in relation to weight has been proposed as an objective measure of carcase blockiness, but again this has not been taken up widely.

Carcase depth and width measurements are equally poor as far as carcase leanness prediction is concerned and appear not to have found a place in any practical situation.

These general and somewhat dismissive remarks do need qualification. There will always be particular situations when such measurements could prove to be useful predictors. For example, in a mixed sample of pig carcases made up of half Pietrain (short, blocky carcases with high meat to bone ratio) and Large White (long, intermediate-shaped carcases with relatively low meat to bone ratio), carcase length would be a valuable predictor of meat to bone ratio. The job of the carcase evaluation specialist is to distinguish between such particular cases and the more general value of predictors. Even in this example, breed (if known) or conformation (as an alternative to breed) would probably both be better indicators of meat to bone ratio than length.

In a more natural mix of carcases of the same weight (with a standard deviation of carcase lean percentage at equal weight of 3.0), we would not expect information on carcase length, depth or width to reduce this below 2.5. Typical levels of precision for different predictors in all three species, based on a review of the literature, are shown later in tables 8.1, 8.4 and 8.7.

FAT THICKNESS MEASUREMENTS TAKEN BY PROBE

The division (quartering) of carcases to expose muscle cross-sections and the overlying fat is often impossible in commercial situations. This has led in recent years to the development of a whole range of equipment for measuring such characteristics on the intact carcase. Instruments range from simple sharpened steel rules which are pushed in until they touch the muscle sheath, through the Danish intrascope which is a simple optical instrument rather like a periscope, to more complex instruments exploiting differences in conductivity or light reflectance between muscle and fat (see chapter 8).

The value of these instruments depends on the circumstances in which they are used, in particular whether pig, beef or lamb carcases are being measured and whether the carcases are hot or cold at the time of measurement. The size of the probe may also be critical, as is the condition of the carcase.

Measurements have usually been taken in the rib and loin region, where the *M. longissimus* provides a suitable base for fat thickness measurements. This region of the carcase is also convenient because anatomical positions may be identified cranio-caudally from ribs and vertebrae and laterally at fixed distances from the dorsal mid-line. Historically it was preferred because the Hammond school identified it as the latest-developing region.

Berg and Butterfield's (31) reminder that live animal measurements should be evaluated by their relationship with carcase composition, applies equally to the assessment of the merits of alternative probe measurements made on the carcase. Yet there are many published reports in which carcase probes have been judged against corresponding measurements made after the carcase has been cut.

The precision of carcase lean prediction achieved with probe fat thickness measurements taken on cold pig carcases is similar to that achieved when the corresponding measurements are taken on the carcase cross-section. The corresponding measurements taken with probes on hot carcases are slightly less precise predictors while the most precise predictions can be achieved by probing in an area in the hind rib region (220, and see table 8.1).

Probed measurements of fat have been less successful with beef and sheep carcases, as their subcutaneous fat is less evenly distributed, less thick and forms a lower proportion of the total fat (see table 8.5).

MUSCLE THICKNESS MEASUREMENTS TAKEN BY PROBE
Muscle thickness measurements have limited practical application. They are poorly correlated with carcase lean content (except in populations containing carcases with extreme differences in muscularity and lean to bone ratio), providing only a marginal improvement in precision of carcase lean prediction when used in addition to carcase weight and fat thickness measurements. Further, they are difficult to measure by probe, because even when the muscle boundaries can be accurately defined, small differences in the angle of insertion can lead to important variations in the muscle thickness measured. Indeed, the use of muscle thickness measurement as one of five measurements in the equation for predicting carcase lean content in the Danish pig carcase grading scheme, is the only significant application known to us.

WEIGHT OF PERINEPHRIC AND RETROPERITONEAL FAT (KKCF)
KKCF weight and percentage has been shown to be a useful predictor of beef and sheep carcase composition in a number of circumstances where it can be removed conveniently during dressing and weighed.

KKCF percentage is used in the U.S.D.A. beef yield grade formula where it makes a marginal contribution to the precision of prediction. It has also been proposed as a means of overcoming the dairy-type versus beef-type bias, brought about when fat thickness measurements are used. This arises because dairy-type cattle have a lower ratio of subcutaneous fat to the sum of inter-muscular fat and KKCF (314, and see chapter 3).

The level of precision of carcase lean prediction achieved within breeds by KKCF weight is similar to that achieved with a single subcutaneous fat thickness measurement.

FAT THICKNESS AND MUSCLE MEASUREMENTS ON QUARTERED CARCASES
In common with probe measurements, the main effort has been in the rib and loin regions where the measurements are more easily defined and the border of the M. longissimus more regular. Such measurements are used extensively in

pig progeny testing and also in some classification and grading schemes where it is possible to expose the surface before measurement.

CROSS-SECTIONAL AREAS OF MUSCLE AND MUSCLE DIMENSIONS

Cross-sectional areas of the *M. longissimus* have been studied over many years as predictors of carcase lean content. An investigation of muscle dimensions and area was made for pigs by McMeekan (271) and many studies have followed a similar pattern. Results have been generally poor, which surprises some who expect the area of a big muscle such as the *M. longissimus* to be well correlated with leanness.

The relationship between muscle measurements and carcase lean content is complicated by several factors and, in particular by the variation that can exist in carcase blockiness influencing muscle area at equal carcase lean content. Variation in fatness may also complicate the relationships as follows:

Among carcases with the same carcase fat content and conformation	Muscle area increases with carcase weight
Among carcases with the same weight and fat content	Muscle area increases with improved conformation
Among carcases with the same conformation and carcase weight	Muscle area decreases with carcase fat content

In populations with variation in lean to bone ratio, muscle area might show a useful predictive relationship with carcase lean content, but as will be emphasised later when conformation is considered, variation in weight and fat content *must* be eliminated.

CROSS-SECTIONAL AREAS OF FAT AND MUSCLE TO FAT RATIOS

More detailed assessments of the leanness of the whole cut surface have been used to improve the precision of carcase lean prediction. An early study by Pearson and co-workers (307) showed that the fat to lean ratio (areas) can be used for this purpose and later studies showed the value of increasing the number of surfaces measured (for example, 312).

Most studies have been carried out using the *M. longissimus* and the surrounding areas of fat on cross-sections in the area of the last rib. The lean to fat ratio of the streak (belly) has seldom been measured because it is time consuming and costly. Where measurements have been taken in this region, they have been found to add useful information to that from other carcase regions as predictors of lean content. Lund and Pedersen (260) using the Danish electronic planimeter obtained a 15 per cent improvement in precision when the streak lean to fat ratio was added to that for the rib region.

With recent developments in scanning techniques, based on reflectance differences between tissues, the measurement of a series of cross-sections to build up a more comprehensive picture of the body is now relatively simple; a more precise prediction of carcase composition is obtained. Butterfield *et al.*

(50) found high correlations with carcase lean content when a series of up to eleven cross-sections were measured using the Leitz Classimat automatic image analyser on photographs of cross-sections of lamb carcases. Unfortunately the precision was not compared with other simpler techniques. More recently Malmfors (263) examined the use on pig carcases of the electronic scanning planimeter (E.S.P.). In contrast to Butterfield's results, a major increase in precision was not obtained from combining different cut surfaces, but the technique was considerably more precise than simple measurements and offered labour savings over simpler scanning procedures. Malmfors estimated that by using the E.S.P. technique, twenty carcases could be evaluated in forty-five minutes, the time taken to evaluate one carcase in the Swedish pig progeny testing procedure, and with similar precision. The study also showed the value of taking fat areas in the streak.

Developments of this kind should be important for progeny test procedures and their use bears examination in more detail for cattle and sheep. Besides the evaluation of whole pig carcases and primal cuts, E.S.P. can be used to determine the leanness of processed and cured meat products and to measure pig meat quality through cut surface colour.

ULTRASONIC MEASUREMENTS ON CARCASES

Ultrasonic equipment can be used to take measurements on carcases to predict composition but there are problems of ensuring good acoustic contact (129). With skilled operators, simple A-mode ultrasonic measurements of fat thickness over the *M. longissimus* in the hind rib region taken on the hot pig carcase, can provide similar precision to the comparable measurements taken by probe (138). Such an approach is unlikely to offer significant advantages over conventional probing techniques unless it is able to provide a cross-sectional picture sufficiently accurately for areas to be measured in commercial situations where carcase quartering is not possible.

There is a case for further study of the use of ultrasonics where probing of pig carcases is unacceptable, for example because the skins are to be removed for tanning.

E.M.M.E. measurements on carcases

As indicated in chapter 6, E.M.M.E. can also be used for carcase evaluation although there are few reports of its use. Koch and Varnadore (237) examined its potential in beef grading and concluded that it offered similar precision to the combination of measurements used in the U.S.D.A. yield grade equation (involving fat thickness, percentage KKCF and *M. longissimus* area).

Density or specific gravity

The use of density and specific gravity in the prediction of carcase composition has been reviewed by Garrett (139) and Miles (281). The volume of a carcase is obtained from its displacement of water using the principle that the difference between weight in air and weight in water equals the weight of the displaced volume of water. Density is then calculated as carcase weight (in air) divided by volume.

The carcase can be considered as made up of fat and fat-free components. Fat has a density of about 0.90 and muscle of about 1.10, so a 0.002 change in carcase density is approximately equal to a 1 per cent change in carcase fat content.

Comparisons of specific gravity with other techniques are rare, interested workers being content to evaluate the technique on its own. Relationships have been rather poor and in some cases over-stated because of the variability in the sample, the failure to take weight into account and the fact that contending predictors were not included. We conclude that the precision of specific gravity for carcase lean prediction is little better than that achieved with the best fat thickness measurements taken in the hind rib region. This implies that the benefit of having a direct measure of total fat (as opposed to subcutaneous fat) is counterbalanced by variations in the composition of the fat-free component.

In principle, specific gravity is relatively easy to determine and there is no loss of value to the carcase. But this technique has never become established in commercial practice, where it could in theory replace fat thickness measurements in carcase classification and grading. There would clearly be complications in the organisation of carcase dressing and also in the standardisation of factors such as water temperature.

In Garrett's view, the precision of the technique is too low for predicting the composition of individual carcases but in experiments where replication is possible, or when progeny test groups are being compared, differences between treatments or groups may be demonstrated. However, this argument can be applied to any predictor and does not alter judgements of their relative precision. Of greater moment is the different dimension that specific gravity adds to prediction: because it measures total carcase fatness, it may add to the precision of carcase measurements and visual scores.

Sample joint dissection

The results in the following chapter indicate that there is a limit to the level of precision that can be obtained with visual assessments and simple measurements. To reach beyond this limit, sample joint dissections (partial dissections) or whole side cutting techniques (see below) are necessary.

Sample joints can be wholesale or retail joints, anatomical regions of the carcase defined by the location of skeletal reference points, or individual muscles and bones. The principle is that they are dissected and the weights of their tissues used to estimate overall carcase composition.

The precision achieved with different sample joints depends on the species and will be considered in more detail for pigs, cattle and sheep in chapter 8. Suffice to say that there is unlikely to be a sample joint which has outstanding value in relation to its size and cost of evaluation, or indeed, that there is a single sample joint which is suitable for all purposes. The relative cost of joints varies considerably from place to place and from time to time, and to choose a certain joint because workers elsewhere find it appropriate for their work may not be a sensible decision. When planning the use of a sample joint in a particular study, a pragmatic approach is appropriate: determine the cost of removal and dissection of different joints in the study and then choose the one that offers the best compromise between precision and cost.

Commercial cutting

Techniques based on fat trimming and deboning similar to those used in commercial practice have been in common use in the U.S.A. and are now increasingly adopted around the world. They are used most frequently in beef evaluation since, in contrast to pig and lamb carcases, the bones are usually removed in preparation of beef cuts for retail sale.

Practice can range from copies of the procedures used in meat plants and butcher's shops, when the cutting lines and trimming will be varied to allow maximum value to be obtained from carcases of different weight and muscle thickness, to standardised techniques where joints are defined by anatomical reference points and cuts are trimmed to the same level of fatness whatever their weight or muscling.

Some regard these techniques as base-line, but as indicated earlier we consider them as predictors. In other words, their use needs to be supported by complete tissue separation data to reveal what constitutes 'saleable meat', to check that their use will not introduce bias into comparative trials and that the results are also relevant where other techniques are used commercially.

Despite their widespread use, little firm information is in fact available on how the results obtained with commercial cutting techniques compare with those from tissue separation. Some points of importance in the relationship will be discussed using some of our own results.

Before the M.L.C. beef breed evaluation programme was set up in 1972, the complete tissue separation of the half carcase was used by M.L.C. in most of its trials. This provided the weights of lean, bone and the various separable fat depots within each of a number of standardised commercial joints (89). This detail was considered necessary because little basic information on the carcase characteristics of cattle in Great Britain existed.

The breed evaluation programme presented quite a new problem in terms of scale and the number of different breeds and production systems involved. Full tissue separation of all carcases could not be justified and alternative predicting techniques had to be considered.

A commercial cutting technique was preferred to the main contender (sample joint dissection) because:

(a) the results obtained would stand on their own without major adjustments, whereas sample joint dissection results would normally have to be converted to estimates of overall carcase composition using prediction equations;

(b) direct information could be obtained on all joints and on how the weights of carcase components (trimmed joints, fat trim and bone) are distributed through the carcase;

(c) the weights of trimmed joints obtained could be easily valued so the results could be presented in a way relevant to meat traders.

These considerations outweighed the following disadvantages associated with the commercial cutting technique:

(a) standardisation between operators and over time would be more difficult as there is inevitably some subjectivity about the amount of fat left on the trimmed saleable meat;

(b) under the particular circumstances of this trial, commercial cutting would be about twice as expensive as sample joint dissection for a similar level of precision in predicting carcase lean percentage;

(c) the technique could provide little discrimination in composition between carcases at low levels of fatness, i.e. those below the threshold where fat trimming becomes necessary. As most cattle were slaughtered at a level of fatness well above the threshold for fat trimming, this was not important.

A further difficulty with the commercial cutting technique, which may not be so obvious, is that an accurate regressor (independent) variate may not be available when comparisons at equal fatness are required. Without tissue separation data, commercial fat trim or some other predictor of carcase fat content has to be used to adjust breed means to an equal level of fatness. In the M.L.C. beef breed evaluation programme, a visual assessment of carcase subcutaneous fat percentage (SF_e) was used for this purpose because this related the results both to the M.L.C. beef carcase classification scheme and to commercial practice in Britain (210, 211). In the U.S.D.A. programme at Clay Centre, Nebraska, where the carcase evaluation was also based on commercial cutting, the ether extract of the *M. longissimus* (Cycle II) (236) and fat trim in carcase (Cycle III) (235) were used as regressor variates for making comparison at 'equal fatness'.

As a check on the commercial cutting results obtained in the M.L.C. beef breed evaluation programme and to provide more detailed information on characteristics such as fat distribution, one side was commercially trimmed and the other side separated fully into component tissues, on about one in four of the carcases. Kempster, Cook and Smith (208) compared commercial cutting and full separation in this sample of carcases. The use of commercial cutting as an alternative to full dissection was supported in the context of the trial where cattle were slaughtered at similar levels of fatness. Breed differences in deboned fat-trimmed joints (saleable meat) as a percentage of carcase weight were in good agreement with those for carcase lean percentage (fig. 7.1) even though it was necessary to rely on SF_e as the regressor variate.

Lean (meat) in carcase (%)   Lean (meat) to bone ratio

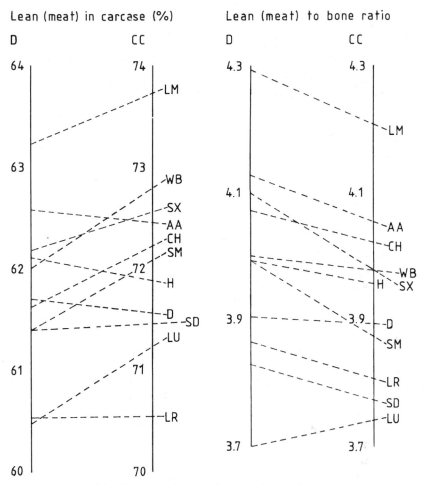

Fig. 7.1 Relationships between sire breed means for beef carcase characteristics obtained by dissection (D) and comparable characteristics obtained by commercial cutting (CC). Data from M.L.C. beef breed comparisons (208)

Breed codes
Crossbred cattle out of Hereford X Friesian and Blue-Grey dams by the following sire breeds.
AA Aberdeen Angus; CH Charolais; D Devon; H Hereford; LR Lincoln Red; SD South Devon; SM Simmental; SX Sussex.
Purebred cattle: LU Luing; WB Welsh Black

It is tempting to be over-critical of cruder evaluation techniques such as commercial cutting. More precise methods are expensive and large numbers of carcases evaluated by commercial cutting will often be more informative than a few evaluated by detailed anatomical cutting and tissue separation.

The dangers of criticising the use of cruder techniques are well illustrated by Berg and Butterfield (31), who said that Willis and Preston (387) '. . . . fell into the trap of interpreting their own results (based on commercial cutting) as indicating that some breeds (e.g. Charolais) have a higher proportion of high-priced cuts than others as a direct result of superior muscle weight distribution'. The implication is that if Willis and Preston had used complete separation they would have reached a different conclusion. Fig. 7.2 based on the M.L.C. breed evaluation data, shows that the conclusion of Preston and Willis was correct: in our sample which involved both commercial cutting and tissue separation, Charolais did have more muscle in the higher-priced joints. Perhaps it was Berg and Butterfield who had fallen into the trap of not taking larger samples in their work, more representative of the breeds available. Berg has since carried out other tissue separation work which indicates breed differences in the proportion of muscle in the higher-priced joints (32). The lesson from these arguments is that the circumstances dictate the technique to be used. Cruder techniques such as commercial cutting may well be the best choice in a particular situation but to make this a rational choice in the first place, some base-line tissue separation work is essential.

Lean (meat) in higher-priced cuts (%)

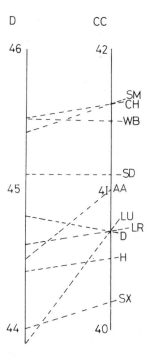

Fig. 7.2   Relationships between sire breed means for another beef carcase characteristic obtained by dissection (D) and the comparable characteristic obtained by commercial cutting (CC). Data from M.L.C. beef breed comparison (208). Breed codes as in Fig. 7.1.

8 Relative precision of alternative methods

Pig carcase evaluation

FAT THICKNESS MEASUREMENTS TAKEN ON THE INTACT OR CENTRE SPLIT
CARCASE

Subcutaneous fat represents a high proportion of total dissectable fat in pig carcases, is fairly evenly distributed over the musculature and is convenient to measure. Its measurement has led much of the development in carcase evaluation techniques over the past fifty years. Early information on pig carcase evaluation was reviewed by Harrington (155).

Several fat thickness measurements along the dorsal mid-line on the split carcase are used in classification and grading schemes. The most common are the thickest point over the shoulder, the thinnest point in the region of the last thoracic vertebra, and points in the rump region over the cross-section of the *M. gluteus medius* or over the cranial or caudal margins of this muscle. In most studies where the relationship between individual measurements and carcase lean content has been examined, measurements taken in the rump region close to the *M. gluteus medius* had the highest correlation, and those over the shoulder the lowest correlation (some recent results are shown in table 8.1). The reasons for this are not clear; possibly the shoulder measurement, being furthest from the initial splitting point, is more sensitive to the accuracy with which carcases are split. Also the shoulder fat is less well supported by vertebral spines than rump fat and the *M. gluteus medius* provides a clear anatomical reference point for measurement.

In the early 1950s, reliance on mid-line fat thickness measurements in breeding schemes gave cause for concern because, although fat thickness had improved in the dorsal line, an increasing number of carcases showed an undesirably thick layer of fat over the *M. longissimus*. This led, via fat thickness measurement on the cut carcase, to the development of probes capable of taking measurements over the *M. longissimus* (lateral measurements) on the intact side or carcase. Such measurements are more valuable predictors of carcase lean content than mid-line measurements (table 8.1).

We have examined the relative precision of lateral measurements along the carcase (cranio-caudally) (220). The precision of probe measurements showed a regular pattern: moving from the most cranial position (fourth/fifth cervical

Table 8.1 Residual s.d. for the prediction of pig carcase lean percentage from different fat thickness measurements taken on the intact carcase

Trial	(1)	(2)	(3)
Number of carcases	104	240	427
Standard deviation of carcase lean percentage	5.13	5.15	3.84
Residual s.d. for			
Mid-line fat measurements:			
shoulder	3.27	3.27	3.32
mid-back	3.01	3.15	3.18
loin	2.91	2.88	2.89
Fat measurements taken by probe over the *M. longissimus*			
4th/5th cervical vertebrae			3.30
7th rib			2.96
10th rib			2.68
13th rib (3rd/4th last rib)	2.62	2.67	2.20
Last rib	2.60	2.61	2.36
2nd/3rd lumbar vertebrae			2.45
5th/6th lumbar vertebrae			2.76

(1) de Boer *et al.* (99); probe measurements taken by Danish M.F.A.
(2) C.E.C. (77); results are averaged over the seven national populations
(3) Kempster and Evans (220); results shown are for the bacon weight group

vertebrae), precision increased to the positions in the hind rib region (third/fourth last rib and last rib) and then declined to the most caudal positions (fifth/sixth lumbar vertebrae) (table 8.1). The hind rib region therefore seems to have some special predictive value. Fat thickness measurements are commonly taken in this region following on from the suggestion of Hammond (148) and McMeekan (271) that the junction of the loin and thorax is the best region for prediction purposes since it is the latest-developing part of the carcase. The results of our study support the hypothesis, or at least the prediction from it.

Experience in Britain is that lateral measurements have the added advantage that they are more resilient than mid-line measurements to differences in dressing procedures, for example whether the backbone has been removed or not. However, this is not supported by Danish results which suggest that lateral measurements are more sensitive to such differences (308).

The addition of a second lateral fat measurement, or a mid-line fat measurement, to an initial fat measurement taken in the hind rib region has generally been found to provide a relatively small improvement in the precision of carcase lean prediction. There are some exceptions to this, particularly in the American literature, but these have involved small samples of carcases and commercial cutting techniques. In most commercial pig populations the residual s.d. cannot usually be brought below 2.0 per cent lean in carcase with the conventional mid-line and lateral fat thickness measurements. The decision to use two or more measurements depends largely on operational efficiency: if two or more measurements can be taken as easily as one, the small improvement in efficiency is worth having.

Some have argued that although additional fat measurements have little value for overall carcase lean prediction, they may have special regional value. For example, mid-line shoulder measurements might be useful as predictors of the lean content in the shoulder region. If this were so, they would be of value for meat traders who are concerned with buying or selling particular joints. Kempster and Evans (220) examined the value of fat measurements additional to a lateral measurement at P_2 for predicting the lean content of particular regions of the carcase (the ham, shoulder, rib back, rump back and streak joints were each considered). There was some slight indication of special regional value but the additional fat thickness measurement which gave the greatest increase in precision over P_2 in predicting the lean content of any cut was always fat thickness at the third/fourth last rib.

DEVELOPMENTS IN PROBING TECHNIQUES

Fat thickness measurements taken laterally over the *M. longissimus* in the hind rib region generally provide the most precise prediction of carcase lean content among measurements suitable for use in commercial classification and grading. In Britain as in several other countries, such measurements have been taken using the optical probe (intrascope).

Several instruments are now available which automatically record fat measurements and offer advantages over the optical probe in terms of improved data handling, labour savings and reduced operator fatigue. The main instruments available are as follows:

(a) The Ulster Probe (U.P.) which was developed for the Pigs Marketing Board of Northern Ireland by the Wolfson Opto-Electronics unit in Belfast University, and is based on the colour difference between muscle and fat.
(b) The Danish Meat-Fat Automatic Probe (M.F.A.) which is manufactured by the S.F.K. Hvidovre, and used in all Danish bacon factories. It is based on the difference in electrical conductivity between fat and muscle.
(c) The Hennessy and Chong Fat Depth Indicator (F.D.I.) which is manufactured by the Hennessy and Chong Company in New Zealand, and like the Ulster Probe is based on the detection of colour differences between fat and muscle.

Probing equipment has also been developed in Australia (C.S.I.R.O. Meat Laboratory).

Results available from different trials around the world indicate little difference between the instruments in the precision with which carcase lean content

Table 8.2 Residual s.d. for the prediction of pig carcase lean percentage using different probing instruments

Trial	(1)			(2)		(3)		
	OP	UP	MFA	OP	MFA	OP	UP	FDI
Standard deviation of carcase lean percentage	4.09	4.09	4.09	3.83	3.83	4.04	4.04	4.04
Residual s.d. for								
Carcase weight (W)	3.54	3.54	3.54			3.46	3.46	3.46
W + fat thickness at:								
3rd/4th lumbar vertebrae	2.64	2.92	2.77			2.29	2.29	2.40
3rd/4th last rib	2.23	2.44	2.24		2.35	2.37	2.56	2.16
last rib	2.30	2.75	2.55	2.70	2.54	2.21	2.27	2.20

OP = Danish optical probe; UP = Ulster probe; MFA = Danish Meat Fat Automatic (KSA); FDI = Hennessy and Chong Fat Depth Indicator.
(*1*) Kempster, Jones and Cuthbertson (225): 158 pigs representative of the British population.
(*2*) Hansson (150): 328 pigs from the Swedish pig progeny test.
(*3*) Kempster *et al.* (207): 110 pigs representative of British population.

is predicted (table 8.2). In addition to the trials comparing probes, there have been several comparing the M.F.A. with other methods of classification (for example, 340, 77). French results with the F.D.I. indicate that there may be problems in defining muscle/fat interfaces in extreme carcases when the muscle is very pale or the fat flecked with blood (316).

The choice of a particular instrument will depend on other factors, mainly their cost and efficiency of operation under commercial abattoir conditions. The cost-benefit ratio of installing automatic probes to replace the simpler optical probe depends critically on whether the number of people involved in taking the classification measurements can be reduced. This in turn depends on the number of measurements taken, line speed, size of abattoir and so on; but it does not depend on subsequent labour saving in data handling since this could be obtained equally well if the optical probe were used and the measurements keyed into a computer system at the measuring point.

The cost of the automatic probes, and of the M.F.A. in particular, is far in excess of the cost of the optical probe; a complete M.F.A. system is likely to cost approximately a hundred times as much as the optical probe. However, the use of automatic probing systems does offer potential labour savings in the operation of grading schemes. Since the M.F.A. lights up the distance from the mid-line at which the probe should be inserted, and a hot branding unit to mark the carcase with the grade may be incorporated in the system, this has potential for greater savings in labour than the Ulster or F.D.I. Probes. These savings are difficult to generalise since they depend very much on the operations in individual abattoirs.

The M.F.A. probe also has the facility to measure muscle thickness although research has shown that this provides a relatively small improvement in carcase lean prediction. The F.D.I. has recently been modified to provide a muscle thickness measurement (17), but there is no evidence on its accuracy in comparison with other measuring techniques. Muscle thickness measurements are much more sensitive than fat thickness to the angle of insertion of the probe; a small difference in the angle can have a major effect on the reading taken.

S.F.K. in Denmark have also developed a modified M.F.A. probe known as the Fat-o-Meater based on the colour difference between lean and fat. (They argue that this will be more accurate than the M.F.A. when used on beef carcases).

A rather different development is that by Pfister, the West German engineering company. Their equipment, under test at the Federal German Meat Research Institute at Kulmbach, is known as S.K.G. (Schlachtkorper — Klassifizierungsgerät) which predicts the percentage lean in carcase from factors similar to those used in the basic E.E.C. pig carcase grading scheme. The dorsal and medial sides of the hind leg and the rear part of the loin are scanned by video cameras under a monochromatic light source. Various shape measurements are taken automatically and used together with carcase weight and mid-line fat thickness measurements, taken automatically on the split carcase, to predict carcase lean content (341). The equipment is expensive, perhaps two hundred times the cost of the optical probe (17).

Is the accurate definition of probing positions really necessary? If not, there would clearly be major implications for automatic probing. Observations of carcase back fat in pigs suggests the existence of an area where there could be minimum variation in fat thickness. If such a general area could be defined, the full automation of back fat measurement would be easier to achieve.

OTHER MEASUREMENTS AND SAMPLE JOINT DISSECTIONS

The range in precision achieved with different measurements and sample joint dissections is illustrated in table 8.3. From among the methods considered, it is necessary to carry out sample joint dissections to achieve a major improvement in precision over that provided by fat thickness measurements.

Trial (2b) in table 8.3 shows how the judicious selection of simple measurements in combination with sample joint dissections can improve the precision of prediction (116). A fat thickness measurement taken over the *M. longissimus* at the last rib (P_2) gave a useful increase in precision when used together with the collar and hand sample joints. However, as one would expect from its location, the measurement did not improve the prediction when used with joints in the rib and loin region (rump back and rib back). When the precision of the joints plus P_2 was examined in relation to the relative cost of the joints (combination of labour and depreciation costs, shown in brackets in table 8.3), the ham followed by the hand joint appeared to offer the best value

Table 8.3 Residual s.d. for the prediction of pig carcase lean percentage using different measurements and sample joints. (Brackets indicate combined joints)

Trial	(1)	(2a)	(2b)**	(3)
Standard deviation of carcase lean percentage	3.74	3.19	3.19	5.0
Residual s.d. for				
M. *longissimus* dimensions taken				
on the cut surface	3.13	2.85		
Carcase dimensions	3.65			
Fat thickness at last rib:				
by probe		2.23		
on the cut surface	2.67	2.33		
Combination of the above		2.05		
Lean in joints (%)				
ham (12)*	1.71	1.37	1.22	1.7
rump back (17)	} 1.79	1.40	1.40	} 1.9
rib back (20)		1.40	1.40	
streak (belly) (22)	1.79	1.34	1.21	1.9
collar (17)	} 1.97	1.95	1.69	} 2.3
hand (12)		1.97	1.53	

* Cost as percentage of side dissection cost under M.L.C. conditions.

(1) Smith and Carpenter (350): 70 castrated male carcases from commercial abattoirs; live weights of 84-98 kg.

(2a) Evans and Kempster (116): 384 bacon weight carcases from M.L.C.'s commercial pig evaluation. The analysis was pooled within company source × feeding regimen × sex subgroups.

**(2b) As (2a) but with P_2 fat thickness used in multiple regression with percentage lean in sample joints.

(3) Schön *et al.* (339): 90 carcases sampled from commercial abattoirs.

for money. These costs are, however, obtained under particular conditions where the deboned defatted ham received a relatively high price.

Beef carcase evaluation

FAT THICKNESS AND OTHER SIMPLE MEASUREMENTS

Fat thickness measurements are not used as extensively with beef carcases as they are with pigs, since more reliance is placed on visual assessments of external fat cover. They are, however, used where the carcase may be cut and measurements taken on the cut surface. Such measurements are commonly taken in experiments and population studies. They are also used in some grading schemes, particularly the U.S.D.A. and Canadian systems for beef (see chapter 13).

In the U.S.D.A. scheme, 'cutability' (the weight of boneless, closely trimmed

Table 8.4 Residual s.d. for prediction of beef carcase lean percentage (defined in various ways) from different measurements.

Trial	(1)	(2)	(3)	(4)
Standard deviation of carcase lean percentage	3.59	2.41	3.0	2.79
Residual s.d. for				
Carcase dimensions	3.43		2.8	
Visual fat score			2.5	2.40
Fat thickness on the cut surface*				
6th rib 7.5 cm				2.27
10th rib 7.5 cm				2.47
10th rib 75% A				2.45
12th/13th rib 7.5 cm				2.38
12th/13th rib 75% A	2.76	1.88		2.25
3rd lumbar 7.5 cm				2.40
M. *longissimus* area				
10th rib				2.53
12th/13th rib	3.54	2.35		2.55
Marbling score	3.32			2.40
KKCF (%)	3.17	1.90	2.6	2.43
Specific gravity		1.65		
U.S.D.A. yield grade equation	2.66	1.62		
Lean in joints (%)**				
Shin				2.56
Fore rib			1.7	1.34
Top piece				1.21

* Fat thickness measured over the *M. longissimus* 7.5 cm from the dorsal mid-line or at a position 75% of *M. longissimus* width (A).

** Included for reference (see table 8.5): the sample of carcases was the same for both the measurement and sample joint analyses.

(1) Crouse and Dikeman (84): 1121 steers pooled within sire breed, dam breed and year subgroups. Prediction of saleable meat percentage in carcase.

(2) Powell and Huffman (317): 41 carcases differing widely in composition. Prediction of carcase protein percentage.

(3) Sornay (354): average result across 220 cattle comprising four groups differing in breed and muscularity type.

(4) Kempster and Chadwick (206): 600 carcases of different breed types. The analysis was pooled within 15 breed types. Prediction of carcase lean percentage.

retail cuts from the round, loin, chuck and rib expressed as a percentage of carcase weight) is predicted from fat thickness over the *M. longissimus* at the twelfth rib, the percentage of kidney, pelvic and heart fat, *M. longissimus* area at the twelfth rib, and carcase weight. It is generally agreed that the fat measurement is of principal importance in the prediction equation (for example, 3 and

84). Early studies of the use of different measurements to predict beef carcase composition were reviewed by Hedrick (173).

Table 8.4 illustrates the range in precision achieved with different predicting measurements. Our results (206) indicate that a fat thickness measurement taken in the twelfth/thirteenth rib region at a point defined from 75 per cent of *M. longissimus* width, known as A, is a useful predictor, confirming experience in the U.S.A. (289).

The use of probes to measure fat thickness presents more difficulties with beef than it does with pig carcases because of the soft consistency of the fat on the warm carcase and the lack of a firm outer surface against which to hold the probe (normally provided by skin on pig carcases). Fat thickness measurements are also generally smaller in beef carcases, requiring greater resolution of the probes for accurate readings, and the fat is less evenly distributed over the carcase, even in the rib region over the *M. longissimus*. Accurate readings may in some cases be difficult or impossible to obtain because of damage to the measuring site by hide pullers.

For these reasons, developments in probes and their use in beef grading and classification schemes are not far advanced. During the 1960s, some interest was shown in the U.S.A. in the use of simple steel probes to measure fat thickness on the cold carcase (4, 248). Later, the automatic probes developed originally for pigs were applied to beef carcases. In Britain, three of these have been compared with a simple steel rule pushed through the fat until the muscle surface is detected. The main results, shown in table 8.5 (64), lead to several important conclusions.

First, the state of the carcase at the time of probing can influence significantly the relative precision achieved with different probes. The automatic probes tended to be better than the simple steel rule when used on the cold carcase but the steel rule was better on the warm carcase. Anyone contemplating the use of such instruments should, therefore, ensure that they are evaluated under the same conditions as those of the intended application. Secondly, none of the rib positions was consistently better than any of the others, and little improvement in the precision of lean prediction was achieved when three fat thickness measurements were used instead of two. Thirdly, there were advantages in using the probe measurements in combination with a visual assessment of overall fat cover.

Our general conclusion would be that the best fat thickness measurements taken by probe can provide as precise a prediction of carcase lean percentage as visual fat scores given by experienced operators. Anyone involved in the development of classification and grading schemes should certainly consider their use.

Trials have been conducted in New Zealand and the U.S.A. to evaluate the Hennessy and Chong Fat Depth Indicator (17) and a series of probes have been evaluated by the Australian Meat and Livestock Corporation (259); results on their ability to predict carcase lean content are still awaited. In the Australian trials, a probe measurement is being taken at the position used in the U.S.D.A.

Table 8.5 Residual s.d. for the prediction of beef carcase lean percentage from different probing measurements and visual assessments of external fat cover (from 64)

Trial	(1a)				(1b)				(1c)	
Probe	MF		RP		FDI		RP		UP	RP
Hot or cold carcase	H	C	H	C	H	C	H	C	H	H
Number of carcases	50	50	50	50	61	61	61	61	33	33
Standard deviation of carcase lean percent	3.65				3.11				3.29	
Residual s.d.* for Visual fat score:										
7-point scale	1.83				2.69				2.42	
15-point scale	1.65				2.51				2.25	
Fat thickness over *M. longissimus*: most precise measurement at:										
6th rib	3.31	2.45	2.47	2.26	3.05	2.61	2.99	2.67	2.96	2.95
10th rib	3.02	2.14	2.47	2.25	3.09	3.00	3.00	3.05	3.15	2.65
13th rib	3.10	2.18	2.07	2.57	3.00	2.60	3.01	2.89	3.13	3.00
Combination of best two fat measurements	2.15	2.04	2.00	2.07	2.53	2.37	2.90	2.61	2.90	2.52
Combination of best three fat measurements	1.99	1.97	1.88	2.06	2.48	2.29	2.90	2.62	2.90	2.48
7-point fat score + two fat thicknesses	1.83	1.62	1.62	1.64	2.40	2.27	2.64	2.49	2.33	2.35

MF = Danish meat fat probe; RP = ruler probe; FDI= Hennessy and Chong Fat Depth Indicator.
* Carcase weight was included as predictor in all cases
(1a) Sample of commercial Hereford × Friesian steer carcases selected to cover a wide range in fatness. RP was a sharpened steel rule.
(1b) Sample of steer carcases of different types from M.L.C.'s beef breed evaluation programme.
(1c) As (1b).

grading scheme (fat thickness at the twelfth/thirteenth rib at 75 per cent of the width of the *M. longissimus*). This position is identified by eye and touch on the intact carcase, following the contour of the *M. longissimus*.

PARTIAL DISSECTIONS OF BEEF CARCASES

Over the years, research workers have been intrigued by the possibility of predicting beef carcase composition from partial dissections. The earliest work was based on a three rib cut (ninth to eleventh ribs) (149), and this has found widespread use for prediction purposes in cattle experimentation. In some cases, little thought has been given to its applicability or whether any differences detected between treatments might be biased (see chapter 18). The composition of this joint is sensitive to the accuracy with which the vertebral column is split and, because the joint is small, to the accuracy with which it is removed from the carcase. The division between rib and brisket position is difficult to standardise, leading some to investigate a single whole rib as an alternative (245).

Butterfield (47) suggested the shin as a possible predictor of carcase composition and developed equations using the weights of the radius and ulna and the weight of associated muscle for predicting carcase bone and muscle content respectively.

During the 1960s and 1970s, precision of different joints was compared in many studies and various prediction equations and combinations of predictors were proposed for general use. Two main types of prediction equation have been used:

$$\text{Equation A:} \quad Y_w = a + b_1 x_1 + b_2 x_2$$

$$\text{Equation B:} \quad Y_p = a + b \frac{100 x_2}{x_3}$$

where:

Y_w = weight of lean in the side
Y_p = weight of lean in the side as a percentage of side weight
x_1 = side weight
x_2 = weight of lean in the joint
x_3 = weight of the joint

The relative precision has appeared to be different depending upon the equation used. In analyses using equation A, little difference has been recorded between the predictive value of the different joints and the shin has usually been nominated as best because it is convenient and cheap to dissect (75, 175). On the other hand, when equation B has been used, the shin joint has been shown to be a poor predictor; other joints, particularly the rib, have been selected (244).

The essential difference between the two equations is that one includes joint weight (albeit as the divisor for percentage lean in the joint) and the other does not. The effect of joint *per se* on the precision of predicting weight of lean in the side could be examined by adding weight into equation A. This was done with benefit by Harrington and King (165) on a small sample of carcases described by Callow (52); on a larger sample, Kempster and Jones (224) showed that the addition of joint weight provided little improvement in precision for the shin and leg joints but a substantial improvement for other joints including the rib. The absolute level of precision with joint weight in the equation was lower for the shin and leg joints than other joints of comparable size (table 8.6). The implication of this is that reports of analyses which did not include joint weight have exaggerated the value of the shin and leg joints by failing to demonstrate the full potential of other joints.

Table 8.6 Residual s.d. for the prediction of carcase lean weight or percentage from different sample joints with the prediction equation constructed in different ways (From Kempster and Jones, 224).*

| | *Type of equation* | | |
	A1 (kg)	A2 (kg)	B (%)
Standard deviation	7.81	7.81	2.79
Residual s.d.			
Shin	2.66	2.66	2.56
Coast	2.57	1.34	1.13
Clod + sticking	2.76	1.82	1.61
Fore rib	2.86	1.58	1.34
· Pony	2.71	1.39	1.17
Leg	2.85	2.74	2.42
Thin flank	3.19	1.84	1.53
Rump	2.83	1.82	1.50
Sirloin	2.79	1.75	1.46
Wing rib	2.94	1.81	1.50
Top piece	2.07	1.37	1.21

* Results are pooled within 17 breed type X feeding system groups.

A1: $Y_w = a + b_1 x_1 + b_2 x_2$
A2: $Y_w = a + b_1 x_1 + b_2 x_2 + b_3 x_3$

B : $Y_p = a + b \dfrac{100 x_2}{x_3}$

where Y_w = weight of lean in side
Y_p = weight of lean in side as a percentage of side weight
x_1 = side weight
x_2 = weight of lean in joint
x_3 = weight of joint

The most likely explanation for this is the low fat content of the shin and leg joints in comparison with others. Addition of joint weight as an independent variate to an equation which includes the weight of lean in the joint is effectively adding weight of bone and fat weight in the joint to the information. The former is closely related to the lean weight in the joint at constant side weight, but the latter is not. So it is the fat content of joints which has the potential to improve the precision of predicting carcase lean content in these circumstances.

An important factor influencing the choice of sample joint for a particular application is cost (labour plus depreciation). This will vary considerably from one set of circumstances to another, depending particularly on the depreciation involved in removing joints from the carcase. The relative weighting given to cost and precision will depend on the trial in question and generalisation about which joints are best is difficult. With M.L.C. costings appropriate to 1980, the rib joints (fore rib and wing rib) appear to offer a useful compromise between cost and precision. (The relative cost of different sample joints is shown later in table 18.4).

Fig. 8.1 shows the relationship between the cost of a predicting measurement (expressed as a percentage of side dissection cost) and its precision in prediction

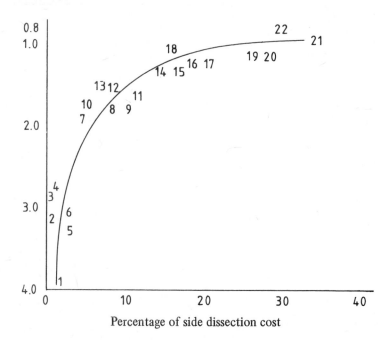

Residual s.d.

Percentage of side dissection cost

Fig. 8.1 Precision (residual s.d.) against cost for predicting the lean percentage of beef carcases from different measurements (216)

1 Eye muscle area 10th rib; 2 Fat over B 10th rib; 3 Best probe fat thickness; 4 Subcutaneous fat score; 5 % lean in shin (A), 6 leg (B), 7 thin flank, 8 clod + sticking (C), 9 A + C, 10 wing rib, 11 sirloin (D), 12 rump (E), 13 fore rib (F), 14 top piece (G), 15 B+G, 16 pony (H), 17 D + E, 18 coast (J), 19 C + H, 20 F + H, 21 H + J, 22 G + J (best pair)

of lean percentage in beef carcases (expressed as the residual s.d.) for twenty-two possible predictors investigated in our work with M.L.C. data.

Sheep carcase evaluation

There have been many trials to compare the precision of different predictors with sheep carcases. The early trials assessed techniques over as great a range of material as possible, so the results are of limited value except possibly in the context of commercial classification. Harrington (156) and Timon and Bichard (365) drew attention to the deficiencies of this approach. Since then, a number of trials have been carried out within breed and sex, and within other factors normally controlled in breeding schemes, population studies and experiments.

Table 8.7 Residual s.d. for the prediction of sheep carcase lean percentage from different measurements

Trial	(1)	(2)	(3)	(4)	(5)
Standard deviation of carcase lean percentage	3.29	3.1	3.6	3.70	3.50
Residual s.d. for					
M. longissimus dimensions	2.83	2.7	3.3	3.65	3.48
Carcase dimensions		2.9		3.33	3.01
Visual fat scores		2.3		2.82	2.60
KKCF in carcase (%)	2.81		3.2	2.98	2.60
Fat thickness over					
M. longissimus	2.71	1.7	2.9	2.80	2.60
Specific gravity	2.83	1.7			
Combination of the above		1.6	2.1	2.40	
Lean in joints (%)					
leg (27)*	1.63	1.6	1.8	2.15	2.34
breast (8)	1.88	1.7		1.82	2.15
loin (14)	1.83	1.2	2.2	1.81	1.80
ribs (13)	1.83	1.2	1.9	1.53	1.92
shoulder (16)	1.58	1.4	1.3	1.62	1.74
legs + loin (41)		0.9		1.23	
loin + ribs (27)		1.0		1.32	
ribs + shoulder (29)				1.04	

* Cost as a percentage of side dissection cost under M.L.C. conditions.
(1) Field, Kemp and Varney (121): 165 Southdown X Western lambs.
(2) Timon and Bichard (365): 83 Clun Forest lambs.
(3) Latham, Moody and Kemp (242): 121 Southdown crossbred lambs.
(4) Kempster *et al.* (204): 424 lambs, pooled within breed groups.
(5) Kempster and Jones (unpublished data): 894 lambs pooled within year, dam breed, sire breed and sex groups.

Results from the more important trials are shown in table 8.7 together with some recent unpublished results from an M.L.C. study. These as a whole present a fairly consistent picture indicating that:

(a) carcase dimensions and *M. longissimus* dimensions are poor individual predictors;
(b) visual fat assessments, KKCF percentages, fat thicknesses and specific gravity determinations provide increasing precision, possibly in that order; and
(c) sample joints are the most precise predictors.

When the simpler measurements not involving dissection are combined in multiple regression, their precision approaches that achieved by dissection of the leg (and is better than that achieved by some smaller joints, such as the neck which is not shown in the table). However, for greater precision, dissection of other joints or combination of joints is necessary.

Table 8.7 also shows the relative costs of the sample joints under the circumstances of M.L.C.'s Carcase Evaluation Unit. The leg does not appear to offer value for money, whereas the breast offers relatively high precision in relation to its cost.

THE USE OF PROBING INSTRUMENTS

The testing of automatic probes is less well developed with sheep than the other species, although this is being explored in Great Britain and New Zealand. Interest has been shown in the use of simple probing instruments (for example 122) and a simple measuring tool is now used in the New Zealand lamb grading scheme to identify the overfat (F) grade (see chapter 12). This measurement is referred to as GR and is the total tissue thickness between the surface of the lamb carcase and the rib at a point 11 cm from the mid-line in the region of the twelfth rib (133). GR has been shown to be as accurate as a fat thickness measurement over the *M. longissimus* in predicting carcase fat content (231).

9 Carcase conformation

Carcase conformation or shape (usually expressed as a score determined by eye judgement) adds a different dimension to the prediction of carcase composition. Careful control of carcase fatness is necessary for it to be useful and then the value of conformation lies more as a means of identifying different breed types rather than as a predictor of individual animal composition. In view of its importance commercially, the characteristic will be considered in some detail.

Debate about the value of conformation (of animal or carcase) as a predictor of carcase composition has continued for many years. Results from carcase evaluation studies have varied, but on balance they indicate that conformation is related to carcase composition in many circumstances. However, the degree of correlation is low, so that predictions based on conformation are subject to considerable error. Scientists have therefore tended towards the view that conformation is an unimportant characteristic. On the other hand, the meat industry has traditionally paid more for animals considered to have superior conformation and most breeders and meat traders still attach importance to conformation as an indicator of commercial value. Conformation assessments are included in the national classification or grading schemes for pigs, beef and sheep operated in many countries, particularly in Europe.

One type of conformation may be considered preferable to another for a number of reasons, additional to its possible value as a predictor of carcase lean content. For example, carcases with better conformation are expected to have advantages in the proportion of higher-priced cuts or in thicker muscle cross-sections.

DIFFICULTIES OF INTERPRETATION

The interpretation of results from published conformation studies is complicated by several factors.

First, many different definitions of conformation have been used. A particular distinction can be drawn between the assessments of shape which attempt to eliminate the influence of fatness on the score given, and those which allow fatness to play its full part. Results can be particularly difficult to interpret if this distinction is not made. An E.A.A.P. working party on reference methods for beef carcase assessment (98) recommended that the former assessment (defined as the thickness of muscle in relation to the skeletal size) should be referred to as *muscularity*, while the latter type (defined as the thickness of muscle and fat in relation to skeletal size) should be called *conformation*. (*Fleshiness* is intermediate, being determined by the thickness of flesh, that is lean plus intermuscular fat, relative to skeletal size).

Secondly, conformation assessments attempt to describe a complex three-dimensional shape by a simple index and many subtleties of definition are possible. For example, more or less emphasis may be given to hind-leg development, to the blockiness of the lumbar region, to shoulder thickness or to carcase length. Such differences may be sufficient to confuse the interpretation of results from different studies.

Thirdly, most conformation assessments are made by visual appraisal and subject to variation in the same way as visual scores of external fat cover (see chapter 7).

These difficulties are such that, while there appears to have been much research on the topic, little sound information is available to answer practical questions.

Conformation assessment

Conformation is most commonly determined by visual appraisal. As a means of improving the consistency of visual appraisal, photographic scales are now sometimes used. Such scales for beef assessment have been published for conformation by the M.L.C. (273) and by O.N.I.B.E.V. (298); de Boer *et al.* (98) published a scale for fleshiness.

The number of points on scales for conformation varies between countries or applications with 5-7 point scales being most common. A 15-point scale, with five basic classes each with three subdivisions, has been proposed as the standard for the assessment of experimental cattle in E.A.A.P. countries (98).

A number of objective methods of conformation assessment have been examined over the years, in particular different relationships between carcase weight and length. Generally, these have been found to be less well related to meat yield than visual scores (for example, 212). However, as indicated earlier, objective methods are normally easier to standardise and they are more easily adapted to automatic recording, so there has been a resurgence of interest. In New Zealand, Bass and co-workers (25) found that measurements of the degree of curvilinearity (convex to concave) of the hind leg in beef gave promising relationships with beef carcase composition. In Germany, the Pfister company have developed automatic measuring equipment, known as S.K.G. (Schlacht-körper Klassifierungsgerät), for pig conformation assessment based on video scanning. The equipment is being tested for use in the E.E.C. grading system (341).

CONTROLLING FATNESS IN CONFORMATION STUDIES
Conformation studies present a different problem from other carcase work in that variation in fatness must be removed before the relationships between conformation and carcase lean content can be examined.

Several methods of controlling fatness are available. In commercial beef carcase classification and grading schemes, visual conformation scores are often used in conjunction with visual scores for external fat cover in a two-way grid. In the E.E.C. grading scheme for pig carcases, as operated in the original six member states, a fat thickness measurement is used with visual conformation (or 'type') score in such a grid (E.E.C. Regulation 2108/70).

More control can be exercised over fatness when data from trials involving detailed carcase assessment and dissection are being analysed.

The accuracy of adjustment for fatness variations is crucial in determining the value of conformation as a predictor of carcase lean content, since conformation and fatness are normally positively associated with one another but related to leanness in opposite directions. Better conformation carcases tend to have higher lean to bone ratios, and hence a higher lean percentage, than poorer conformation carcases of the same fatness. But, in a group of carcases differing in fatness, there may be some which have good conformation because they are fat (fat has the effect of filling in the indentations between muscles giving a rounded appearance) so having a lower lean percentage than poorer conformation carcases of comparable (or poorer) lean to bone ratio but less fat.

The effect of fatness on carcase lean content is often large in comparison with the effect of lean to bone ratio, so an imprecise adjustment to equal fatness can easily obscure the relationship between leanness and conformation (212). By the same token, the value of conformation when used with a poor control over fatness, needs to be established if this is how it has to be used in practice.

Carcase weight may also influence relationships between conformation and carcase characteristics. The effect may be important when tissue weights and dimensions (such as muscle thickness) are involved, but are likely to be smaller when tissue weights are expressed as percentages of carcase weight.

The basic question is: 'What additional information is provided about carcase composition by an assessment of conformation among carcases of similar weight and subcutaneous fat percentage?'.

Conformation in pig carcases

The value ascribed to pig carcase conformation differs markedly between countries depending on the types of pigs in their individual populations. In Britain, we have found that carcase conformation assessed visually or by length or muscle depth measurement has virtually no value as a predictor of carcase leanness (159, 221). Our most recent results, given in table 9.1, show only a small effect of conformation overall, given weight and P_2 fat thickness, despite the superficial evidence of the extreme groups based on small numbers of carcases.

Such results conflict with those studies in Germany (337) and the Netherlands (for example, 97) which indicate that conformation (muscularity) as assessed there increases the accuracy of predicting lean content among carcases of the same weight and fat thickness.

Table 9.1 Residual s.d. for the prediction of pig carcase characteristics from different combinations of predictors including conformation, with means for different conformation classes. Based on 1385 carcases from years 3 to 6 of M.L.C.'s commercial pig evaluation (221)

	Lean in carcase (%)	Lean to bone ratio	Lean in higher-priced cuts (%)*	*M. longissimus* area (cm^2)
Standard deviation	4.39	0.56	1.29	9.7
Prediction from:				
carcase weight (W)	3.67	0.54	1.28	6.0
$W + P_2$ fat thickness	2.45	0.53	1.28	5.3
$W + P_2$ + conformation (C_f)**	2.44	0.51	1.28	5.2
$W + P_2$ + company (Cy)***	2.31	0.51	1.25	5.2
$W + P_2 + Cy + C_f$	2.30	0.50	1.25	5.1
Means for conformation classes+:				
1 (worst)	47.6	5.20	38.2	32.9
2	48.5	5.51	38.8	40.2
3	49.0	5.74	38.7	45.8
4	49.5	5.95	38.8	49.2
5 (best)	50.7	6.30	38.9	52.2

* Percentage of total lean occurring in back and ham.
** Conformation was assessed on a 5-point scale.
*** The breeding company from which the pigs originated used as predictor.
+ At equal W and P_2

We now know that genetic differences between pig populations, and in particular the frequency of the halothane gene (see chapter 15), contribute to the contrasting results between countries. The relationship between conformation and composition in pigs will be considered in more detail in the section dealing with the development of classification and grading schemes in different countries, and in the section on the use of carcase evaluation techniques in breeding programmes.

Conformation in beef carcases

Cattle have generated the most debate about the importance of conformation. The scientific literature, although apparently extensive, provides little useful practical information on the relationships involved. This may reflect the cost of carrying out detailed evaluation of beef carcases; sample sizes have generally been small and research workers have tended to select cattle of different (often extreme) shapes with little regard to breed differences.

Several reviews have been made of published trials on beef conformation, for example those of Oliver (300), Barton (22) and Preston and Willis (319). Reviewers have drawn attention to the fact that results from different trials are confusing and difficult to interpret as a whole, and have generally concluded that conformation is a poor indicator of carcase composition. But they have not tried to explain why the confusion exists, or to suggest ways in which it might be overcome in future trials.

Table 9.2 Residual s.d. for the prediction of beef carcase characteristics from different combinations of predictors including conformation, and regressions on conformation. Based on 805 carcases from M.L.C.'s beef breed evaluation programme (223)

	Saleable meat in carcase (%)	Meat to bone ratio	Meat in higher-priced cuts (%)	*M. longissimus* area (cm^2)
Standard deviation	1.83	0.36	1.05	10.9
Prediction from: carcase weight (*W*)				
+ fat class (*F*)	1.81	0.35	1.04	8.1
W + *F* + conformation*	1.68	0.29	0.98	7.5
W + *F* + breed**	1.45	0.27	0.92	6.5
W + *F* + breed + conformation	1.41	0.25	0.91	6.3
Regression on conformation***:				
computed over all data	0.77	0.23	0.37	5.6
computed within breed	0.29	0.15	0.15	3.6

*   Conformation was assessed on a 6-point scale.
**   Breed used as predictor.
*** Change in the characteristic per one point change on the conformation scale, carcases in the same fat class.

Results from large-scale analyses using accumulated M.L.C. data for mixed breed samples have shed light on some of the underlying problems in conformation studies (223). Correlations between conformation and composition among carcases of equal weight and fatness were moderate to low, conformation rarely accounting for more than 30 per cent of the remaining variation (table 9.2). Similar relationships were recorded by Colomer-Rocher, Bass and Johnson (76) in a mixed breed sample of cattle in New Zealand. The practical significance of these relationships depends on the circumstances in which they may be used. Those calculated from the bulked data were sufficiently precise to confirm a role for conformation in classification under commercial conditions when breed cannot be identified.

During the early 1980s particular concern was expressed by the meat industries in Britain and several other European countries about the increasing influence of the Canadian Holstein, with its poor conformation, on beef carcases coming as a by-product from the dairy herd. Canadian Holstein cattle were not included in the samples of cattle in the study of Kempster and Harrington (223), but information has accumulated from a number of British studies, including later runs of M.L.C.'s beef breed evaluation programme. These indicate that Holsteins have 1-2 percentage units less saleable meat in carcase than British Friesians with the same external fat cover (200). They also have conformation scores one to two classes lower than British Friesians on the 6-class conformation scale used in M.L.C.'s beef carcase classification scheme. The increasing use of the Canadian Holstein at one end of the conformation scale and of muscular Continental breeds, in particular the Limousin, at the other, is increasing the range and importance of conformation in the British cattle population.

Conformation is not a particularly good breed indicator in our samples since breed explains a substantial proportion of the remaining variation in carcase composition among carcases of the same weight, fat class and conformation class (table 9.2). Our data were, therefore, examined to see how well particular breeds fitted the between breed regression of saleable meat to bone ratio on conformation. Some breeds differed in characteristic ways from the regression, for example Aberdeen Angus crosses had higher meat to bone ratios than would be predicted from their conformation (196). Such effects may be caused by basic differences in the relative thickness and/or density of bone.

Conformation in sheep carcases

Sheep do not show such a wide variation of conformation types and the importance of conformation as an indicator of carcase composition has not caused the debate or generated the research effort for sheep that it has for beef cattle. Nevertheless, there is still uncertainty about the emphasis that should be given to conformation in sheep breeding programmes and commercial classification and grading schemes.

Most sheep conformation studies have been carried out within breed and without adjustment to equal fatness. Predictably the general conclusion has been that lambs selected as of good conformation tend to be fatter than poorer conformation carcases, with little difference in muscle thickness or proportion of higher-priced cuts (for example, 184, 326). As before, an association between fatness and conformation is expected when carcases with thicker fat cover are judged to have better conformation.

Detailed information on the value of conformation among British breeds became available in the early 1980s from two large-scale ram breed trials (212). 'Fat-corrected' conformation was not found to be a valuable predictor of composition in sheep carcases (table 9.3). At best it only contributed marginally to prediction and was sensitive to the accuracy with which fatness was controlled. Indeed, poor control of fatness, as would occur in commercial classification

Table 9.3 Residual s.d. for the prediction of sheep carcase characteristics from different combinations of predictors including conformation, and regressions on conformation. Based on 1475 carcases from M.L.C.'s ram breed trial (Trial I) and 920 carcases from a joint A.B.R.O./M.L.C. trial (Trial II) (212)

	Lean in carcase (%)		Lean to bone ratio		Lean in higher-priced cuts (%)		M. longissimus depth (mm)	
	Overall	Within sire breed	Overall	Within sire breed	Overall	Within sire breed	Overall	Within sire breed
Trial I								
Standard deviation	3.83	3.58	0.38	0.36	1.70	1.64	3.14	3.10
Prediction from:								
Carcase weight (W) + fat class (SF_5)*	2.97	2.88	0.35	0.33	1.67	1.62	2.68	2.61
$W + SF_5$ + conformation (C_4)*	2.96	2.88	0.34	0.33	1.66	1.61	2.64	2.59
Regression on C_4**	−0.52	NS	0.15	0.12	0.43	0.40	1.04	0.83
W + fat class (SF_e)*	2.61	2.56	0.35	0.33	1.68	1.62	2.68	2.62
$W + SF_e$ + conformation (C_{15})*	2.61	2.56	0.34	0.32	1.65	1.60	2.60	2.56
Regression on C_{15}**	NS	NS	0.05	0.04	0.16	0.14	0.37	0.35
Trial II								
Standard deviation	4.36	3.89	0.39	0.35	1.80	1.77	3.22	3.10
Prediction from:								
$W + SF_5$	3.29	2.96	0.37	0.33	1.76	1.74	2.89	2.79
$W + SF_5$ + conformation (C_5)*	3.29	2.96	0.37	0.33	1.75	1.73	2.82	2.74
Regression on C_5**	NS	NS	0.14	0.12	0.44	0.40	1.30	1.20

* Visual assessment of external fat cover: SF_5 = 5-point scale, SF_e = carcase subcutaneous fat percentage estimated to the nearest percentage unit; Conformation: C_4 = 4-point scale; C_{15} = 15-point scale; C_5 = 5-point scale.
** Partial regression coefficient (change in the characteristic per one point change on the conformation scale) with carcase weight and fat class constant.

when a visual score into one of a limited number of fat classes was used, could mean that conformation would identify fatter rather than leaner carcases. In view of this, there is a case for ignoring conformation in the current sheep population in Britain, unless it can be demonstrated that such carcases are more valuable because of shape *per se*. Such a conclusion would, of course, have to be reviewed if radically different breeds were introduced in significant numbers into the British population.

The marginal advantage of conformation as a predictor of leanness appears to lie in the identification of differences in lean to bone ratio, although examination of breed differences indicates that breeds with better conformation do not necessarily have higher lean to bone ratios. Suffolk crosses, for example, have relatively low lean to bone ratios in relation to their conformation, whereas Texel crosses have a high lean to bone ratio but do not have sufficiently high conformation scores to identify their advantage. The poor relationships between breeds may again reflect differences in bone structure.

Summary

Results for cattle, sheep and pigs present the same general picture. In a mixed breed population including types of extreme conformation, 'fat-corrected' conformation is positively related to lean to bone ratio and muscle thickness.

The contribution that the relationship of conformation with lean to bone ratio can make to the prediction of carcase lean percentage depends on how effectively the variation in fatness is controlled. For cattle and pigs, with control achieved by fatness measurements suitable for use in commercial classification schemes, conformation (at equal 'fatness') is positively related to carcase lean content. However, considerable error is involved in the prediction of leanness for individual carcases, showing for example that large numbers of beef and pig carcases would need to be purchased before wholesalers or butchers could confidently assume that the choice of carcase based on superior conformation would give the expected advantage in yield of lean meat.

Conformation provides little information about the proportion of the total lean located in the higher-priced joints. This is to be expected from the limited variation existing in this characteristic. The largest increase in precision in predicting this trait has been recorded for cattle, because the muscular Continental breeds have a slight advantage in lean distribution in combination with better conformation compared with traditional British beef and dairy breeds.

Conformation appears to be of some value as a predictor of *M. longissimus* area or depth, however these characteristics are dominated by carcase weight and the most effective way of achieving bigger muscle cross-sections is to slaughter at heavier weights.

The value of conformation in a population drawn from mixed breeds essentially depends on its ability to identify breed differences in carcase characteristics. Although of some value in this respect, actual breed identification is much more effective, since breed differences in lean to bone ratio and fat partition are not always evident from visual assessments of overall shape.

SECTION 3
Commercial grading and classification

10 Role of grading and classification in marketing

In early agricultural societies, as in many underdeveloped countries today, domestic animals were used mainly as providers of milk, wool and pulling power. The killing of immature animals specifically for meat was a luxury, most meat coming as a valued by-product along with skin and bones when the animal's working life was complete. Over the years, as productivity improved and as non-agricultural communities developed, meat became an important part of the total output of the animal and trade began. Initially this trade was in surplus live animals, which were killed by the buyer for his own family's use; these buyers then began to sell their surplus. The distributive trade became progressively more sophisticated and several different kinds of middlemen emerged, providing services and adding value.

Until recent times, most trade was on a personal basis. The middleman bargained face to face with the farmer or his agent for the purchase of stock, and with the buyer or his agent for the sale of carcases and cuts. Even today, such personal bargaining accounts for a significant section of the business in developed countries and much of the trade in less developed countries.

The need for methods of carcase description arose primarily from the lengthening of the distribution chain and the decline in face-to-face bargaining. So it first became a matter of importance in the export trade which developed from Australia, New Zealand and South America particularly to the United Kingdom, for many years the largest importer of meat. This blossomed after the introduction of refrigerated transport in the second half of the nineteenth century.

Carcase description, introduced to facilitate trade at a distance, quickly took on a promotional significance. In most countries where the export of meat became an important factor in the national economy, government departments or quasi-government bodies, such as producer marketing boards, developed to influence or control the pattern of trading. Some of these organisations have traded in meat, some have been merely regulatory. They have been concerned to protect the image of their meat exports in the eyes of the traders in the recipient countries, and have introduced methods for safeguarding quality. An essential tool in these disciplines was usually some form of export grading. The foremost examples are Danish bacon and New Zealand lamb, for both of which the United Kingdom was the dominant market, although the same principles applied to a lesser extent to the export of beef from Australia and Argentina.

In the U.S.A. carcase grading arose from a different background. By the turn of the century, buyers and sellers in the United States had developed their own broad terminology for different categories of live cattle. They knew what the terms meant and anyone who was engaged in trade was well advised to be familiar with them before he spent his money. Nevertheless, similar terminology inevitably began to mean rather different things in different areas and was unsatisfactory as a basis for sensible market reporting.

The U.S.D.A. recognised that effective market price reports were dependent on a uniform grading system, but the proposals quickly took on two new dimensions. First, those concerned with regulating trade, ensuring fair competition and encouraging improvements in the distributive system, began to talk of the need for a 'common language'. Then, as now, this need was less readily appreciated by those actually engaged in buying and selling. Secondly, beef quality was highly prized and excellence was closely associated with particular breeds, fed in particular ways. This led the protagonists of the traditional beef breeds to demand differentiation of their product from beef produced in other ways which they considered to be inferior in eating quality. They argued that this inferior beef might damage the image of the product and, indeed, the whole market potential. Consequently there was strong pressure to base the grades on criteria believed to be closely related to eating quality, particularly marbling and maturity, and to structure them in such a way that only beef considered of high quality would achieve the higher grades to which names attractive to the consuming public could be applied.

Naturally, these developments were controversial and controversy about meat grading, particularly beef grading, continues to this day in the U.S.A. with an intensity unknown elsewhere. Proposed changes have been fiercely resisted by one sector or another of this vast industry. Changes proposed in 1974 were even resisted right up to the Supreme Court and Presidents have become involved.

The grading system adopted in New Zealand, where lamb and mutton exports have contributed substantially to the Gross National Product, similarly has considerable repercussions for whole sectors of the economy. Although the intensity of the debate has not approached the American level, since the consumer is less directly involved, controversy and argument have flared up several times in the history of New Zealand lamb grading. A false step in adjusting the system might have led to a change of direction by the industry which in the long term could undermine the confidence of the British retailer.

SITUATION IN EUROPE

The above are two cases where grading systems devised for specific purposes — price reporting in the U.S.A. and exporting from New Zealand — have developed to become more and more significant in livestock improvement. With the sole exception of the trade in bacon from export-orientated Denmark and the Netherlands to Great Britain, the same incentives to create grading systems have not until recently existed in Europe. The industries have been on a much smaller scale than those of South America, the U.S.A. or the Antipodes, and trade has been essentially local; meat factories and trade between countries in carcases and cuts have been a post-war development. As production and trade built up, grading systems were introduced in countries like France and Germany, essentially as part of regulations controlling official price reporting, but they have not been widely adopted in trade.

Grading was developed in the U.K. for bacon pigs as part of an attempt to compete with Danish imports. The desirability of introducing schemes of carcase description for beef, sheep and other types of pigs was promoted in the 1960s but the debate in Great Britain has had an important additional dimension.

For many years, the U.K. market for finished livestock was supported by government schemes whereby the difference between the market price and a predetermined guaranteed price was made up to the producer on an individual animal basis. To operate such support systems, the classes of stock which were eligible for this payment had to be defined, and their average market price calculated. The concept of a Certification Standard was introduced, and only animals (or their carcases) above this standard were eligible for the so-called 'deficiency payment'. In some variations, the acceptable animals or carcases were further subdivided into statutory grades receiving different levels of government support.

So in Britain 'grading' came to be thought of as a process carried out by government employees or their agents as an integral part of the market support system, rather than as a device to facilitate trading or provide market information to producers. Since the 1960s, it has been argued in Britain that improvements in production and distribution efficiency depend on producers being given strong signals about the type of carcase in demand by the wholesale trade to supply to their retail customers (375). Grading has not been seen to have a role in promotion or consumer information.

Despite the laudable objectives, the subject has been as controversial in Britain as elsewhere (161). To many academics and economists, it seems self-evident that the efficiency of the distribution system must be open to improvement if the basic product being traded – the carcase – is described in a uniform manner understood by all parties. The fact that such a description can never describe the infinite variations of carcase and meat qualities, or even of the factors which would be brought into his assessment by any individual buyer, is not seen as negating the basic principle. Benefits are seen to accrue even when the quality of the information falls short of perfection, provided the net benefits in improved efficiency exceed any costs added to the distributive process by the introduction of grading.

While some traders can see benefits to their own business in such carcase description, the majority remain sceptical. They suspect that the short-term added costs will fall on them, while the benefits, if any, are long term and realised elsewhere. Perhaps, most important of all, they are concerned that their individual skills in sorting, allocating and the associated bargaining will be devalued and even, in due course, superseded. More realistically, economic circumstances will dictate that the traditional skills in disposing of variable supplies to customers with varying demands and varying degrees of market power will have to be replaced gradually by new skills of minimising variability and assuring the retail buyer and his customers that tighter control of the product itself has been achieved. In these circumstances, effective methods of carcase description will prove a valuable component but not the 'be-all and end-all' of the process.

The European aspect of this subject is now dominated by the Common Agricultural Policy of the E.E.C. The European-wide systems of supporting the market for beef, pig meat and sheep meat involve standardised methods of reporting national prices to the Commission headquarters, so that various support measures can be triggered. Effective management control of this huge and costly system depends on introducing precision into the prices reported and the subsequent actions – the levies on imports, the subsidies on exports, the aids to private storage, intervention buying or various sorts of premium schemes. There has been a common pig grading scheme used for price reporting since the early 1970s and a common beef scheme was introduced in 1981. While it has been the somewhat idealistic intention of E.E.C. officials that these schemes should also be used as a common basis of trading throughout the Community, such a development is now seen as being some years away.

Grading principles

Most of the early grading schemes for cattle and sheep were designed to focus attention on a top quality, a top grade from which were excluded carcases with meat considered likely to be of inferior eating quality. This was particularly the case in countries where extensive systems of production were the rule. Such systems led to animals varying widely in age at slaughter, and certainly the meat of older animals is likely to be tougher than that of younger animals. Further, good eating quality of meat has been associated traditionally with a certain amount of fat on the carcase.

Elimination from the top grade tended to be on the evidence of excessive age, inadequate fatness and a carcase shape which suggested that the animal had been poorly grown or had been on a production system in which its weight had fluctuated from year to year. Top grades were reserved for youthful animals with an adequate amount of fat, coupled with shape consistent with well grown animals of the meat type breeds. Second and lower grades tended to be the aggregation of carcases which failed to meet the top grade for one reason or another.

So although top grades were relatively homogeneous, second grades tended to be a mixture of carcases deficient in a number of different respects. Attempts to make the second grade more homogeneous by rejecting extreme types into a third grade, inevitably led to the problem of establishing the relative importance of the various deficiencies. For example, was a carcase which was somewhat deficient in fat but youthful, likely to be better than another which was acceptable in fatness but rather older? This led to the concept of 'compensation' whereby the rules for balancing excellencies or deficiencies in one factor with those in another were laid down. Compensation reached its ultimate in U.S.D.A. beef grading where marbling was allowed to compensate for maturity deficiencies, and where marbling/maturity was amalgamated with conformation in a sophisticated way, the scientific basis of which came under ever-increasing attack.

The changes in systems which have been seen in world beef production in the last forty years have had marked effects on the basic assumptions underlying such long-standing grading schemes. In particular, systems have tended to become more intensive and a higher proportion of the animals marketed are youthful. In many beef and sheep producing countries, most animals now slaughtered for meat, with the exception of cull breeding stock, are youthful by traditional standards and their further subdivision by age is unlikely to be relevant to eating quality variation. Exceptions might be milk lambs, those slaughtered straight from suckling the ewe, and 'baby beef', an intermediary between veal and mature beef. In some situations, the colour of the lean meat and of the fat are important consumer characteristics in their own right and the darkening of lean meat with age and the yellowing of fat following a period of grazing may be considered reasons for rejection from the top grade.

With a relatively uniform pattern of production, for example that for lamb in New Zealand, carcase weight itself may provide a useful index of the levels of fatness and age; so New Zealand grading has always been based on rather narrow ranges of carcase weight. Other grading systems have used minimum weights for beef carcases on the basis that anything lighter than that weight was either immature or had grown so slowly as to raise doubts as to its eating qualities.

YIELD

Few of the early systems paid any direct attention to the yield of lean meat from the carcase. Poor conformation, which was rejected anyway because of its expected relation to eating quality through age and breed, was also thought to indicate a high yield of bone and therefore a poor yield of meat. But otherwise the systems tended to favour animals with a low ratio of lean meat to fat because of the requirement that top grades should have a certain (frequently substantial) level of fatness, again because of the expected relationship with eating quality. As the pattern of meat distribution has changed, traders have become more conscious of the yield of deboned trimmed lean meat obtained from carcases, while at the same time consumers have tended more and more to reject excess fatness. Accordingly there has been a swing from interest in the grading of carcases according to expected eating qualities to grading according to expected yield of saleable meat. Beef grading in the U.S.A. was among the first to make this distinction, with the addition of a yield-grading parameter to the long-standing quality component.

The introduction of direct estimates of yield factors into grading schemes has caused a re-evaluation of their whole purpose. Clearly, throughout its history, grading has had the intention of picking out top qualities and distinguishing them from poor qualities thought to be much less desirable in the market. The expectation was that top grade would be worth more than second grade which was worth more than bottom grade. In recent years, in several countries including Great Britain, this concept has been rejected in favour of descriptive carcase classification.

Classification principles

The principle of classification is that carcases are described, using a common language which is understood by everyone trading in the market. The language involves characteristics known to be relevant to traders — some are of importance in determining yield, some are of importance in determining consumer reaction, some may influence both. The essence of classification is that individuals may pick out different classes as being best for them and worth more to them.

A good example is provided by the differentiation between young, lean, well-fleshed beef carcases produced by intensive systems in Great Britain, compared with the long-standing 'quality' beef which is grass-fed to an older age, to a higher level of external fatness and with the lean meat being darker and more marbled. Each of these types can be described by a classification scheme, which takes account of age, fatness and conformation, but different class combinations would be considered best and most valuable by different traders in the market. There is no way that a grading system which amalgamated both types into a top grade could, of itself, be of much value in trading or price reporting, or indeed as a vehicle for attempting to extol the virtues of beef to the consumer or to guarantee its qualities.

A similar situation can exist in the descriptive classification of pig carcases, whereby different traders may prefer different ranges of fat thicknesses according to the way in which they propose to utilise the carcase. Those who use pig carcases in ways which involve the sale of meat fresh or cured with the skin still attached may set one preferred range of fatness measurements, while those who are trimming excess fat may be quite content with other ranges.

Another example of the distinction is provided by Australian lamb which for many years was sorted into a top, a second and a third grade, with the first two grades generally referred to as 'G.A.Q.' (Good Average Quality) and 'F.A.Q.' (Fair Average Quality). G.A.Q. was originally a genuine 'top grade' as far as the British market was concerned, with its preference for a certain level of fatness and the shape that generally went with it in early-maturing breeds. But with the development of other markets, such as those in the Middle East, which discriminate firmly against any more than a minimum wafer-thin layer of fat, the traditional grade names have come to be misleading, particularly in the guidance they give to producers.

TWO MEANINGS OF 'CLASSIFICATION'

In the context of carcase evaluation, classification has two distinct meanings. Originally, the use of the term was confined to a preliminary sorting of carcases into categories of age, sex and breeding status. The grader 'classed' a carcase as veal rather than beef, as lamb rather than mutton, as a steer rather than a bull, as a heifer rather than a young cow, and then went on to make further distinctions of 'grade' according to criteria applicable to that class and in a way that stated or implied 'best', 'average' or 'worst' within the class.

More recently, as has been shown, the term classification has come to mean the process of describing carcases in terms of importance to traders and consumers but in a way which does not necessarily impute value. Most schemes for commercial assessment developed in recent years are, therefore, schemes of descriptive classification rather than grading, and the classification is usually carried out in a way which ignores the category of age, sex and breeding status — although carcases of different sexes, of different age and of different breeding status will usually show a different distribution over the descriptive classes.

WRITTEN DEFINITIONS

One notable difference between the many grading and classification systems devised around the world which employ visual assessments is the extent to which they rely on written definitions of the classes or grades. Some schemes attempt to spell out the class definition in great detail, while others, such as the M.L.C.'s classification schemes for beef and sheep carcases in Britain, have had no written descriptions but rely on visual demonstration supported by photographic reference scales and, if appropriate, an underlying objective definition.

For example, the M.L.C. fat classes for beef were defined by ranges of subcutaneous fat percentage. In training, a small number of carcases (usually borderline examples) may be dissected to demonstrate the true class according to the objective criterion.

No such fall-back objective criterion is generally available for conformation. Attempts to write down conformation requirements for grades or classes inevitably involve adjectival graduation — the muscles of the loin, for example, may be 'very thick' for the top class, through 'thick', 'moderately thick', 'slightly thin', 'moderately thin', 'thin' or 'very thin'. Clearly these adjectives have no meaning in isolation; the thickness defined as 'moderately thick' and 'thick' has still to be demonstrated. There is no way that an intelligent observer, shown the definitions for the first time, could interpret them accurately without demonstration.

Written definition may have some value in stressing the relative importance of different factors and underlining the particular features to be given emphasis in forming a judgement, but two graders in disagreement may well use the same written definition to justify their position. In addition, the struggle to express on paper what can only be discerned by the eye can lead to linguistic absurdities such as 'slightly bare'.

We believe that written definitions should only be used in support of photographic scales as indicators of visually assessed fatness and conformation classes.

Carcase weight definition

The treatment of carcase weight in the various grading and classification schemes to be described is variable. At one extreme (U.S.D.A. beef quality grading, for example) weight is not considered a part of the system at all, but as a separate issue. In others it is crucial, being an integral part of the carcase description or involved in the grade definition in the form of a minimum weight, maximum weight or acceptable weight range.

Whether or not it is a formal part of the grading or classification scheme, precise weight definition is clearly important in trading; this is particularly so when farmers sell stock on a deadweight basis, when the whole animal (including the so-called fifth quarter, the valuable non-carcase parts) is valued on the basis of a negotiated price per kilogram of the dressed carcase weight. Small differences in definition or failure to adhere closely to the definition can affect the farmer's return, often by an amount comparable with his net margin.

The range of methods of carcase definition will not be reviewed here, since there is little of fundamental interest in the definitions which are largely arbitrary. There are, however, two variations of particular interest which have already been mentioned in chapter 2.

HOT WEIGHT

In many cases, dressed carcase weight relates to the cold carcase after 24 hours chilling. However, because the actual weighing is carried out at the completion of the carcase dressing process, 'cold' weight is estimated from the 'hot' weight by a deduction determined from a conversion scale calculated on a percentage basis. (Deductions are usually of the order of 2 per cent). While there may have been some historical logic in paying farmers on the basis of the cold carcase weight, in that this is the weight available for sale by an individual who retains possession of the carcase through from farm to wholesale market, there no longer seems to be any case for the additional records and calculations involved. North America, Australasia and Denmark have adopted hot weights as the basis of trade but, generally, Europe is finding it more difficult to change from the long-standing cold weight convention.

FAT TRIMMING

In most circumstances, the trimming of external carcase fat is not allowed before weighing. However, it has become common practice, in France particularly, to trim external fat from carcases of above average fatness while they are still hot, the so-called *émoussage*, because it is easier and in some ways more efficient to do this than to trim cold carcases. Various conventions may be adopted. The organisation O.N.I.B.E.V. has attempted to lay down firm guidelines to minimise the extent and variation of the trimming, and to adjust the basis of payment to producers, but these clearly involve an element of estimation. If this practice were to spread, it could undermine producer confidence in selling by deadweight.

Cost-benefit

Grading as a concept lends itself to economic analysis. The theoretical benefits in the context of meat trading have been explored by Williams and Stout (386) and Brayshaw and DeLoach (39), and the framework for detailed cost-benefit studies of the proposed Australian classification systems has been laid down by Griffith (145) and Todd and Cowell (366). However, factual information on the detailed structure and costs of current meat marketing systems is limited, and so no one has yet been able to present a cost-benefit analysis of a proposed scheme which is sufficiently convincing to influence the degree of acceptance.

We have attempted an unsophisticated item-by-item approach to beef and pig classification in Great Britain (158). Each potential area of impact was considered separately and the scale of the advantage (for example, in accelerating improvement in carcase quality, in protection against mis-pricing and in facilitating carcase sales) estimated. Under each heading, the potential benefits of the classification information, if used, appeared to exceed substantially the costs and it seemed reasonable to deduce a substantial cumulative net benefit, even though some of the individual benefits to successive participants in the distributive chain cancelled out.

Although the theoretical approach may assist policy-makers, it is of limited value in practice because the costs are likely to fall on the abattoir operator (who may be able to share them to a limited extent with his producer suppliers) while the short-term benefits will be spread out through the industry, and the longer-term benefits in terms of 'marketing efficiency' will basically benefit consumers and surviving meat producing and trading firms.

The remainder of this section will seek to describe the essential features of some of the more important methods for grading and classification of pig, sheep and beef carcases throughout the world. This cannot be an exhaustive review, but the systems which have been most widely used and the systems which have included important innovations of principle or technique will be mentioned. (A detailed report of the systems operating in European countries twenty years ago was published by the O.E.C.D., 304).

11 Pig carcase grading and classification

Grading and classification schemes for pig carcases throughout the world tend to concentrate on grouping carcases by their estimated composition. Meat quality factors, such as colour and wetness of the lean and softness and oiliness of fat, are sometimes taken into account but have not until recently had the same importance relative to compositional variations as they have for beef. Some schemes have dealt with meat and quality defects by an exclusion clause, which identifies only carcases extreme in some quality factor. This inevitably leaves a good deal of variation in meat quality within the main grades. Modern developments in meat processing and distribution, coupled with the improvements in meat yield which have been achieved since the 1950s, may lead to a shift in emphasis to meat quality characteristics. There have been suggestions, for example, that muscle pH should in future be a factor in pig carcase grading (101).

United States

In North America, pigs have traditionally been produced on systems which lead to wide variations in weight, fatness and degree of muscularity. They have been processed in packing plants where the chilled carcases have been broken into a variety of trimmed cuts used for a range of different purposes. The trimmed loins and some shoulder cuts are used for sale as fresh meat, the legs for ham production, the belly for curing into bacon, while the trimmings and lower-valued cuts are utilised in various forms of sausage.

Since the turn of the century, the value of the trimmed cuts has increased relative to the value of the fat trimmings. It is now a matter for some surprise that in 1908, the wholesale market value per lb of lard was the same as that of the trimmed lean cuts (at 125 per cent of the live pig's value per lb); by 1975 the ratio had become more than 6 to 1. This widening gap, reflecting changes in consumer preference and eating habits, has made the yield of trimmed cuts from the carcase a more and more important index of economic value.

Grading schemes have therefore been developed to divide carcases into groups by the estimated yield of cuts (usually the four 'lean' cuts – the ham, loin, picnic and Boston Butt – the yield of which is related to carcase lean content). Because virtually all pigs changed hands in the United States until the 1940s on a live weight basis and because most carcases are cut at the buyer's plant, the original work on carcase grading (for example, 92) had little practical impact. However, the schemes developed were translated back into live pig grades particularly for use in price reporting.

In the period 1949-55, there was a spate of activity in the state universities to establish the relative pricing efficiency of alternative methods of pig marketing which included examination of alternative grading methods. In general these showed that grades based on weight and back fat would be effective (for example, 113) although others did find some additional value in carcase length (42).

To facilitate grade and deadweight buying, federal carcase grade standards were drawn up and publicised by the U.S.D.A. in 1949 and on several occasions thereafter. Promotional material related these grades to estimated yields of trimmed lean meat and they became an important component of the thrust towards the 'meat-type hog' in the 1950s and 1960s (for example, 369).

The U.S.D.A. method is of interest since it was one of the first to attempt a systematic adjustment of provisional grades, determined by objective criteria, by subjectively assessed variations in 'muscling' (372).

Average thickness of back fat is determined from measurements taken in the mid-line level with the first and last ribs and the last lumbar vertebra, but the grader is empowered to adjust this average up or down (usually by one tenth of an inch) if he considers that variations in fat thickness over the carcase at other positions suggest the carcase has 'a greater (or lesser) degree of overall fatness than that normally associated with its actual thickness of back fat'. The adjusted level of average back fat thickness in conjunction with carcase *length* determines the provisional grade. The method is based on an assumption that weight and length are closely related, but where the weight/fatness ratio suggests a different provisional grade to that based on length/fatness, the latter is the one used.

Six degrees of muscling are recognised, with the degree of muscling typical of the bottom of the four basic grades being specified. If the degree of muscling is considered to be different from that typical of the grade provisionally determined from the length, weight and average back fat, a complex system of compensation, summarised in fig. 11.1 and based on one degree of muscling equating to one tenth of an inch of fat, comes into play. This has to be read in conjunction with detailed definitions since the chart specifies only minima for each grade.

Fig. 11.1 also shows the expected yield of the four lean cuts in each of the four grades. Finally, the lean is required to be of 'acceptable quality' determined by an examination of any cut surfaces available, the bellies to be adequately thick, and the fat not to be soft or oily. Failure on any of these criteria, irrespective of the factors related to carcase yield, causes the carcase to be put into a bottom grade — U.S. Utility.

In effect, the scheme attempts the practical application under commercial conditions of a regression predicting yields of the trimmed cuts from weight,

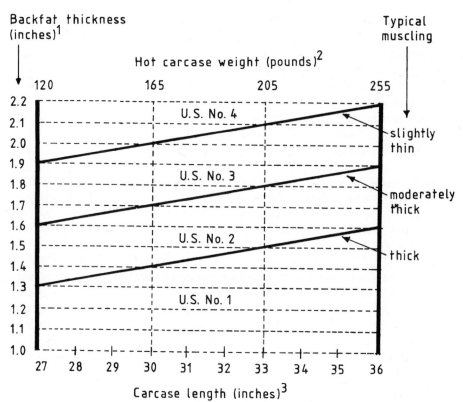

Fig. 11.1 The relationship between average back fat thickness, carcase length or weight, and U.S.D.A. grade for pig carcases with muscling typical of their degree of fatness (372)

1 An average of three measurements including the skin made opposite the first and last ribs and the last lumbar vertebra. It also reflects adjustment, as appropriate, to compensate for variations from normal fat distribution.
2 Carcase weight is based on a hot packer style carcase.
3 Carcase length is measured from the anterior point of the aitch bone to the anterior edge of the first rib.

length, average back fat and muscling. The intentions are laudable, but the very complexity may have been a factor both in the poor uptake and their failure significantly to stimulate the development of grade and deadweight selling and associated pig carcase improvement in the U.S.A.

Further, the grades are based on the premise that a carcase grader, working at speed in a packing plant, can distinguish degrees of muscling in pig carcases varying widely in weight, length and back fat thickness. In practice, only small differences of muscling (one or at the most two steps on the 6-point scale) will be likely to occur at a given weight and back fat (except in a small minority of unusual carcases), and the ability to distinguish these consistently must be in doubt.

Unlike the grading methods promulgated by the U.S.D.A. for beef and sheep, these grades for pig carcases do not appear to have been preceded by published research evidence on the relationships between the various factors involved and the underlying trait of value – in this case the yield of trimmed cuts. Subsequent published studies by several groups, albeit on rather small numbers of carcases, tend to suggest that muscling score had indeed been given too much weight (81) and that intact carcase measurements and judgements (such as length and muscling score) could add little to the information provided by average back fat in the grading situation (82, 111).

Despite the concerted efforts of agricultural economists, meat scientists, their extension colleagues and government agencies to encourage grade and deadweight selling of pigs as an essential element in improved marketing and the thrust towards a leaner more efficient pig, sales remain predominantly by live weight – not even of the individual pig but of the truck load.

It is not difficult to see this from the meat packers' point of view. There is a highly developed intelligence on the market valuation of individual cuts and the products derived from them. Packers are large businesses, which can afford to employ their own economists and use computers to convert the current value of the component parts back to a live pig valuation, and can communicate this to their buyers in the field instantly. In addition, sophisticated techniques allow variations in weight of component parts actually bought to be utilised most efficiently – by varying cutting specifications under computer instructions, for example, or by instant adjustment of least-cost formulations for sausage-type products. Generally there is an ample supply of cheap pigs, being bought by a small number of sophisticated packers (with access to a lot of detailed market information) from large numbers of relatively small producers with little information.

The packers believe, as middlemen who sort and add value to whatever raw material is available, that they do not themselves necessarily gain by paying more for pigs that are leaner and worth more as cuts, particularly as they would have to meet the cost of the grading process. They recognise the longer-term argument that more efficient conversion of corn to lean meat will lead to relatively cheaper and therefore more competitive pork products, but argue they cannot risk their short term individual competitive positions against other packers by introducing price differentiation for pigs of varying leanness.

At some point in the historical development of other industries, such as those of Denmark, Canada and the U.K., this vicious circle has been broken, usually by government action in imposing export standards, paying premiums over and above market price differences, or by linking support payments to carcase quality; but it is difficult to see such intervention occurring in the American pig industry.

Canada

The complexity of the U.S.D.A. grading approach is contrasted by the simplicity and effectiveness of the Canadian method.

In Canada, pig packing plants developed along similar lines to those in the U.S.A. although in the first half of this century there were several attempts to build up an export trade in Wiltshire bacon to the U.K. While Canadian sides of bacon were never able to compete with the Danish product on the British market, these attempts did focus attention on the relative quality of the Canadian pig and did encourage livestock improvement programmes earlier than in the U.S.A.

Carcase grading, as opposed to live pig grading, became the only official system in Canada in the early 1940s (267). The Canada Department of Agriculture used it to encourage sales on a grade and deadweight basis and as a stimulus to livestock improvement. From 1940 to 1968 there was a conventional visual system dividing pig carcases into A, B and C grades (referred to for a time as 'choice bacon', 'secondary bacon' and 'non-bacon'), plus a variety of lesser grades for extreme carcases. Visual assessment included reference to muscling, joint proportions, uniformity of fat thickness, fat and flesh colour. A feature of this system was the addition of criteria for weight, length and two mid-line back fat thicknesses to the detailed subjective descriptions (54). However the following extract of how the grader worked from Maybee's official publication is instructive:

The grader rapidly attains speed and efficiency in grading the carcasses as they pass along the moving rail. He must exercise judgment on about two-thirds of the hogs since around one third falls automatically into grade because of weight and sex. A glance at the outside of the carcase indicates whether the type and conformation warrant first, second or third grade. A glance at the thickness and distribution of fat complete the appraisal. Graders have convenient measuring tools at hand to check an occasional carcass for length of side or thickness of back fat. This confirms the grade for the odd 'liner' and helps keep the eye in trim.

This approach is typical of the attitude adopted towards nominally objective grading criteria in many countries, including France and Germany (see below). However, grading is extremely sensitive to the assessment of back fat thickness in these circumstances; graders can develop small unconscious biases which distort the grade distribution. Measurement of back fat thickness to the nearest millimetre is sometimes derided as inappropriate in view of the relatively low predictive accuracy of the measurements on individual carcases. But in fact, it is the only way to minimise the cumulative influence of graders' preferences and opinions on the grading profile of a large number of pig carcases.

A conference of producers and packers in 1964 resolved that research should be devoted to developing 'a system of grades that would more accurately identify the value of the hogs, measured by out-turn of lean cuts', and the needs of the market for factors such as colour and texture of flesh, which were not then given major weight in grading, should be taken more into account.

The following year a technical conference concluded that the job being done by the weight, length and back fat categories in predicting carcase value was inadequate, primarily because the categories were too few in number, but also because weight and length added little information on yield over and above that provided by back fat. They accepted a new principle for commercial evaluation whereby pig carcases would be rated according to predicted yield of trimmed cuts expressed as a percentage scale rather than by a specific grade, the prediction being arrived at by taking appropriate carcase measurements (57).

In reaching this important conclusion, they argued among other things that there would be wider variation in the returns for pigs, payments for individual carcases would better reflect relative values and the price incentive for quality production would increase with increased price rather than the reverse; also the system could be readily adaptable without changing its basis.

The essence of the method (55) is a table of value differentials (the latest version is given in table 11.1) developed from an analysis of cutting data on large samples of pigs. The predicted variable was not simply yield of trimmed cuts, but a value measure which took into account the relative value of the different joints of various weights. Carcase weight appeared in the prediction equation, not because it added to the precision with which fatness measurements predicted yield, but because the value of trimmed cuts from carcases of different weights varied. The sum of shoulder and loin back fat thickness in the mid-line continued to be used as the measure of back fat; the potential of probe measurements of fat thickness off the mid-line had not then been demonstrated in Canada but if they did eventually prove to provide a better prediction, the predictive measurements involved in grading could be readily changed without altering the basic principle.

Using the prediction, a value/yield table was constructed in a grid of cells of weight and fat categories. Predictions were found to be acceptable in the core of the table but needed some adjustment at the fringes to fit more closely commercial value. Each entry in the table was then converted to a percentage of the entry in the cell representing 150-59 lb weight and 3.2-3.3 in of back fat. Weight classes outside those of the table were assigned specific index value.

In most Canadian packing plants, hot dressed carcase weight is automatically printed on a scale ticket, but under the supervision of Canada Department of Agriculture officials. They also take the two back fat measurements and then decide any necessary penalties (called 'demerits') as follows:

(a) type deficiencies in ham, shoulder, belly, length or roughness, resulting in a reduction in the index of 3 per cent;
(b) quality deficiencies such as abnormal colour or texture of lean, abnormal fat (soft, oily etc.), resulting in a reduction in the index of 10 per cent;
(c) deficiencies leading to trimming on the killing floor — deformities, pathological conditions, skin conditions, etc. The actual weight removed is

Table 11.1 Value differentials that form the basis of the Canadian pig grading system. This is the revised table published in 1978 (135), the original having been published in 1969 (55)

Back fat (in)	Predicted Yield (%)	Carcase weight (lb)											Ridgling
		90-124	125-129	130-139	140-149	150-159	160-169	170-179	180-189	190-199	200-209	210-	
≤ 1.9	69.7	87	105	107	108	110	112	113	114	114	90	80	67
2.0-2.1	69.0	87	103	105	107	108	110	112	113	113	90	80	67
2.2-2.3	68.2	87	103	103	105	107	108	110	112	112	90	80	67
2.4-2.5	67.5	87	100	102	103	105	107	108	110	110	90	80	67
2.6-2.7	66.7	87	98	100	102	103	105	107	108	108	90	80	67
2.8-2.9	66.0	87	97	98	100	102	103	105	107	107	90	80	67
3.0-3.1	65.2	87	95	97	98	100	102	103	105	105	90	80	67
3.2-3.3	64.5	87	93	95	97	98	100	102	103	103	90	80	67
3.4-3.5	63.8	87	92	93	95	97	98	100	102	102	90	80	67
3.6-3.7	63.0	87	90	92	93	95	97	98	100	100	90	80	67
3.8-3.9	62.3	87	88	90	92	93	95	97	98	98	90	80	67
4.0-4.1	61.5	87	87	88	90	92	93	95	97	97	80	80	67
4.2-4.3	60.8	85	85	87	88	90	92	93	95	95	80	80	67
4.4-4.5	60.1	83	83	85	87	88	90	90	90	90	80	80	67
4.6-4.7	59.3	82	82	83	85	87	88	88	88	88	80	80	67
4.8-4.9	58.6	80	80	82	83	85	87	87	87	87	80	80	67
≥ 5.0	57.8	80	80	80	80	80	80	80	80	80	80	80	67

deducted from the hot dressed carcase weight for payment purposes, but not for the purposes of calculating the index.

Marketing systems for pigs subsequently introduced involve bids for lots while still alive, but expressed in terms of cents per unit of carcase weight. Bids are made on the assumption that the pig carcase will fall in the base cell, that is 150-59 lb carcase weight with 3.0-3.1 in total back fat. Settlement for a particular carcase, therefore, involves reading the index from the table using its weight and back fats, adjusting for type or quality penalties if any, multiplying this index by bid price to calculate the price relevant to the category and finally multiplying this calculated price by the actual hot dressed carcase weight, or the adjusted weight if any trimming had to be carried out. The necessary calculations can be carried out speedily from prepared tables or by computer.

The decision to base the index on a commercial characteristic (the yield of trimmed cuts, weighted by value) rather than on estimated lean content has been the subject of some criticism (388), the argument being that indices based on estimated lean content would show wider variation and provide a greater stimulus to improvement. However, when adjustments were made to the index table in 1978, they reflected the marked increase in the carcase yield of Canadian pigs that had been achieved at the same time as the average carcase weight had increased (135). The original scale showed a sharp fall-off in the calculated value of pig carcases over 180 lb, due to uncertainty about market acceptability of their cuts; but by 1978 the cut-off point for index valuation could be raised to 200 lb. Detailed work on further samples of carcases may lead to further modification (138, 266).

The basis of the system, the prediction of yields of trimmed cuts, whether weighted with relative values or not, is of course only appropriate to an industry or sector of an industry mainly involved in cutting and trimming before retail sale in fresh or processed form. An established wholesale market and wholesale valuation of the individual parts is an essential prerequisite to this approach.

Of more general interest, however, is the principle adopted whereby divisions into grades or classes (usually arbitrary in any case) have been abandoned in favour of a continuous categorisation. Whereas division into grades or classes has some merit from the selling point of view (in connection with promotional or branding operations, for example), the Canadians have rightly recognised that there is no reason why producers should not be paid in a manner which links price more directly to measurement, provided the recording, calculation and accounting problems can be surmounted. The only other system that approaches this degree of sophistication is the Danish.

Australia

The relatively small pig industry of Australia was, for many years, modelled on that of Britain, with bacon factories increasingly using measurements of carcase back fat thickness as a basis for purchase of bacon pigs, and a separate fresh pork industry using visual grades to a limited extent. Wilson and Campbell (390) reviewed the Australian problem in the light of progress in Canada, New Zealand and Great Britain, and recommended the introduction of a national pig carcase classification scheme similar to that operating in Great Britain.

The unique feature of this Australian plan is that an integrated approach to industry information flow has been attempted. Called a National Pig Carcase Measurement and Information Service, and co-ordinated by a committee consisting mainly of senior pig production extension officers from each state, the aim has been to introduce a systematic approach throughout the industry for identification, weighing, back fat measurement by probe and recording of observations by meat inspectors (389).

The aim is to publicise widely the relationship between fatness and weight, so that producers may put their own carcase records into perspective whatever their buyer's payment system; a common deadweight price reporting system is planned and forecasting methods improved. Considerable emphasis has been given to the automation of procedures for weighing, measuring and recording in the abattoir, so that eventually the full potential benefits in terms of information flow, competitive pricing and operating efficiencies, right through to central accounting, may be realised. Early hopes were, to some extent, frustrated by problems with the automatic and semi-automatic recording equipment introduced experimentally into abattoirs.

West Germany

The German Federal Republic is one of Europe's largest pig producers. Like all other European countries, it has seen the development of larger pig slaughtering plants, remote from consumption areas and procuring pigs direct from farmers valued on the basis of carcase weight, and selling carcases and cuts to butchers and manufacturers in the consumption areas. Mandatory trade grades were introduced in 1965 (335) to provide a common basis for trade and valuation, for price reporting and for producer information. The grades for pigs other than sows stipulated maximum mid-line fat thickness measurements for each 10 kg carcase weight range, in addition to requirements for degrees of muscularity in the major cuts.

The range of carcase meat contents then considered to be appropriate to each grade, and their relative value, is given in table 11.2. These data suggest a very marked degree of discrimination between classes in estimated lean meat content and the presumption of wide price differentials between grades.

Revisions were introduced in 1972, following the adoption by the E.E.C. Council in 1970 of Regulation 2108/70, requiring average pig prices by grade to be reported weekly by member governments to the Commission in Brussels. Whereas some other member governments confined their application of the E.E.C. grading system to reference market price reports only, the German legislation made it mandatory for all carcases in trade to be graded by this system and marked accordingly.

Table 11.2 Information presented in promotional literature concerning the German pig carcase grading scheme in 1966 (335)

Grade	Range of carcase lean content (%)	Average of a sample of carcases (%)	Calculated relative value	Approximate % of carcases in grade
E	Over 50	50.2	105	15-20
I	45-50	46.3	100	45-55
II	40-45	41.3	92	20-25
III	Under 40	35.2	84	5-10

The E.E.C. system was, in its original form, clearly considerably influenced by German and Dutch experiences; its adoption in Germany represented a logical development of the 1965 method. The grade targets in terms of estimated leanness ranges were raised, a more formal procedure for balancing variation in fat measurements with variations in shape introduced, and producers given clearer guidance on why their carcases were downgraded.

The possible combinations of type and back fat thickness are given in table 11.3. The back fat measurement used is in the mid-line at the level of the last rib or that over the loin muscle, whichever is the greater, and this represented a change of practice in Germany.

Class II for fatness in combination with type A gave a grade II carcase, as did the combination of class I for fatness with type B. The type classification is, in fact, even more dominant than the table implies since the back fat, in practice, is seldom measured. The type classes AA and C represent very extreme differences in shape as fig. 11.2 shows.

Schön (337) claimed very marked differences in meat yield between class combinations (table 11.4).

The value differences are wide and impute considerable significance to type classification. For example, IIA appears to have 2.6 per cent more trimmed boneless cuts than IIB, and IA nearly 4 per cent more than IB. Such differences reflect a much bigger effect of conformation on composition at constant carcase fatness than has been found elsewhere. While the genetic variation of the sample of pigs is no doubt one factor, there are others which could have contributed to an exaggeration of the effect. The sample was, in fact, quite small (about 150) and carefully selected rather than random. Further, there is evidence that the type classification is partially making up the shortcomings of the fat measurement technique; if fat is measured off the mid-line accurately, then the additional information provided by type classification is much less.

Nevertheless, effects of conformation on meat yield of this order have been found in some other European pig populations. Fig. 18.1 shows the range in

Table 11.3 Description of the German pig carcase grading scheme following adoption of E.E.C. Regulation 2108/70 (337)

Grade (or trade class)	Weight of two sides (kg)	Fat thickness (mm)	Type	General characteristics
E (extra)	60-70 70 and over	up to 15 inclusive up to 20 inclusive	AA	Excellently developed in all meat-bearing parts
I (very lean)	60-70 70-80 80-90 90 and over	up to 20 inclusive up to 25 inclusive up to 30 inclusive up to 35 inclusive	A	With very good development of all meat-bearing parts
II (lean)	60-70 70-80 80-90 90 and over	up to 25 inclusive up to 30 inclusive up to 35 inclusive up to 40 inclusive	IIA	With good development of all meat-bearing parts
				or
	Measurements, weight of two halves and fat thickness as in grade I		IB	As in grade I but with a defect in one meat-bearing part
III (not so lean)	60-70 70-80 80-90 90 and over	up to 30 inclusive up to 35 inclusive up to 40 inclusive	IIIA	Moderately well developed meat-bearing parts
				or
	Measurements, weight of two sides and fat thickness as in grade II, type IIA		IIB	As in grade II but with a defect in a meat-bearing part
				or
	Measurements, weight of two halves and fat thickness as in grade I		IC	As grade I but with defects in two meat-bearing parts
IV	All pig sides that do not conform to the requirements of the preceding grades, and also pig sides from under-sized and old animals.			
S	Pig halves from sows			
V	Pig halves from boars			

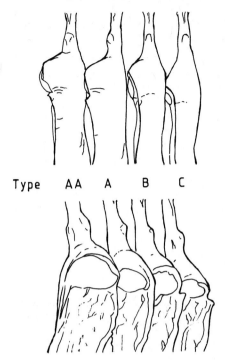

Type   AA   A   B   C

Fig. 11.2 Type variations differentiated in the German pig carcase grading scheme (337), following adoption of E.E.C. Regulation 2108/70

Table 11.4 Yield, relative valuation and approximate percentage of pigs falling into each German pig grade for carcases 80-90 kg (337)

Grade	Class combina- tions	Range of carcase lean content (%)	Average carcase lean content (%)	Calculated relative valuations assuming fat is worth 40% of side value	Calculated relative valuations assuming fat is worth 20% of side value	Approximate % of carcases in grade
E	EAA	Over 55	60.2	117	120	1-3
I	IA	50-55	52.9	106	107	15-20
II	IIA	45-50	47.6	99	98	55-60
	IB		49.0	100	101	
III	IIIA		43.3	94	91	
	IIB	40-45	45.0	95	94	15-20
	IC		44.7	94	93	
IV	Others	Under 40	40.2	89	86	4-5

pig carcase lean content at equal fat thickness found in the pig populations of some E.E.C. countries (77).

A further problem with the application of this sytem in Germany is that, although mandatory for pig carcases in trade, it is applied by the staff of the abattoirs under a degree of supervision by officers of the Länder (Provincial) governments. The level of accuracy in application has been criticised and there is some pressure for independent application of the grading system (for example, 20).

France

Price quotations for pigs from major livestock markets such as La Villette were reported according to grades along the following simple lines:

(a) well-muscled pigs weighing 90-120 kg, good conformation with lean bellies;
(b) fat pigs over 120 kg;
(c) inferior quality pigs, too lean or poorly conformed.

Eventually, these were supplemented by price reports for the following carcase types from wholesale meat markets such as Les Halles (400) formalised in 1953 (modified in 1960).

(a) *Complet*: lean carcases weighing 65-77 kg, with back fat (the average of two measures in the mid-line) 20-29 mm, well conformed, full hams, thick loin, lean belly, and firm dry lean meat of good colour.
(b) *Belle Coupé*: 60-77 kg carcases with fat less than 35 mm, the same meat qualities as *Complet* but less good conformation.
(c) *Coupé*: good lean meat quality, up to 85 kg, with fat thickness less than 50 mm.
(d) *Lourd et gros*: overweights and over-fats.

Application of these market classes to the buying of pigs by abattoirs proved difficult because of their imprecision. The Institut Technique du Porc devised a more precise system for this purpose, based on weight, fat and conformation combinations. Février and Zert (120) showed how this could be used to define the differing requirements of different sectors of the pig meat market, thus introducing the concept of a descriptive classification system used to define specialised grades.

The market preference was and remains quite different from that of the side-bacon dominated approach of Denmark and Britain, or the mixed industry of the Netherlands. Considerable importance is attached to the shape and muscularity of leg, loin and shoulder, with the *charcutier*, or small local trader, who combines the sale of fresh cuts with his own extensive range of manufactured products, including many local specialities, setting the tone of the market. He prizes most highly short, muscular, thick pigs, with exceptional ham shape.

But this scheme was overtaken, as in other countries of the original Six, by the introduction of the common E.E.C. system in 1972, applied by the trade now under the supervision of O.N.I.B.E.V. However, research subsequently demonstrated that in France, as in England, fat measurements off the mid-line had greater predictive value (for example, 147).

The Netherlands

As early as 1933, the 'Dutch Pig Board' introduced payment according to slaughter quality for bacon pigs. This came to be in the form of a contract between the regulatory body, the Productschap, and those meat manufacturers who wished to participate. Until 1971, a national grading scheme was used involving the combination of weight, back fat thickness (average of several mid-line positions) and 'type', although for the top grade there was also a minimum length measurement reflecting the fact that for a period the Netherlands were involved in producing Wiltshire sides. Grade II was made up of subgrade IIA (with the same type as Grade I but slightly fatter) and subgrade IB (same weight and fatness as Grade I but less well muscled) and similarly for the subclasses IC, IIB and IIIA that made up grade III. From 1972, the E.E.C. system in its original form, which differed only in detail from the long-standing Dutch scheme, was adopted.

Studies carried out at the 'Schoonoord' Institute confirmed that, for Dutch pigs as for British, probe measurements of back fat thickness off the mid-line are markedly better predictors of lean content than the mid-line measurements of back fat used in the original E.E.C. scheme (97). Type classification (or alternatively a measure of lean meat thickness) added much less precision than had previously been assumed in the original Six, but it added more to the mid-line measurements than to probe measurements. This may account to a degree for the different emphasis attached to type in continental Europe at that time, although the main reason is likely to have been the different breed mix providing a wider range of carcase shapes.

Application of the system in the Netherlands is by government employees (though paid for by industry through a levy). But the unique feature of pig marketing in the Netherlands was, for many years, the fixing of the price differentials between grades, whatever the base price variation. This principle was carried on when the E.E.C. scheme was introduced and the differentials were then set as follows (given a base price of 3 Fl/kg for grade I):

Payment grade	Price (Fl/kg)	Index
EAA	3.05	101.7
I	3.00	100.0
II	2.85	95.0
III	2.75	91.7
IV	2.70	90.0

The small differential for EAA over I was due to uncertainty over the desirability of pressing for further improvement of pig carcases beyond the norms of grade I because of the suspect meat quality of very lean muscular pigs. Since then, differentials have been widened.

The principle of sale by grade with fixed differentials is important and has clearly contributed to pig improvement in the Netherlands; other countries have found that the proportions of pigs sold by deadweight with or without grade (as opposed to live sales), fluctuate with the state of the market as do the price differentials between grades of pigs. When pigs are in short supply, more are sold by live weight, by flat rate or with narrow differentials between qualities. The differentials widen when pigs are in plentiful supply. Such fluctuations undermine incentives to livestock improvement and if the differentials can be maintained, despite the degree of market distortion involved, then progress is likely to be faster.

Denmark

The Danish exploitation of the British market for bacon is a classic example of market research followed by product development and an integrated industry marketing effort. The success of the Danish pig farmer and processor in gaining a consistent high share of the British bacon market has been possible because of government support — moral, financial and regulatory — for this important export business, and the exercise of firm disciplines throughout the industry.

The curing of whole sides of pigs was a technique developed in the Wiltshire area of Britain in the eighteenth century, and by the mid-nineteenth century it had grown from a cottage industry to a small factory operation. As the standard of living improved in the industrial centres so did the demand for bacon, particularly for rasher bacon.

About 1887 the Danish pig industry found itself cut off from its main market in Germany because of the new disease restrictions. A plan of radical readjustment to attack the British bacon market was drawn up and implemented about 1895, involving a full range of activities from breeding through to export controls. The factory cure was developed and advances in technology were made. In recent years, more sides have been cut, deboned and prepacked before distribution to retailers; nevertheless, the operation was and remains essentially one based on whole side cure.

Reliance on whole side cure requires a highly specialised form of pig production, leading to pig carcases which are satisfactory in terms of fat/lean proportions without trimming. The desired uniformity can only be achieved by tight weight restrictions. Ideal conformation in the eyes of the trade involves long pigs with a light and narrow shoulder, because of the relative value of the untrimmed cuts of bacon (155), in marked contrast to utilisation methods elsewhere which allow a wider, deeper shoulder provided it is meaty and where fatness can be adjusted by trimming.

From the earliest days of the implementation of the Danish plan, pigs were sold to curers on a carcase weight basis and in due course graded according to a standard national procedure. Although length was important in the selection of sides, for many years it was not incorporated in the grading procedure because it was controllable through breeding programmes. (More recently length was briefly reintroduced following an increase in variation due to greater use of cross-breeding). For export, however, sides had to meet certain criteria of back fat thicknesses and these were used in determining the grades for pig carcases. Three measurements were used, at shoulder, mid-back and loin, all in the mid-line of the split carcase. The fat measurements required for the top grades have been regularly reduced and published reports show a steady increase in the proportion of top grade pigs, both from the testing stations and in the commercial kill.

As the level of fatness has decreased, the consumer has become continually more discriminating against fatness in the rasher or joint and because of this, subtle variations in the distribution of fat periodically came to the attention of processors and pig breeders. In particular, the development of a bulge of fat away from the mid-line and in some cases intruding into the muscle cross section has received considerable attention. Such problems are of importance in the Wiltshire bacon market, because of the commercial significance of the visual appeal of the rasher which is cured and sold in untrimmed form.

Although there was interest in the inclusion of subjective type classification in the early 1950s, when grading was reintroduced after the War, later research did not establish a need for this with Danish pigs (311). Instead, development has concentrated on improving the precision of the objective method in predicting lean meat yield in conjunction with appropriate equipment to minimise operator differences and to facilitate recording. Thickness of fat off the mid-line was measured from 1970 with the M.F. probe based on differences in electrical conductivity between fat and muscle. This procedure was automated with the introduction of the M.F.A. (or K.S.A.) in 1974 (plate 4). Individual measurements continued to be the basis of grades up to 1977 (because of their importance in ensuring satisfactory fat distribution on bacon sides), but thereafter grading, and hence prices to producers, have been based on estimated lean percentage in the carcase.

The estimating equation chosen was as follows:

Lean in carcase (per cent) = 51.5601
+0.0565 (carcase weight in kg)
−0.3525 (fat depth in the loin, mm)
−0.0923 (fat depth at third lumbar vertebra, 8 cm from the mid-line, mm)
−0.1857 (fat depth at third/fourth last rib, 6 cm from the mid-line, mm)
+0.1396 (muscle depth at the same position, mm)

Subsequently modifications were made but these five items were retained:

weight, three fat depths (two off the mid-line), and one muscle depth. The latter adds little to the predictive accuracy, and even the second and third fat measurements provide relatively little additional information (reference to the precision of the method was made in chapter 8). However, these measurements are included because they are important in their own right and because the automatic recording process allows them to be taken and incorporated at little extra cost.

A feature of this revised method of grading was a decision to reward producers for each additional increment of lean content.

Plate 4 M.F.A. probe in operation in a Danish bacon factory. (Photograph from S.F.K., Hvidovre, Denmark)

Instead of having a payment system with a large differential between top and second grade and a high proportion of pigs falling within the top grade, there are in effect many more grades and prices with small steps or increments between them (but still a major step between export quality and the rest). A producer who can already achieve a high proportion of pigs in the conventional top grade is, by this method, provided with a greater incentive for improvement.

Great Britain

Since the Danes became a force in British bacon in the early part of this century, the domestic bacon industry, which is only a part of the British pig industry, has benefited from the developments and promotional work carried out by the Danes for their own bacon. For many years there has been a wish to mimic and eventually overtake the Danish producer in the British bacon market. Accordingly bacon factories introduced payment for pigs on a carcase weight basis with common grades involving mid-line back fat thickness being laid down by the Pigs Marketing Board in 1933. Shoulder fat was used first, but loin and mid-back were added later; for a period belly thickness was assessed.

Moreover, because the British bacon industry did not have the same control over the length of the pigs through systematic breeding as had the Danes, length has, since 1956, featured in its own right in bacon pig grading. While it has never been possible to demonstrate that length added anything to back fat measurements in sorting carcases by any compositional factor, the British bacon curing industry, because it was selling its product in competition with a Danish product conspicuously uniform in shape and length, has considered that length must be included as a criterion in its purchasing of pigs whatever its predictive value.

The most important development in the grading of bacon pigs in Britain was the introduction, about ten years before the Danes adopted the M.F. probe, of measurements off the mid-line determined with a probing device (in this case the optical probe or intrascope) (plate 5). This now forms the basis of classification for all pigs in Great Britain, although bacon curers continue to buy pigs on a contract in which a single probe measurement is used in conjunction with the traditional measurements of shoulder fat, loin fat and length.

Grading of pig carcases other than those going to the specialist bacon factories was rare before the 1960s. Under the stimulus of the Pig Industry Development Authority, the grading of pigs for other purposes based on probed fat measurements was gradually introduced. The optical probe was particularly valuable for lightweight pork pigs which had to be measured without being split down the mid-line.

Slowest to develop was the grading by objective measurements of pigs heavier than those of the bacon range purchased by processors for part curing and the manufacture of a full range of pigmeat products. This form of pig processing is most closely akin to that of North America and parts of continental Europe; for many years British manufacturers argued that it was uneconomic to encourage the production of pigs into a particular grade straight-jacket and that the 'tailoring' was best done in the factory. However, with many alternative

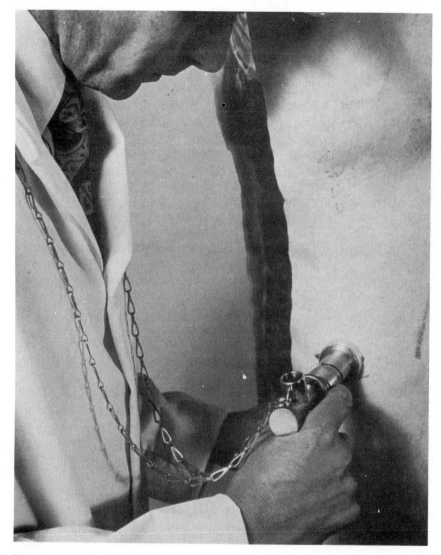

Plate 5 Optical probe in operation

outlets for British pigs, each making differential payments favouring leaner types, the manufacturer eventually had to give in to the general trend or be left with a preponderance of fatter pigs. The single P_2 fat measurement is used most commonly for the classification of heavier pig carcases, whereas the sum of two probe measurements ($P_1 + P_3$) is used for pork and cutter pigs (fig. 11.3).

Until 1974, there was a government-financed support scheme for the British pig industry, based on a deficiency payment principle. That is, the difference between the market price achieved by pigs in any week and a predetermined

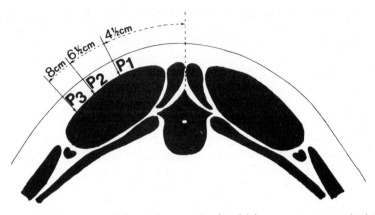

Fig. 11.3 The positions of the various probe fat thickness measurements, taken at the level of the head of the last rib, used in the M.L.C. pig carcase classification scheme (277)

guaranteed price was paid to producers who marketed pigs in that week. To facilitate the administration of these schemes, government departments carried out the weighing of pig carcases in abattoirs to provide an acceptable basis for subsidy payments. At some times, these independently employed staff carried out not only the identification, weighing and certification of pigs eligible for subsidy, but also determined the measurements involved in the grading process. Between 1955 and 1967, the amount of deficiency payment was directly linked to the carcase grade for bacon pigs. This provided a government-financed incentive towards quality improvement.

Even when this phase ceased, the official graders continued to record the measurements as a service to the industry. When the probe measurement was introduced into grading however, the government decided they could not justify meeting this extra cost and indicated that if these measurements were to be made by the official graders a charge would be made. For a period, the abattoir operators decided to carry out the additional measuring with their own staff.

These anomalies were resolved in 1971 when the Meat and Livestock Commission introduced a comprehensive system of pig carcase classification, whereby weighing and measurement were to be carried out by employees of the Commission as an independent third party, a service for which the pig industry has paid since 1975. By 1977, some 80 per cent of all British pigs were being weighed and classified under this scheme; all pigs in participating centres are weighed and measured in a standard manner, the abattoir operator and the person from whom he purchased the pigs being informed of the weight and measurements as recorded. The buyer may convert this information to his own grades, specified to sellers in advance of purchase. There remains considerable diversity in the grade schedules used by individual buyers but, given the basic measurements, producers can make accurate comparisons of the prices offered. Such a classification scheme is inevitably labour intensive, given the structure of the slaughtering industry in Great Britain with a rather large number of plants that are small by international standards. Attempts have been made to reduce labour costs by automation using the Danish or other equipment (225).

An essential feature of this scheme is its simplicity. In the early days of pig classification in Britain there was, of course, considerable resistance from the trade to the low importance attached to conformation, only the most extremely poorly muscled pigs being identified. Sometimes buyers added their own conformation assessment to the independently determined weight and back fat measurements in formulating their grades. However, retail butchers and processors increasingly became aware that, taking account of the variations in British pigs then current, conformation was not important in determining the yield of trimmed lean meat and had little effect on the appearance of individual cuts.

Enlarged E.E.C.

When the U.K. joined the E.E.C. in 1971, together with Eire and Denmark, the new members had to adopt the Common Agricultural Policy, and specifically the Pigmeat Regime, including the requirements of Regulation 2108/70, stipulating a common pig carcase grading method for price reporting and other market management purposes. As has already been described, this E.E.C. scheme gave considerable weight to classification by type (that is shape or conformation). Representations were made that this approach was inappropriate to British, Danish and Irish pigs which showed less variation in conformation and the variation which did exist was not significantly related to compositional factors or widely valued by the trade (159). A sharp contrast was drawn between research results relating conformation and composition at similar back fat measurements in Britain and Denmark, and those found in France, Germany and the Netherlands.

After considerable negotiation, the Regulation was amended to introduce a different approach for price reporting purposes. Under the revised Regulation 2760/75, pig carcases are classified into ranges of estimated lean meat content by the method considered most appropriate for its pigs by each member state. In Denmark, carcase lean percentages have been determined using the combination of measurements used for domestic grading purposes. In the Irish Republic, two mid-line fat measurements have been used together with P_2, whereas in the U.K. the P_2 measurement has been used alone. The original six states chose to continue their former system based on type in conjunction with weight and mid-line back fats.

Since implementation of this dual scheme, concern has been expressed about the consistency of the standardisation of lean percentages used to define the grades in different countries, and a trial was carried out to examine this (77, 202). A team of dissectors from the Federal German Meat Research Institute at Kulmbach visited carcase evaluation centres in Belgium, Denmark, France, Italy and the U.K. and compared the methods applied in the individual centres with a standard reference method. The results indicated that different standards were being applied, leading to a reappraisal by the E.E.C. of their scheme.

Significant changes are now taking place in the British pig industry, which raise several questions to be resolved in the coming years.

(a) Will the low importance currently attached to conformation continue to be appropriate? Certain breeding companies, which came to dominate pig breeding in the U.K. in the 1970s, developed strains for European markets where special attention was given to the size and meatiness of the ham and to shorter, thicker, heavier and meatier types of pig. If the British pig population were to absorb a significant number of pigs of this type, variation in conformation and meat distribution and their commercial significance could increase.

(b) There is evidence that pigs from certain breeding sources are disadvantaged when they are sold for slaughter to buyers on the basis of simple back fat measurements (see chapter 19). This may create problems which cannot be resolved by the introduction of further measurements into the scheme. The payment grades of individual buyers may have to take account of the source of each pig as an important supplement to the carcase measurements in estimating carcase composition.

(c) Will meat quality factors show more variation, achieve more commercial significance and in some way have to be built into the classification and pig buying procedures?

12 Sheep carcase grading and classification

New Zealand

The first shipment of lamb from New Zealand to Britain, on the *Dunedin* in 1882, was made possible by the development of refrigeration (293). This followed the coincidence of an acute food shortage in Britain with a surplus of sheep in New Zealand so serious that some flocks were destroyed. The trade grew gradually and, for a period in the early part of this century, the whole exportable surplus was on contract to the British Government. Termination of this contract caused a crisis and a cost/price squeeze that led to legislation providing for the establishment of a Meat Producers' Board with powers to control the export trade. One of the Board's functions, and a key one in the development of this trade, was to grade carcases at export abattoirs.

Most of the lambs are selected (drafted) for slaughter at three to six months of age, while still suckling their mothers, and this is frequently carried out by a fieldsman of the exporting freezing works. The favourable environment, the remarkably uniform production systems, the breed crosses employed and the systematic selection for slaughter against a price schedule related to grade, has made New Zealand lamb a relatively consistent carcase meat.

In practice, lamb and mutton grades are applied by factory personnel under the supervision of the Board; during the height of the season, the larger plants will operate as many as six separate slaughter lines each at 480 lambs per hour. So the weighing, grading and tagging operation has to be completed within eight seconds per carcase. A Meat Board supervisor would be expected to examine graded carcases almost every day in such plants. By inspecting lines of carcases, sorted by grade in the holding chiller, a supervisor can detect aberrations quickly, can re-grade as necessary, and so exercise a tight control over the standard applied.

The grading procedures have traditionally allowed the British wholesaler and retailer to order with confidence lambs by grade from the importer's cold store. Some more sophisticated buyers have also chosen to specify the individual area or freezing works in addition to the export grade, in a belief they can achieve even greater uniformity. In some years, the traditional service butcher, who retails a substantial part of the New Zealand lamb imported into Britain, may complain about the prevailing standard of the lamb carcases. A grading system applied to a highly seasonal product may be difficult to standardise from year to year, particularly as one year may differ from another in environmental factors, causing variations in the rate of growth and of fattening, and in the phasing of slaughterings as the season progresses.

Because of the reliance on two breeds, the Southdown and the Romney, plus common production and drafting techniques, carcase weight has played a central role in New Zealand lamb grading. Not only do other characteristics vary less, at a particular carcase weight, than is the case with the production of many other countries, but the British retailer seeks New Zealand lamb carcases to a tight weight specification. This is to allow whole and half joints (shoulder and leg) to be cut consistently to a similar weight; in the days before inflation became a major factor affecting meat prices, this led to a level total cost. It was accepted wisdom in the British meat trade for many years that the housewife sought a joint of meat for weekend consumption with a particular total cost in mind; carcase weight just a few pounds too high on average would lead to too many joints priced above this target figure and so damage sales.

Within the weight ranges, grading has traditionally involved the separation of well-finished, short, thick, full-legged carcases from those which are longer and leaner with a less desirable leg shape. The Southdown is early maturing and the pure-bred lambs are fat at an early age and lightweight, with the smoothness and blockiness of the well-fattened animal beloved in the British show ring and carcase competition for many years as the acme of 'quality'. The Romney, on the other hand, is later maturing and the carcases of the pure-bred lambs of this breed are larger, generally less fat and with a more variable and less desirable conformation in these traditional terms.

Because of the breed mix, the top grade was eventually subdivided to differentiate the lighter down-type from the heavier, but still well finished prime-type that was typical of the cross-bred lambs. Further refinements introduced were the rejection of grossly over-fat lambs from all export grades, the separate grading of very lean lightweight carcases (Alphas) in demand in some new export markets, and the differentiation of long, leggy lambs with poor loin development (Omegas) but enough fat to otherwise carry them into the Prime grade.

The Omega grades were introduced following a Committee of Enquiry (347), which provided the first clear indication to the New Zealand producer of a growing aversion in the British market to the fatness of the down-types despite the excellence of its conformation.

The early forms of the scheme have been listed by Frazer (133). At the end of the 1960s, the grading for lambs (all of which carry the distinctive stamp 'New Zealand Lamb') involved Primes (graded for flesh content with an adequate covering of fat and in four weight ranges), Omegas (derived from the Prime grade, but different in conformation and with more fat than Y), and Ys (with less flesh or more fat cover in three weight ranges but not graded as Prime).

Although the Meat Board has recently argued that the grades have always been essentially descriptive and did not impute value, there is no doubt that producers and many British retailers have thought of the Prime grade (and the Downs before them) as being the better 'quality'. This is partly because the shape was seen as desirable, but also with the implication that the meat would be more flavourful and succulent when cooked. This was reflected in the way the grades were referred to in price reports (229).

But as consumers turned increasingly against fat, the New Zealand producer began to receive puzzling price signals from the British market — at times the Ys achieved better prices than the Primes. New Zealand meat scientists weighed into the debate with the view that the grading system was misleading the producer on consumer demand in the medium-term, favouring as it did smallness, good conformation and fat development rather than a larger leaner lamb with less emphasis on conformation. In particular, they showed that the Y grade carcases certainly had more bone than the Prime grade — but also more lean meat, the lower bone yield of the Primes being more than outweighed by the extra fat (195).

They showed that, among the breeds then used, desirable shape was achieved by the fat covering and not by a markedly superior thickness or yield of the lean meat. So the Board found itself in receipt of conflicting advice, since many of the leaders of the retail trade in Britain were themselves fighting a rear-guard action against the 'obsession with leanness'.

Accordingly a second major enquiry was set up (262), and although not all the recommendations were accepted, this did lead to further changes in the grading system in 1975. Kirton and Colomer-Rocher (230) have described the grades operating in 1978 in a way which emphasises that they have, in fact, now moved more towards descriptive classification (see table 12.1). Further changes of detail have been made since then; plate 6 illustrates the differences between major grades in 1981 (294).

Table 12.1 The New Zealand lamb export grading system in 1978 (230)

Present grade symbol		A	Y	P	O	F[1]
	Earlier grade name	Alpha	Y	Prime	Omega	Overfat
Weight range class	Fat cover	Absent or minimal	Light	Medium to heavy	Medium to heavy	Excessive
kg	Description / Conformation	—	—	Compact	Leggy	—
Under 8.0	Very light	A				
8.0 - 12.5	Light (L)		YL	PL	OL	
13.0 - 16.0	Medium (M)		YM	PM	OM	F
16.5 - 25.5	Heavy (H)		YH	PH		
% of total export kill		0.5 - 2.0	30 - 45	55 - 65	1 - 3	0.1 - 0.5

1. F carcasses must be cut and trimmed of excess fat before export.
2. Carcasses that would have been placed in one of the above grades but which are not eligible for export due to trimming or mutilation are classed as Cutter 1 or Cutter 2. Cuts from these carcasses may be exported.

Most lambs slaughtered in New Zealand are born between the beginning of August and the end of October, and slaughtered from October to June. Up to 31 August, sheep born in the previous year are classed as 'lambs' for grading purposes provided their weight does not exceed 25.5 kg. A hogget carcase should

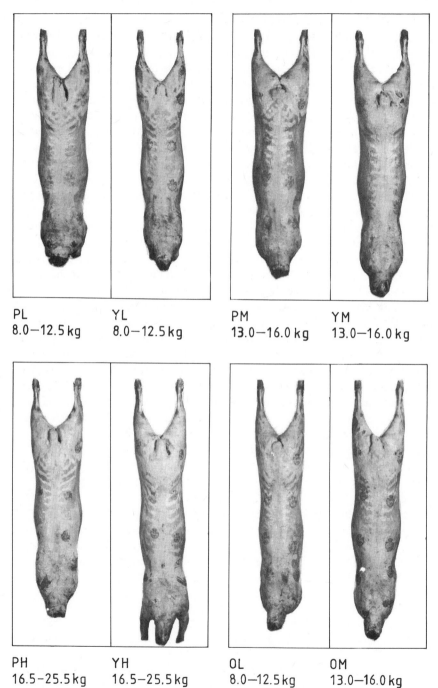

PL   YL   PM   YM
8.0–12.5 kg   8.0–12.5 kg   13.0–16.0 kg   13.0–16.0 kg

PH   YH   OL   OM
16.5–25.5 kg   16.5–25.5 kg   8.0–12.5 kg   13.0–16.0 kg

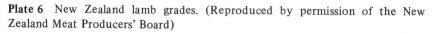

Plate 6 New Zealand lamb grades. (Reproduced by permission of the New Zealand Meat Producers' Board)

come from a sheep between twelve and twenty-four months of age, and thereafter it is classed as mutton, for both of which types of sheep descriptive grades on a similar basis to those for lamb are available. Dentition may be examined in the lairage to establish the age category of particular batches if there is doubt.

This system has worked well for New Zealand and indeed, as indicated above, there is little evidence from any source that there are significant changes in the palatability of sheepmeat during the first year of its life. New Zealand will therefore resist any attempt under international legislation or terms of trade to differentiate lambs up to six months of age from those six to twelve months old. In particular, the method proposed for such differentiation by Schön (332) in the context of Codex Alimentarius, involving examination of the fusion of bones of the pelvis, has been shown to be insufficiently accurate as well as impractical in a high throughput plant (232).

The only measurement currently in use in New Zealand lamb grading is the GR measurement of tissue thickness. This is taken with a ruler probe between the surface and the twelfth rib bone at a point 11 cm from the mid-line, to pick out the over-fat (F) lamb carcases, which must be cut and trimmed before export. The maximum fat thickness allowed is being progressively reduced: 18 mm in 1973/74; 15 mm in the 1978/79 season; and possible further reductions to a target of 10 mm (231, 233). But there is evidence that the current measuring method leaves something to be desired. With the tool available, GR is proving difficult to measure at normal New Zealand freezing works line speeds of 6-8 per minute, and many over-fat lambs are missed. Also the system, when based on a single maximum thickness, penalised heavier carcases because they have less fat at a given GR measurement; this would tend to encourage the production of lighter lambs to the disadvantage of the industry's total output and efficiency.

Considerable interest is being shown in New Zealand in automating the measuring and recording process (396) and also in automatic measuring equipment which might eventually allow objective criteria to be introduced into the grading of all sheep carcases (17) (see chapter 8). But as Kirton and Colomer-Rocher (230) have pointed out, the existing subjective system (applied to 21-27 million lambs and 4-7 million mutton carcases annually) has proved generally effective in maintaining confidence among producers, retailers and wholesalers. This is still the case despite a greater diversity of crosses now in use in New Zealand and inevitably a greater variation in the kill than was traditionally the case. Although major fears about the importation of disease remain, should European breeds that have excellent muscling at very low levels of fatness eventually be introduced into New Zealand, and their production grow to a significant scale, it will be interesting to see how the grading system is adjusted to accommodate them. At the moment, such carcases would have to be graded Y and bracketed with a large number of carcases of much poorer conformation and muscling.

Australia

The sheep industry of Australia differs in several important respects from that of New Zealand. There is a much wider range of environments in that huge country, many unfavourable, so there is much greater variation in sheep carcases produced in all respects, including age.

A smaller proportion of the kill has traditionally been exported and, although for many years there was a Meat Board with somewhat similar terms of reference as that in New Zealand, in practice it has had less tight control of the export trade including the export grading systems and their application. In particular, the Australian Meat Board has not employed supervisory graders (since in theory the meat inspection service oversees the system) nor provided central training of abattoir staff, so the application of the Australian export grading system has proved to be more variable than in New Zealand.

The grades were for many years of a conventional nature involving adequate even fat cover over well developed legs, loins and shoulders in the top grade, with deficiencies in any respect causing downgrading, coupled with New Zealand-type weight ranges (286). Some or all of these grades were applied to eleven age/breeding status categories, with age being formally defined by dentition. During ante-mortem inspection, if the veterinary authorities considered a batch did not conform to the description given for it in advance by the supplier, they could require each lamb to be mouthed during the dressing operation. These distinctions are important in Australia because of the high proportion of sheep grazed extensively and coming to slaughter as hoggets or young sheep rather than 'lambs'.

From 1972, the Board and its successor (the Australian Livestock and Meat Corporation) experimented with alternative classification systems for Australian sheepmeat. A committee recommended the retention of the same age and sex categories, but coupled with separate fatness and conformation classifications as in the British system developed by M.L.C. (see below).

The proposed fatness scale is similar to the British (differentiating five levels of fatness) but a different approach to conformation classification was proposed. Under the stimulus of beef research by Yeates, there always has been an interest in Australia in the value of the so-called 'fleshing index', or carcase weight per unit length, as an objective measure of conformation. (Earlier studies sought other measurement combinations to pick out the conformation differences between the export grades, 329). Three categories for conformation determined on this basis were proposed, and as might be expected the measure proved to be related closely to fatness (286).

Data have been presented which show some relation between length, weight and carcase composition, but it is a matter of judgement whether insistence on objective classification (in order to avoid visual judgements and the potential problems in their standardisation) should override other considerations such as the weakness of the underlying correlations or a poor relation between the objective and subjective assessment of the same characteristic. In this case the length definition could be important; total length of the hanging carcase (which has to be used if automatic measurement is the aim) may not sufficiently differentiate length of body and length of leg. Further, the visual assessment of conformation has, over the years, tended to give more and more weight to the hind leg.

As with their pig and beef systems, the Australian sheep classification procedures were planned with the maximum automation of operations in mind. Given an appropriate definition of length, then the length to weight ratio can be measured automatically as the carcases pass the weigh point in the abattoir, and various probing equipment has been tried to determine and record fatness automatically. Comprehensive automatic print-out of carcase tickets etc. has been developed (fig. 12.1) (286).

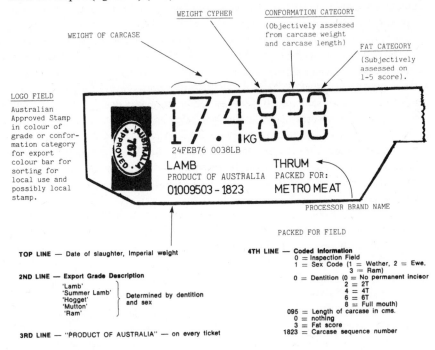

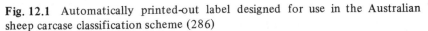

Fig. 12.1 Automatically printed-out label designed for use in the Australian sheep carcase classification scheme (286)

United States

In the U.S.A. sheep feature well behind beef cattle and pigs in the meat league. Nevertheless, following the development of beef grades in the early part of this century, the U.S.D.A. formulated and publicised grades for lamb, yearling mutton and mutton carcases in 1931. The grades have been amended in detail but not in principle several times since then.

The procedure adopted closely followed the beef system, relying on the amalgamation of 'quality' factors (that is palatability-indicating characteristics of the lean meat) with the conformation of the carcase. But since sheep carcases, unlike beef, are intact at the time of grading, the texture, firmness and marbling of the cut surface of the eye muscle cannot be directly observed. Graders therefore have to rely on indirect assessment via the fat intermingling with the lean as seen between the ribs ('feathering'), and the streaking of fat within and on the inside flank muscles, coupled with the firmness of the fat and lean. Their assessment of quality is amalgamated with the apparent maturity of the carcase, and that combined assessment amalgamated with conformation to determine the grade.

Because of the contribution of fat deposition both to the shape of the carcase and to the assessment of the quality characteristics of the lean meat, these grades inevitably show a gradation of fatness down from the top grade Prime through Choice, Good and Utility to Cull. Increasing rejection of fat by consumers and discontent among the traders who had to trim carcases, particularly of Prime and Choice grade, to meet their requirements, led to the introduction of an additional element, the yield grade, in 1969.

Designed to categorise carcases by their estimated yield of closely trimmed, boneless, most-valuable retail cuts, the yield grade was developed by searching for an appropriate and practicable estimating procedure (for example, 188). The method chosen was to amalgamate external fat thicknesses (1½ in from the mid-line between the twelfth and thirteenth ribs, taken by probe or by eye judgement, adjusted for unusual fat distribution over the rest of the carcase if necessary), with estimated percentage of kidney and channel fats, and the conformation of the hind leg. The inclusion of conformation was justified to achieve acceptability with the trade rather than for the information it provided in improving the accuracy of estimation.

The yield grades are defined as follows:

Grades	Boneless, trimmed retail cuts from leg, loin, rack and shoulder as a percentage of carcase weight
1	47.3 +
2	45.5-47.2
3	43.7-45.4
4	41.9-43.6
5	below 41.9

These measurements are estimated from the equation:

Yield grade = $1.66 - (0.05 \times$ leg conformation grade code)
$$+ (0.25 \times \text{KKCF as percentage of carcase weight})$$
$$+ (6.66 \times \text{adjusted fat thickness in inches})$$

The leg conformation grade is coded from 1 for low Cull up to 15 for high Prime. After the calculation, the fractional part of the estimate is dropped.

Promotional leaflets claimed (373) that yield grade 4 carcases were worth 8 per cent less per unit weight than yield grade 2 carcases.

An interesting feature of the American scheme is the method of differentiating lamb, yearling mutton and mutton. In addition to observations of the shape of the rib bones and the colour and texture of the lean, the metacarpal bones are examined for the state of the 'break joint' at the zone of growth, that is the junction of the epiphysis and diaphysis. The joint must have broken on both front shanks for the carcase to be classed as lamb. If both show 'spool joints' rather than broken metacarpals then the carcase must be classed as mutton. The intermediate 'yearling mutton' may have one of each. It is known that metacarpals may break even though they come from sheep as old as fourteen months, but sheep over ten months are likely to be classed as 'yearling mutton' on the basis of colour and texture even if one or more bones break.

Although producers and packers have been encouraged to adopt sale of lambs by U.S.D.A. carcase grade and weight, and some exploratory studies were carried out on weight loss and carcase grade estimation on live sheep (291, 292), this method of marketing sheep remains relatively rare in the U.S.A. However, a high proportion of sheep carcases are graded for sale on from slaughterers to retailers.

West Germany

Despite the low production and consumption of sheepmeat in Germany, official grades for sheep carcases for price reporting purposes were published in 1971 (338). They distinguish four levels of conformation (E, I, II and III, based on development of the 'value-determining parts of the carcase') and in the better conformation classes, three levels of fatness (g, slight; m, medium; or s, considerable). They had the avowed aim of improving market transparency and the encouragement of quality by relating the price paid to farmers to the carcase quality of the sheep they produce.

Five age/sex categories of sheepmeat are specified: milk-fed lamb not more than six months old (M); fattened lambs less than twelve months old (L); castrated males and non-bred females less than two years old (H); mutton (S); and ram meat (B).

The regulation demands that the conformation class has to be marked on the carcase in addition to the category, but the fat subdivision need not be. Further (with the exception of frozen lamb), 'lamb and mutton may be offered, displayed, supplied, sold or otherwise brought on the market only in accordance with the statutory (conformation) grades. . .'

As with pigs, the dissection data used in promotional material shows a much

Table 12.2 Composition and relative value of milk lamb carcases in each grade of the German lamb carcase grading scheme (338)

Grade		Lean Total	Carcase composition (%) Fat Internal fat	Subcut- aneous	Inter- muscular	Bone	Calcu- lated relative carcase value
E	g	71.5	9.1	1.0	3.2	4.9	16.7	117
	m	62.9	18.2	1.9	6.0	10.3	15.8	103
	s	55.7	26.8	2.2	9.9	14.7	14.8	91
I	g	67.8	10.5	1.1	3.8	5.6	17.9	111
	m	61.0	18.5	1.8	6.8	9.9	17.1	100
	s	51.4	29.6	2.8	12.9	13.9	16.0	84
II		57.2	21.5	1.9	9.6	10.0	17.9	94

bigger effect of conformation on composition than does British data (table 12.2). However, more detailed data presented elsewhere (333) showed small differences between the yield of individual cuts and their lean content when milk lamb carcases in conformation classes E and I are compared at the same average level of fatness.

France

Sheep production in France is second only to that of the United Kingdom among European countries; but sheepmeat is a luxury food and production is a specialist business among predominantly small farmers.

Attempts to grade sheep in France originate with price reports for live sheep (La Villette) and for carcases in the wholesale meat markets such as Les Halles. By 1971, details had been published of a carcase classification scheme developed by the Institut Technique de l'Elevage Ovin et Caprin (I.T.O.V.I.C.) for wider purposes, involving five classes for conformation (A to E) and five classes for fatness (1 to 5) (246). Diagrams to show the shape requirements and the development of the surface fat layer were supplemented by very detailed written descriptions. For example, for each conformation and fat class, requirements are given separately for hind leg, rump, loin, back and shoulder, and the weight to be attached to each part of the carcase is specified. Diagrams showed how the angle of the hind leg relates to the conformation assessment for that part of the carcase.

An official regulation of 1973 specified this system for price reporting purposes for slaughter lambs and ewes, slightly simplified in its descriptions and with the conformation classes renamed, F, R, A, N and C. The scheme was adopted in 1976 by the new regulatory body O.N.I.B.E.V. who renamed the

Table 12.3 Descriptions of the conformation classes specified in the French EUROP sheep carcase classification scheme (299)

	E	U	R	O	P
General	Superior, all profiles are convex and show a very full muscular development	Very good, the profiles are not so convex overall and show a good muscular development	Good, all the profiles are at least rectilinear and show a thick musculature	Fairly good. The profiles are on the whole rectilinear, some may be concave, showing musculature of average thickness	Fair, all the profiles are concave and show a poor muscular development
Leg and saddle	Short, rounded and very thick. The saddle is more wide than long	Rounded and thick, the saddle is again more wide than long	More elongated, but always thick. The saddle is about as wide as it is long	Very elongated, lacking thickness in all the parts. The saddle is longer than it is wide	Concave in all their parts. Less thick, long and flat. The saddle is much longer than it is wide
Back and loins	Very wide and thick up to shoulder level	Thick, wide and without hollows nearly to shoulder level. Spinous processes not apparent	Less full, but always wide at the base. The back may lack width at shoulder level. Spinous processes very slightly apparent	Narrow, lacking thickness. Spinous processes slightly apparent	Very narrow and hollow, completely lacking in thickness. Spinous processes prominent
Shoulders	Rounded and very thick	Rounded and thick	May lack some thickness	Lacking in thickness	Flat, shoulder blades are prominent

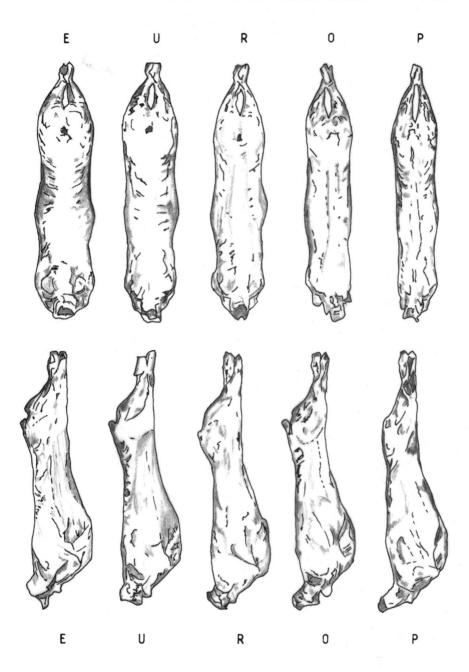

Fig. 12.2 Lamb carcases of the various conformation classes of the O.N.I.B.E.V. scheme (299)

conformation classes, E, U, R, O and P (299). The current descriptions are given in table 12.3 and the conformation classes are illustrated in fig. 12.2.

The classes of this scheme reflect the range of breeds used in France for sheep meat production (some of which are very muscular) and the market requirement for very low levels of fat covering. The carcases in the middle class for conformation (R) appear from the illustration to be quite muscular but in fact they are comparable to the M.L.C. 'average' conformation class (see below); the method of hanging the carcase, with hind legs crossed, emphasises the thickness of the hind leg musculature. Although the classes for fatness appear to be comparable to those in the M.L.C. system, the distribution of fatness in France is weighted much more towards the leaner classes.

Sweden

All carcases produced in Sweden intended for sale on the open market have to be classified according to rules issued by the Swedish Board of Agriculture. In addition to category (suckler lamb, lamb or sheep), and classes of conformation (varied according to category), the Swedish sheep classification system differentiates seven classes of fat (8). These range from M (completely lacking) through L (light), N (normal), B, C, D, and E (for varying degrees of over-fatness).

For these fatter classes, a linear measurement of the subcutaneous fat layer is taken between the tenth and eleventh ribs over the *M. longissimus* by making a cut and inserting a rule. Class B has a range in thickness of 3-5 mm; C, 5-10 mm; D, 10-15 mm; and E has more than 15 mm.

Great Britain

Although Britain continues to import a substantial proportion of its requirement for sheepmeat from New Zealand and Australia, a significant export trade in selected fresh lamb to other parts of Europe and to the Middle East has been built up and, given the right political climate, could be increased.

The traditional pattern of sheep production in Britain involves a stratified cross-breeding system, related closely to the altitude of grazing. Starting with pure-bred flocks in the harsher hill areas, the second stage is the transfer of older ewes from these flocks onto lower ground for mating with rams of the longwool crossing breeds. The cross-bred ewes from these matings are, in turn, put to rams of down breeds to produce slaughter lambs, mainly on lowland farms. To cope with the variety of environmental conditions under which sheep are bred and finished, a multiplicity of breeds and crosses has been developed.

Lamb slaughterings follow a seasonal pattern increasing steadily from May to November and then declining. As the season advances after May, there is an increase in the proportion of heavier lambs which partly reflects regional differences in breeds and systems of production. British lamb carcases, therefore, are variable: the extent of the variation was shown in a national survey (213).

There is, nevertheless, scope for increasing uniformity by more careful selection of lambs for slaughter. But due to the absence of clear price differentials against fatter lamb carcases, the farmer may well obtain a better financial return by taking lambs on to heavier weights even if they do become fat. In the long run, the lack of adequate differentials between different carcase types may be prejudicing consumer demand for lamb due to its fatness and variability.

Despite some years in which plentiful supply has been absorbed, at a price, the general trend of consumer demand for sheepmeat in Britain has been to fall. One reason is that consumers consider mutton and lamb to be disagreeably fat; the quality of the product has failed to keep pace with changing consumer attitudes.

In an effort to provide the common framework upon which price differentials could be based, the M.L.C. introduced a sheep carcase classification scheme in 1975 (91). This is purely descriptive, concentrating on the characteristics of importance to meat traders when they cut up and prepare meat for sale. It does not attempt to rank or group carcases in terms of their ' quality' since there is much regional variation in demand. The classification scheme was devised so that meat traders could express their own requirements for different types of lamb, linked to price, so encouraging a better matching of supply with demand.

The M.L.C. classification scheme describes carcases by weight, category (age/sex group, for example, lamb, hogget, ewe), fatness and conformation. Weight is determined after the carcase has been dressed in a specified manner. An independently recorded weight linked to a firm dressing specification for identified carcases is seen as an important contributor to successful deadweight marketing in Britain.

A fundamental difference between this classification scheme and the grading method in, for example, New Zealand is that the latter includes weight ranges. Attempts to reach decisions on such ranges in Britain would undoubtedly have led to prolonged negotiations with the different trade sectors, whose current requirements differ and overlap; so weight is merely described to the nearest ½ kg and any buyer (whether wholesaler or retailer) may specify his own weight range requirements.

The distinction between lambs and hoggets is on the basis of a date. Lambs born before 1 October in any one year are classed as hoggets at the beginning of the following year.

Fatness is described by a visual judgement of the level of the external fat cover. Five levels of fatness are distinguished ranging from 1 (very lean) to 5 (very fat) (plate 7). (In addition, the letter K is applied to carcases which are judged to have excessive kidney-knob and channel fat development, that is, with more than 5 per cent of the carcase weight as KKCF, regardless of the level of external fatness.) There is an underlying objective base in that each class is defined in terms of the percentage of subcutaneous fat in the carcase (91).

The description of carcase conformation is based on four classes: extra (E); average (no distinguishing letter); poor (C); and very poor (Z). Conformation is assessed as the thickness of lean meat plus fat in relation to the size of the

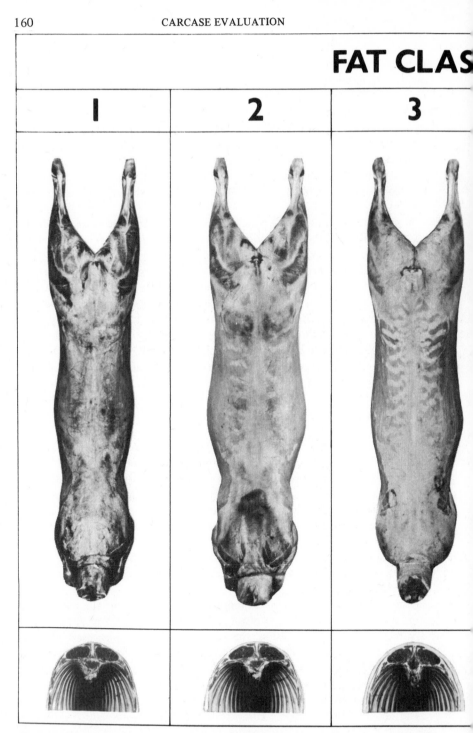

Plate 7 The scale of fatness used in the M.L.C. sheep carcase classification scheme.

4	5

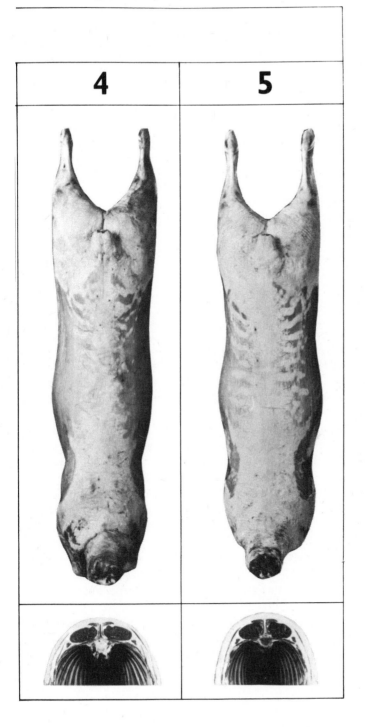

skeleton, and fatness is allowed to play its full part in influencing conformation. Given the separate fat class, this approach to classification of conformation is considered preferable to attempts at adjusting the conformation judgement for fatness. The average group is deliberately wide, reflecting that for most of the British trade, only extremes of conformation have commercial significance.

Table 12.4 The form of the grid used in the M.L.C. sheep carcase classification scheme, with the percentage (shown in brackets) of lamb carcases in Britain in 1977 falling into each cell (198). This is based on 102 000 carcases, a random 1 in 20 sample of those classified

Fat class

1	2	3L	3H	4	5
1E (−)	2E (1.0)	3LE (6.0)	3HE (3.5)	4E (4.3)	5 (1.6)
1 (0.4)	2 (22.5)	3L (34.2)	3H (15.0)	4 (9.0)	
C (2.3)					
Z (0.2)					

This led to the grid in table 12.4. Trade reaction to this attempt at simplification was mixed. Some found the loss of symmetry confusing and would have preferred a 5 × 5 grid allowing, as it would, subdivision of the average conformation group and easier comparisons with other schemes. Others accepted the simplification as both desirable and successful.

The extent to which this scheme has been integrated on a formal basis into trading is limited; some wholesalers use it informally as their basis for producer payments and in sorting carcases for different retail outlets. Others continue to express a fear that encouraging the use of classification as an aid to the selling of carcases into the retail trade will allow, and indeed encourage, multiple retailers in particular to become more demanding in their requirements, leading to situations when wholesalers are unable to meet a demand for volume supplies of specified weights and types. Clearly retailers need to be aware of the difficulties facing a wholesaler if he is set too tight a specification by buyers. He may not always be able to meet requirements from supplies available at the time, so buyers need to indicate not only their basic preference but, in addition, acceptable alternatives for negotiation at different prices where the first choice cannot be met in full. Some such procedure is necessary if the wholesaler is to feel the full pressure of differential demand; without such pressure developing, reflection of market needs back to producers is bound to be incomplete.

13 Beef carcase grading and classification

United States

No carcase grading scheme has had more influence on an industry than that for beef in the U.S.A. That country has a huge beef industry based on large herds of beef cows producing calves under range conditions, a high proportion of which are finished in feedlots. Per capita consumption of beef is high, with increased expenditure on beef being seen by many as an index of affluence and indeed national prosperity. This has ensured that the grading scheme itself has been in the forefront of industry politics.

The promotion of the scheme in the early days was resisted strongly by the packing industry and since then the proposed changes have been advocated or resisted by various pressure groups with a fervour not seen elsewhere. The U.S.D.A. Grading Chief has claimed '. . . . . the United States remains the largest and only significant (sic) producer of high-quality beef in the world' (146) and reminded meat packers that the grading service shares responsibility with them for the product's integrity. So beef grading, which is all about expected eating quality, is clearly fundamental to industry thinking.

The intention has always been to identify segments of beef within the entire range produced having similar palatability characteristics. The traditional thinking that has always determined the structure of the scheme, despite many changes of detail, has been that the achievement of good consistent eating satisfaction needs youthfulness, marbling in the lean meat and evidence, through conformation, that the animal is from a breed expected to provide the right palatability, if fed correctly.

Grading is carried out on cold sides quartered, or at least 'ribbed', to reveal the cross-section of the *M. longissimus* and overlying fat. Maturity is assessed from the condition and colour of the bones and the lean meat. The scheme assumes that beef from the older animal will eat less well than that from the younger animal, unless it has more marbling fat to compensate. Conformation, when used, could only reduce the provisional grade determined from marbling and maturity, not improve it. The common use of high-energy feeding systems for beef cattle achieved high levels of marbling as well as rapid growth. So 'quality' was usually associated with high levels of external fat deposition. The highest grade with the most succulent meat has been 'Prime', the second 'Choice', the third 'Good'.

Even from the earliest days of the scheme, Prime was too fat for most domestic consumers and tended to be reserved for high-class restaurants. So the second grade, Choice, has always been the main retail grade; indeed, the selection of names has proved particularly apt, since the term 'Choice' has proved to be appealing in its own right to the housewife. Consumer reaction has been important because the graded carcases are roller-branded and the grade name is used at point of sale.

Most of the changes proposed over the years have been aimed at watering-down the basic concept, requiring less marbling at a given level of maturity, and diminishing and eventually eliminating the importance of conformation. A reason some sectors of the industry have given for proposing changes (though not the U.S.D.A.) has been the need to reduce feeding costs, as the price of grain has increased because of world demand. In fact, rising feed costs caused a major crisis in confidence in the American beef industry. This led to the introduction of a yield grade in 1962 designed to sort carcases by yield of trimmed, deboned cuts, by taking account of weight, fat thickness, *M. longissimus* area and the KKCF percentage in the carcase. 'Choice 2' became the most desirable grade describing beef that had achieved the necessary marbling for Choice without excessive external fat.

Because of the seminal nature of this scheme and the interaction of interests — breeders, feeders, packers, retailers, the catering trade, meat scientists and, not least, government agencies — the historical changes in the grading scheme will be listed in some detail. Further analysis, particularly of the economic effects, can be found in Williams and Stout (386) and Kiehl and Rhodes (227).

By 1880 Various agencies were publishing private market sheets but each used terms that had grown in usage in the particular markets.

1917 Tentative grading standards based on university research (287) were issued by the U.S.D.A. and began to be used as a basis for uniformly reporting beef markets. (The revised form was published in 1924, 93).

1925 The 'Better Beef' campaign was initiated mainly at the stimulus of the pure breeders, although supported by the U.S.D.A. and the National Livestock and Meat Board. Its objective was to promote quality finished beef from pure-bred beef cattle, and grades were to be stamped on the carcase so that consumers could discriminate. Marbling began to emerge as a major guide to tender and juicy beef, and the campaign sought to denigrate 'lean beef' using a variety of derogatory names (324).

1926 The Secretary of the U.S.D.A. offered to stamp beef grades on carcases on request and free of charge to all packers operating under Federal inspection. Conflict began to emerge between different sectors on whether all beef should be graded and stamped, or whether stamping might be confined to top grades only, or whether stamping should be completely voluntary. Some beef was graded and stamped for a few institutional buyers like the Pennsylvania Railroad.

1927 Grade marking began at the buyer's request.

1930 There was a concerted move by packers to establish packer grades rather than to use the U.S.D.A. grades. Differences of opinion between large packers (favouring private marks) and smaller packers (favouring U.S.D.A. marks) were already apparent.

1930-35 Reports of co-operative research on meat quality began to question both the assumed differences between breed types and the dominant effect of marbling. By 1935 24 per cent of federally inspected steer and heifer carcases were being graded.

1942-46 Compulsory grading was introduced during the War (and later again during the Korean war) as a part of a price control programme.

1950 The former 'Prime' and 'Choice' grades were combined to form a new 'Prime', and 'Good' became 'Choice'. Other changes were also made lower down the scale. This was the first major dilution of the marbling requirements for the most widely used grade.

Interest in marketing cattle by grade and deadweight was stimulated by agricultural economists (for example, 103). Growth of this method of marketing was slow but had reached some 25 per cent by the 1980s.

1953 Objective as opposed to subjective grading was investigated (72), the aim being to predict the subjective grade rather than to alter the basic criterion from meat quality to meat yield. This approach attracted little attention from U.S.D.A. or elsewhere.

1955 About half of the beef slaughter was being graded. The greatest growth in demand had coincided with the increasing trend towards large chains of supermarkets with central procurement organisations and considerable buying power. The full benefits of the grading system became apparent; it allowed new packers to compete with long-standing firms, and small packers to compete with large packers in supplying a distant retail customer with beef of known standard. Federal grades began to be featured more and more in consumer educational material and it became common for grade marking to be carried through to the supermarket cabinet.

1956 Meat scientists began to question the relevance of conformation as an index of the yield and distribution of trimmed deboned retail cuts (46). Because of the importance of finish and conformation in determining the grade, it had always been possible to make an estimate of grade on live cattle. Indeed, this had to be the basis of livestock price reports. Estimates of grade are also used in livestock trading, not only of finished cattle but of cattle for further feeding. Here the grade essentially describes a beast by its potential carcase grade if fed properly. Students are trained to estimate subdivided carcase grades on the live animal, but the errors involved can be substantial even for experienced traders and reporters (272).

1960-65 Cost pressures and a growing consumer aversion to fat (stimulated by newspaper stories concerning the health risks in eating too much saturated fat) caused a re-evaluation of grading standards. The highest grade carcases, Prime and Choice, were very fat in relation to consumer demand and also very variable in the yield of trimmed boneless retail cuts which determined the supermarkets' profit from the carcase.

  Investigations by U.S.D.A. (for example, 288) led to the development of dual grading, whereby two separate grades would be attached to the carcase: one similar to the previous grade and with the same names, based essentially on quality but also involving conformation; and another based on the predicted yield of trimmed boneless retail cuts from the round, loin, rib and chuck (the highest priced parts). The original intention was that the quality grade would always be accompanied by a yield grade (hence the name 'dual grading') but, due to opposition of packers and producers of pure-bred beef cattle, yield grade was treated as a separate issue.

1965 Following a period in which yield grading was offered to the industry on a pilot basis, some modifications were made and the revisions incorporated in the official grade standards and offered as an alternative to, or in addition to, quality grading (371). As with quality grading, yield grading required that carcases be cut to reveal the *M. longissimus* cross-section. Although yield grades are defined in terms of objective measurements of *M. longissimus* area, the thickness of fat over it and carcase weight in combination with KKCF percentage, graders are trained to assess all features by eye to provide a subjective estimate of yield.

  In practice, the procedure is to determine a provisional yield grade from the fat thickness (adjusted by eye for unusual fat distribution across the carcase), to adjust this for carcase weight variations from 600 lb, then for estimated KKCF yield, and then for estimated *M. longissimus* area. Although calculated to one decimal place, the figure is always rounded down to provide the yield grade.

  The yield grades are defined as follows:

Grade	Boneless closely trimmed retail cuts from the round, loin, rib and chuck as a percentage of carcase weight
1	52.3 +
2	50.0-52.3
3	47.7-50.0
4	45.4-47.7
5	Below 45.4

These are estimated from the equation (288):

Yield of cuts = 51.34
  − 5.78 (fat thickness, inches)
  − 0.46 (KKCF percentage)
  + 0.74 (area of *M. longissimus*, sq. in)
  − 0.0093 (carcase weight, lb).

1968 Some 15 per cent of graded beef was yield graded, although most of this was in the Choice quality grade favoured by the supermarket chains. The proportion of graded beef falling into the various grades does not reflect the proportions occurring in the population of beef animals. Packers indicate which carcases they wish graded and, subsequently, which they wish stamped with the grade name, their purpose being essentially to pick out the higher yielding Choice grade animals and to get them marked as such.

The 1960s saw a spate of reports on the extent of eating quality variations within and between the beef grades − particularly the key grades, Choice and Good. These tended to show wide variations within grades and only small differences between adjacent grades in average meat quality (in the sense of taste panel judgements and shear force values). They also caused surprise by showing a high degree of acceptance of beef even at the lower end of the Good grade. Nevertheless, the variability was such that the percentage of poorly accepted steaks in particular, was greater in the lower half of the Good grade and there did tend to be more consistency among steaks from carcases in the upper half of the Choice grade (325).

1973 The percentage of beef graded had increased to 57.5 per cent. Information on the distribution of carcases of 'fed' beef (that is cattle finished on high-energy rations) was published by Abraham (2). He showed that at this time, an estimated 97 per cent of beef eligible for the Choice grade was so graded and marked, whereas only 25 per cent of the beef eligible for Good grade was graded. Within the Choice grade, 22 per cent of the beef carcasses would have been yield graded 1 or 2. Overall, 12 per cent of beef graded would have been Choice 1 or Choice 2.

1973 Young bulls were separately graded for the first time. The confusing name 'bullock' was chosen to distinguish them from mature bulls, a factor which may have contributed to the slow adoption of young bull production in the U.S.A.

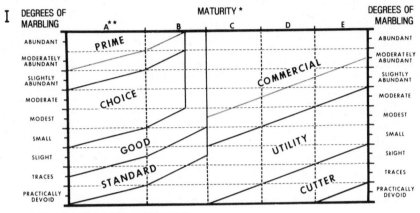

★ Maturity increases from left to right (A through E)
★★ The A maturity portion of the Figure is the only portion applicable to bullock carcasses.
.... Represents midpoint of Prime and Commercial grades.

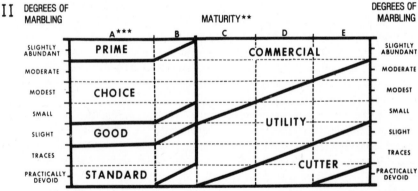

★ Assumes that firmness of lean is comparably developed with the degree of marbling and that the carcass is not a "dark cutter."
★★ Maturity increases from left to right (A through E).
★★★ The A maturity portion of the Figure is the only portion applicable to bullock carcasses.

Fig. 13.1 Comparison of the marbling and maturity relationship applying in the official U.S.D.A. grade standards: I, in effect 1965-75, II, in effect from 1976 (2)

1976 After a prolonged debate (and several court injunctions), the grade standards were again changed to require less marbling and to remove the emphasis on degrees of maturity in younger cattle. The relationship between marbling, maturity and quality in the 1965 and 1976 schemes is illustrated in fig. 13.1.

Conformation was at last eliminated as a quality grade factor. And the requirement that whenever a carcase is graded both the yield grade and the quality grade should be applied and marked, was finally achieved. The two opposing camps in the bitter argument that preceeded this change were made up as follows:

First, those in favour of change were:

(a) consumer activists who believed consumption of high levels of saturated fats was bad for the health of Americans, and who believed that feeding high levels of corn to cattle to achieve the high marbling required was immoral in a world where many were starving;

(b) meat scientists who increasingly doubted the contribution made by marbling to eating quality, stressed the advantages in efficiency in reducing the finish requirements, and who insisted that conformation made no contribution to eating quality, and a minimal contribution to yield estimation;

(c) breeders and feeders of dairy-type cattle, and of the 'exotic' breeds recently imported from continental Europe, who found difficulty in getting cattle into the Choice grade — in the former case because of the conformation requirement, and in the latter because of the marbling requirement.

Those against change were:

(a) consumer representatives who believed that the proposed changes were a trade device to sell an inferior product under the Choice label;

(b) retailers and restaurateurs who believed the variability of the beef they sold and consumer complaints would be increased (watering down the Choice grade to the point where it had no meaning);

(c) breeders and feeders of traditional beef-type cattle who naturally wanted to keep beef from other breeds and crosses out of the most desirable grades, in many cases genuinely believing it to be an inferior product.

Much of the debate was about the marbling requirement and eating quality, but the proposal to require yield grade always to accompany quality grade (and so be marked on all graded carcases) was considered by some to be the most significant for the industry's economics (321). (Packers objected to any degree of compulsion and, in any case, the requirement would add to their costs).

The yield grading formula came under some criticism as information accumulated. In particular, attention was drawn to the loss of information through subjective application by graders rather than by rigid adherence to the measurement requirements. There was also criticism of the amount of fat allowed on the trimmed retail cuts in defining saleable beef yield. One school suggested that marbling would be beneficial in the prediction of yield grades, replacing carcase weight and KKCF percentage, presumably because it might provide a better estimate of carcase fatness than one fat thickness measurement could (193).

The changing breed mix was a factor that might lead to a need to change the method of prediction; some results (for example, 85) led the U.S.D.A. to review its procedures. However, Abraham (1) reported that no basis for change had so far been found; while weight added little to the predictive value of the yield grade equation, the procedure for adjusting fat thickness according to a visual appraisal of fat distribution was entirely justified.

1976-78 Clearly the changes implemented substantially affected the make-up of the Choice and Good grades (2). Restaurateurs and their suppliers continued to insist that the new Choice grade was more variable and that the change had led to an increase in consumer complaints. Further, they argued that feeders carry cattle only to the bottom of the grade since to go further adds costs with no improvement in price per 100 lb live weight. So, even if they introduced into their own specifications a division of the Choice grade (as they have done), supplies of the top half of the new grade were difficult to obtain in quantity. Attention to ageing and other forms of ensuring greater consistency in tenderness (needle-tenderisation, for example) was said to have increased to correct the adverse effects of the grade change.

In total contrast to this view, Campion and Harrison (53) carried out taste panel studies on 500 carcases of mixed breed distribution and could find no difference in the eating characteristics of rib steaks from carcases in a particular grade determined under the 1965 and 1976 systems. They claimed, '. . . consumers will not get lower quality for their money by buying Choice grade beef'. From an economic analysis, moreover, Nelson (290) found that the demand for beef overall, or for Choice grade specifically, had not been damaged. Price differentials between quality and yield grade combinations had widened, consistent with the aims of the change. Meat scientists also felt that no harm had been done; indeed it was seen as a step in a direction which should be continued (59).

1978 Procedural changes in carcase grading were proposed by the new administration in Washington. This new thinking was much influenced by consumer activists introduced into the leadership of the U.S.D.A. and aimed at minimising the possibility of fraud, improving information for consumers and operating efficiency. The most controversial of the proposals was seen as an attempt to achieve mandatory grading by the back door; the suggestion was that carcases not presented for grading would have to be marked 'U.S. ungraded'. The proposals were described at a public hearing as 'illegal, conflicting, demeaning, confusing, arbitrary, capricious, costly, wasteful, misleading and unwise . . .' (14), confirming that the stormy history of beef grading in the States was as alive as ever.

1979 The 1978 plans were withdrawn and replaced by new proposals that clarified the procedural changes, omitting any reference to the compulsory marking of ungraded beef. Despite packers' concern that the seemingly innocuous changes proposed would affect operations and costs considerably, the changes were, in most respects, made by the U.S.D.A. in 1980. Proposals to alter the grade names for beef to facilitate a common food grading structure were fiercely resisted by the trade.

1980-81 Following this preoccupation with detail, recent thinking about beef grading in the United States has been of a much more radical nature, summed up in the following quotation (349):

If the purpose of beef grades and of a beef quality grading system is to provide the American consumer with a means of purchasing the quality of beef desired, but if the present grades do not do this with a high degree of accuracy, then the salient question is — why guess what the palatability might be, when we can better assure what it will be?

To make effective use of the technology developed over the last twenty-five years, the requirements for a U.S. Choice grade might be:

(a) a basic minimal marbling/maturity combination;
(b) a 'certification' that the animal from which it was produced had been fed for a specified time on a ration of specified energy-density;
(c) a specified subcutaneous fat thickness;
(d) treatment with an appropriate pre- or post-*rigor* tenderisation technique.

Compliance by the packer with the technical factors would, it is suggested, make one full grade difference, in effect upgrading a carcase that would be Good on the basis of its marbling/maturity, into Choice. Support for these ideas or variations of them is current among meat scientists in the United States, causing nervousness among traders who believe the continuous dilution of the basic concept is damaging the demand for beef.

However, there has been some packer support for simplifications of this type. One has advocated a minimum of 140 'days on feed', 0.3 inches of fat, 'modest' marbling, and a yield grade of 3.9 or better, to achieve a composite Choice grade; and 109 'days on feed', 0.1 inches fat, a 'trace' of marbling and the same yield grade, defining Good grade, but with electrical stimulation or 10 days' cooler ageing moving a carcase from Good defined in this manner up to Choice (15).

What is needed in the view of the purveyors and restaurateurs, on the other hand, is a joint effort to do a better job of marketing the leaner, less costly product (i.e. the existing Good grade). Although certification of 'days on feed' has its attractions, it is probably impracticable particularly for cattle from hundreds of small feeders, so producers' organisations favour the introduction of a minimum fat thickness in conjunction with a further reduction in the marbling requirement for the Choice grade. The fat thickness is seen as an assurance that the animal has received a minimum amount of grain feeding and is coupled with a proposal to reject a carcase for the Choice grade based on a fat colour indicating the animal was grass-finished.

Like all subjective grading, the U.S.D.A. beef scheme has always had its criticisms of inaccuracy and lack of repeatability. The most recent and most extensive investigation involving over 5000 carcases, found that individual U.S.D.A. grader's quality grades deviated from that of a three-member expert review panel in 7.3 per cent of cases and it was felt that little could be done to further improve this figure (80). But the percentage error for yield grades was 11.6 per cent, and the authors considered this could be improved by more attention to the actual measurements, particularly in borderline cases. In both cases, there was a slight bias in favour of the plant.

It is our impression that the mechanics of this grading system have clearly become an obsession with many practitioners; the whole process of determining grades and making subtle alterations to the standards has acquired its own status and is its own justification, far beyond the predictive value of the indices. The grading system and the way it has become built into the industry's marketing and merchandising practices, appears to us to have restrained the introduction of breeds and feeding systems capable of reducing the cost per unit of lean beef produced.

There is, of course, another school of thought that the industry has been entirely right to resist such changes for as long as possible, since the American consumers' satisfaction with their beef could have been severely damaged and aggregate demand would have suffered. The independent observer has to say that there is a substantial body of research evidence against this last claim and little to support it. The increasingly wild ideas for modifications to the scheme, involving records of the animal's history and the carcase treatment, suggest that a major breakdown of the system might be near.

One final point: grading has always been applied to cold carcases. Any new system must surely accommodate major technological changes at the abattoir, such as hot boning. There is a good deal of interest in this technique, plus accumulating evidence that it could make a substantial contribution to increasing efficiency at the abattoir. But in the U.S.A. the major obstacle to its wider adoption is seen as the grading system (16), surely a clear example of the servant becoming the master.

Canada

The origins of beef grading in Canada also arise from the attempted resolution of a paradox. Consumers found difficulty in purchasing beef of assured eating quality, while the market failed to provide incentives to producers to increase production of the type of cattle considered likely to provide that assurance. The availability of a good deal of dairy by-product beef was said to be the difficulty (268).

So the industry collectively asked the Department of Agriculture to differentiate qualities of beef presented to them and to mark it accordingly. Marking of Red (Choice) and Blue (Good) beef carcases began in 1929, but was based on grading by meat packers' own staff under loose supervision. Packers were encouraged to use their own brand names, but where these incorporated the official designations their brand marks had to be approved. The quantity of branded beef grew until the war period when new arrangements were introduced, but so did dissatisfaction with the standard of grading.

Since 1947, all beef slaughtered at inspected plants has been graded in accordance with national grades by government staff at no direct cost to the user (256), although marking with the grade is carried out only at the packer's request. In practice, most of the top two grades, A and B, is branded while much of the third grade C is not. Carcases are divided into nine categories of sex, weight and breeding status and thereafter into grades taking age (by bone criteria), adequacy and completeness of fat cover, conformation and flesh characteristics into account. The criteria were designed to put well-fed well-bred beef-type cattle into the top grades and to relegate the predominant dairy-type into the third and fourth.

An additional grade (Standard) was introduced in 1958 after which the following grade percentages were achieved (268):

	1959 (%)	1962 (%)	1969 (%)
Canada Choice	28.0	32.0	42.0
Canada Good	17.0	14.9	20.5
Canada Standard	9.3	8.5	7.4
Canada Commercial	9.4	8.0	3.2
Canada Utility	21.3	20.3	} 26.9
Canada Manufacturing	14.9	16.2	

The percentages of the Red and Blue brands had increased appreciably to about 63 per cent (or 85 per cent of 'youthful' cattle).

Fredeen and Weiss (137) showed, from study of a large sample of carcases, that differences in area of *M. longissimus* between grades were negligible (despite the conformation criterion), but Good grade carcases had 25 per cent less fat cover over the eye muscle than those in the Choice grade. In Canada, as elsewhere, there was therefore a conflict between the need to increase lean meat yield (and so to decrease fat cover) to reduce waste and minimise cost, and the finish and conformation requirements of the grading standards which had their basis in 'quality' considerations. This conflict coupled with research on possible 'cutability' criteria (30) and measurement methods (181) eventually led to a revision of the grading system in 1972.

The new system amalgamated the quality and quantity dimensions into what the promotional literature described as 'the most precise and modern beef grading system in the world' designed to identify market demand to producers better and to enable the trade to meet consumer demands more precisely. The top grades, Canada A and Canada B, are divided into four classes (called A1 to A4, etc.) based on fat cover, measured after the carcase is 'knife-ribbed' — that is, cut open between the eleventh and twelfth ribs without sawing the bones; this also allows the grader to examine the lean meat of the *M. longissimus* (56). Canada C is for carcases of intermediate age and Canada D for cows, subdivided by muscling and quality. The ribbon brands incorporate information on both the grade and the fat classification. The range of fat measurements applicable in each grade are dependent on carcase weight (table 13.1).

Table 13.1 Level of fat thickness in inches on the surface exposed between the eleventh and twelfth rib ('the minimum point in the fourth quarter from the vertebrae along the longitudinal axis of the rib eye') for back fat class within the grades of Canada's beef grading system (56)

Warm carcase weight (lb)	Fat levels			
	Canada A			
300-499	0.20-0.30	0.31-0.50	0.51-0.70	over 0.70
500-699	0.20-0.40	0.41-0.60	0.61-0.80	over 0.80
700 and over	0.30-0.50	0.51-0.70	0.71-0.90	over 0.90
	Canada B			
300-499	0.10-0.30	0.31-0.50	0.51-0.70	over 0.70
500-699	0.10-0.40	0.41-0.60	0.61-0.80	over 0.80
700 and over	0.20-0.50	0.51-0.70	0.71-0.90	over 0.90

The criteria for Canada A include bright red lean colour, firm and fine-grained lean texture, a slight degree of marbling, white or slightly tinged fat colour, firm fat extending well over the carcase, and the muscling 'free from marked deficiency'.

The system combines all the desirable features of a modern beef grading scheme while retaining the essential merit of simplicity. Yield is predicted from weight and one fat measurement; conformation and marbling are included only as minimum requirements, but the elements of attractive appearance of the carcase and of the meat are not abandoned. Hawrysh and Berg (169) found that beef from grade A and from grade B1 was comparable in eating quality and all judged acceptable.

However, one aspect of the system has gone rather too fast for the trade; unofficially they have designated dairy-type beef (that is, carcases with dairy-type conformation) within the Canada A1 grade as A1X and established a price differential against this inferior conformation.

A further interesting feature of the grading service in Canada is that a more detailed carcase report will be provided to producers and others who request it. The method is for special tags to be purchased by interested owners; once the tag is fitted, and provided it is not lost, it indicates to the grader at the abattoir that a detailed carcase report is required. Meat inspectors transfer the tags to plastic bags on the dressing-line and affix these to the carcases; the grader completes the report and returns it to his headquarters who forward it to the tag owner. Such a system would only work, of course, in a situation where graders were present at all abattoirs of significance and where the whole distribution chain was sympathetic to its purpose so leaving the tags intact.

Australia

The long-standing export grades for beef laid down by the government in Australia (under the advice of the Australian Meat Board or, more recently, the Australian Livestock and Meat Corporation) differentiate three qualities of carcase by reference to ten separate characteristics: sex, youthfulness, carcase weight, conformation, colour, freedom from blemishes, freedom from bruises (both deep-seated and superficial), internal and external fat development and distribution.

References to colour, blemishes, bruises and a minimal fat cover to 'reasonably protect the underlying muscle while the hindquarter (or forequarter) is being frozen, stored and transported' are evidence of the fact that the grades are drawn up to ensure maximum satisfaction with this important product of Australia (for many years the world's largest beef exporter) among the trade buyers in the importing countries. Originally the U.K. dominated the trade, but more recently as many as 160 other countries have taken Australian beef in quarter, cut or boxed boneless form.

However, while such a method provides a good system for selecting a 'top grade' for those buyers to whom it was originally aimed, producers are not informed how their cattle perform on each individual criterion, nor does it deal effectively with product specification for more diversified markets. Further, being essentially subjective, not only in the assessment of the individual criteria but in their amalgamation and the weighting implicitly applied, standardisation is particularly difficult from plant to plant, season to season, and year to year, especially when applied by the staff of the abattoir — an interested party in the purchase of the cattle and the sale of the meat.

From 1950 to 1970, scientists in Australia pressed for major modifications in the approach with two particular objectives in mind:

(a) replacement, as far as possible, of subjective grading with objective methods more easily standardised and controlled;
(b) breakdown of composite grades into descriptive classes to allow a more systematic approach to the improvement of product quality.

Yeates (397) proposed a quantitative definition of cattle carcases to embrace objective criteria for conformation, finish and 'quality' (involving colour of fat, firmness of fat, marbling and lean meat colour). The methods proposed were more suited to the judging of carcase competitions than to commercial grading, but the proposed method did introduce for the first time the 'fleshing index'. This is the ratio of carcase weight to carcase length and Yeates found it was related to subjectively assessed carcase conformation. He established the average relationships between weight and length and argued that the extent to which the weight of a carcase exceeded or fell short of the average weight for its length was a measure of its 'fleshing'. A slide-rule was developed to facilitate the calculations.

Recognising that the lean fraction of the total flesh was more important than the fat, Yeates (398) described how his index could be adjusted for fatness, but using a measure that could only be established after quartering at the tenth rib. A particular ratio of lean to fat thickness at this point was considered to be the upper limit of acceptable fatness at that time; ratios lower than this lowered the fleshing index by an amount said to be the weight of excess fat.

In a further refinement, Yeates (399) proposed grades whereby the required fleshing index for a particular grade was increased as the age increased, the rationale being that 'a high fleshing index in an animal not overfat is indicative of superior growth. This can only be obtained in a healthy, well nourished animal of suitable breeding; and these are all the ingredients of quality.'

Given this adjustment for fatness, the index was in effect estimating the yield of deboned cuts, trimmed to a constant level of fatness. However, Yeates assumed that conformation was closely related to meat yield and concentrated on the index as a predictor of conformation; he did not publish any evidence to justify the use of the index as a direct predictor of meat yield. In fact, as we have seen, much data collected since in other countries indicates a poor relationship in young well grown cattle. There may be a rather better basis for a relationship in Australian cattle populations, which include a wide range of ages and many animals that have suffered periods of under-nutrition followed by re-alimentation. Although the index was eventually incorporated, with a different method of fat adjustment, in the Meat Board's recommended Beef Carcase Appraisal System (19) it never had an influence on official grading methods.

The approach promoted by Charles (65, 66) was fundamentally different. He argued that beef production had been seriously misdirected by the subjective grading system with inadequate indices of expected eating quality and reliance on conformation as an index of the proportion of high to low valued cuts.

Basing his arguments on the recent work of Butterfield (49), he proposed a practical commercial classification system based on sex, age, carcase weight and the thickness of fat over the *M. longissimus* at the tenth or twelfth rib. He emphasised that the combination of these four factors was necessary to provide an adequate beef carcase description under Australian conditions, and that the trade specification for any particular market could be spelled out in these terms (68).

The Board began to study the Charles system in the late sixties, and following a committee report initiated practical investigations (44). Since then, the Australian workers have been preoccupied with the problems of achieving consistent application in commercial plants, with particular reference to alternative fat measuring equipment (100), their automation and the automatic recording of all items of the carcase description on tickets and producer records (258). Many problems have been encountered, not only with the equipment but also from the damage to the fat layer caused by mechanical methods of hide removal.

More recently, the state governments have pressed ahead with the development of beef carcase classification based on manual fat measurement with rather greater success. Because of the importance of conformation to buyers in the domestic market, the commercial application has included length per unit weight in some plants. Some state Livestock Market Reporting Services have been allied to the new classification approach, the reporters being required to estimate fatness within specified ranges which vary for different sex/age groups.

The ability of the classifications to specify trade requirements, the other uses of beef carcase classification in marketing, and its potential in cost-benefit terms have been the subject of intensive study (34, 352).

New Zealand

Although New Zealand has been a substantial exporter of beef, this has been predominantly in the form of boxed boneless beef for manufacturing purposes, plus some boneless cuts mostly frozen but some chilled. Procurement of beef cattle by freezing works is universally on a deadweight basis, with payment to producers based on grades laid down by, and whose application is supervised by, the New Zealand Meat Producers' Board.

Table 13.2 describes the grades for steers and heifers operating in the late 1970s and the distribution of carcases across grades in 1978/79. Similar classes exist for cow carcases. The carcases are graded hot and intact; graders may cut the fat at the measurement point to obtain a measure of fat thickness in borderline cases, but according to Barton (23) this is seldom done. Conformation is less important in this system than in the earlier more conventional approach. This change followed the report by MacIntyre and others (262) analysing beef grading systems used elsewhere and the scientific evidence on the relation of conformation to yield and eating quality.

South Africa

Hirzel (176), describing the South African controlled market procedure of which carcase grades formed an integral part, claimed that it had had a considerable benefit to farmers in teaching quality differentiation and had stimulated both demand and production of better beef.

Revised regulations promulgated in 1981, applying to the grading and roller marking which remains mandatory in certain areas, set out the first official

Table 13.2 New Zealand beef carcase grades for steers and heifers in 1978/79 and the distribution of carcases between grades (23, 295)

		Steers (%)	Heifers (%)
M	Fat depth over *M. longissimus* at 12th rib less than 1 mm (Also yellow fat and carcases under 160 kg)	5	15
L	Fat depth 1-3 mm		
	Thickly muscled L1	6	5
	Less well muscled L2	3	2
	(Subdivided into four weight ranges)		
P1	Fat depth 4-12 mm		
	Thickly muscled	66	49
	(Four weight ranges)		
G	Fat depth 13-18 mm		
	Thickly muscled	19	26
	(Four weight ranges)		
T	Fat depth 19-24 mm	2	2
E	Fat depth 25 mm or more	<1	<1

scheme to adopt a policy of defining grades in the terms of a classification scheme (323).

The classes for beef carcases are given in table 13.3. Grade is then defined within age groups. Fig. 13.2 shows how the main grades, Super A, A1 and A2, are defined in age group A.

Within the age group B, grades Prime B, B1 and B2 are similarly defined and appropriate definitions are given for the lower grades. The measurements for fatness and conformation (based on the length per unit weight criterion developed in Australia) are provided as guidelines only and will presumably not be applied to all carcases. Such measurements may be of value in borderline cases, but more importantly as a basis for ensuring that individual grader's judgements are unbiased.

Zimbabwe

Cattle in what was formerly Rhodesia have to be sold through an official agency and are priced according to classification. Table 13.4 shows the price differentials that were applied at the beginning of 1980. Clearly, with such wide price differentials, enforced by regulation, the incentive towards improvement should be very considerable. A table is provided in the regulations to convert length and weight into the fleshing class.

Table 13.3 The definitions of the classes used in the South African regulations (323) as a basis for defining beef carcase grades

Characteristic	Code	Description	Guideline
Age	A	0 teeth	—
	B	1-6 teeth	—
	C	7 and more teeth	—
Fatness (uniformity is taken into account)	1	Very lean	Less than 1 mm
	2	Lean	1-3 mm
	3	Medium	3.1-5 mm
	4	Fat	5.1-7 mm
	5	Slightly over-fat	7.1-10 mm
	6	Excessively over-fat	More than 10 mm
Conformation	1	Emaciated	Less than 1.30 kg per cm carcase length
	2	Flat	1.30-1.55 kg per cm carcase length
	3	Medium	1.56-1.80 kg per cm carcase length
	4	Round	1.81-2.05 kg per cm carcase length
	5	Very round	More than 2.05 kg per cm carcase length
Sex	1	Heifer	—
	2	Ox	—
	3	Cow	—
	4	Bull	—
Internal fat	1	Little	Less than 1.5% of carcase weight
	2	Medium	1.5-3.3% of carcase weight
	3	Excessive	More than 3.3% of carcase weight

South America

The development of the export of chilled beef from Argentina to Europe led the major trading companies to introduce house-grading systems, differentiating beef carcases according to conformation, finish, quality and, in some cases, weight ranges.

When the Argentine government took over control of the meat trade in that country, they introduced a common grading system in 1961, modified in 1973. The grades were named after the controlling body, the JUNTA, with some

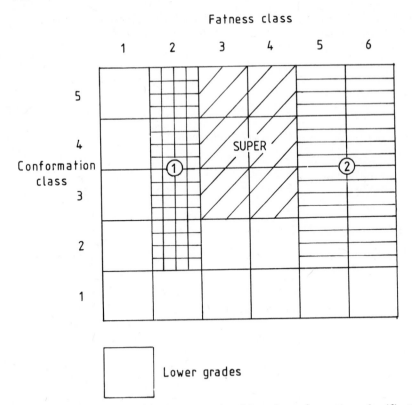

Fig. 13.2 The relationship between the fat and conformation classifications specified in the South African beef carcase grading scheme and the official grades for beef carcases in age code A (no permanent incisors) (323)

subdivisions. This was a mixed system, based on type (with definitions spelled out for each individual part of the carcase), with subsidiary fat classifications and age/weight requirements in some grades (189).

Brazil, however, has followed European developments and introduced a classification scheme based on category (twelve divisions), conformation (six divisions which are, following the growing fashion, named BRASIL) and fatness (five divisions).

Here, the fat classification is linked to a measurement of fat thickness: class 1 corresponding to no fat; class 2, 1-2 mm; class 3, 2-5 mm; class 4, 5-10 mm; and class 5, over 10 mm. The last is described as 'excessive' and it is of interest to contrast this scale with those given above for South Africa, Canada and New Zealand, reflecting as they do the variations in local market demand.

The conformation classes are described by reference to profiles. For example, B is 'hyperconvex' and S 'rectilinear' (i.e. profiles are on the whole straight). From published data the Brazilian cattle population — said to have the greatest potential for expansion anywhere in the world — appears to be concentrated well towards the bottom of this conformation scale (13).

Table 13.4 The terms of the beef carcase classification procedure laid down by the Cold Storage Commission of Rhodesia (74) and price differentials applying to the week of 1 January 1980

			Price or price differential (cents per kg carcase weight)	Price or price differential as a % of top price
Age	Up to 2 teeth		81	100
	4-6 teeth		80	99
	Full mouth		72	89
	Full mouth (aged)		68	84
Fleshing	A	(very well fleshed)	+17	+21
	B		+15	+19
	C		+ 8	+10
	D		− 3	− 4
	E	(very poorly fleshed)	− 6	− 7
Fat Cover	1	(uniform and fairly well covered)	+ 6	+ 7
	2	(lacking uniformity or amount)	+ 4	+ 5
	3	(little or no sub-fat)	− 2	− 2
	9	(excessive fat)	− 5	− 6

International methods

From 1961 to 1965, the Organisation for Economic Co-operation and Development (O.E.C.D.) attempted to draft an 'International System for the Identification of Beef, Veal and Pork Carcases' but agreement between member countries proved difficult to achieve and the systems developed were far too complicated to stand any chance of commercial use.

For example, the draft report includes the following as an example:

The coded statement 4/5/5/70/3/3/2/1/8-3/5/3 signifies a hind-quarter cut between 8th and 9th rib from a 5 to 8 year old cow, weighing 70 kg, with a straight profile, medium bone yield, fat 1 to 3mm thick, KKCF 1–2% of carcase weight, *M. longissimus* area 50-55 sq cm, fair marbling, meat colour red and fat colour white.

Although the work was taken over by the F.A.O./W.H.O Codex Alimentarius Committee on Meat, and some simplification was achieved (73, 332), member governments have not given the work any great encouragement and its reports lie unused.

More significant has been the development of common European schemes at both scientific and commercial levels. This began with a study by experts from each of the six original members of the E.E.C. who made one of the few systematic attempts to compare different grading methods between countries. In order to compare live grading standards operating in the different countries, they first agreed a uniform carcase description method (381).

This group toured some member countries and examined samples of cattle at a number of livestock markets in each. The cattle, having been graded alive by the method of the country (which in some cases varied from market to market) were followed through to carcase assessment, based on points for muscular and fat development, some on a whole side basis, some derived after carcase cutting. The results were combined into an index, which ranged from the highest value for exceptional cattle in the Paris market, to the lowest for manufacturing cows in the same market. The study showed much less variation between the various grades when applied to German cattle than to those in French and Belgian markets, primarily due to the breed mix.

But the study also confirmed the close relation in these particular cattle between carcase weight and the grade awarded to them alive. Indeed, many more formalised live cattle grading systems (but not that of the U.S.A.) feature a minimum estimated killing-out percentage for each grade, generally accompanied by the presumption that better killing-out percentage is related to the muscular development of the animal and indicative of high meat to bone ratio.

Shortly afterwards, the E.A.A.P. set up a working group from a wider circle of countries to devise a method of common carcase description for use in research on beef production and improvement. This working group has concentrated on achieving comparability in judgements of carcase fatness and shape by means of clear definitions of what is being assessed (with particular reference to the distinctions between muscularity, fleshiness and conformation), and by establishing photographic reference standards for the 15-point scales for both fat covering and fleshiness (5 basic classes, subdivided with −, 0 and +).

Following the publication of the agreed method (98), experts from the various countries involved have participated in training and standardisation sessions. The application of the 'fleshiness' assessment (thickness of muscle plus intermuscular fat relative to dimensions of skeleton) creates problems with cattle carcases which are well covered with subcutaneous fat. De Boer (95) reported that very fat carcases scored for fleshiness before and after removal of subcutaneous fat, resulted in a score two subclasses lower than that which would have been awarded for 'conformation' (thickness of muscle, intermuscular and subcutaneous fat relative to dimensions of skeleton). De Boer has argued that fleshiness defined in this way does relate to variations in lean, fat and bone proportions at a given level of fat covering and has presented figures for the relative importance of the two criteria in predicting composition, based on dissection data accumulated at the Schoonoord Institute (96).

Of particular interest is the attempt to disentangle the effect of carcase weight from that of size (linear dimensions) on the relationships between fleshing, fat cover and carcase composition (see fig. 13.3).

Muscle in carcase (%)

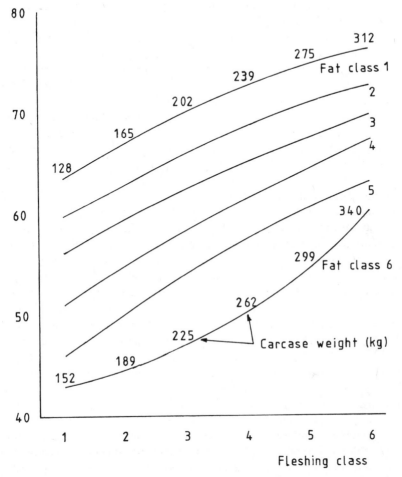

Fig. 13.3 Relationship of fat cover class and fleshing class, among Dutch beef carcases of the same size (124 cm long, 37 cm deep), to carcase muscle content and to carcase weight (96)

Given this background work by scientists in the E.E.C. member countries (plus others), the development of a common classification scheme for the market management purposes of the E.E.C.'s Common Agricultural Policy should have been greatly facilitated. Harrington (163) analysed the problems in detail and proposed the E.A.A.P. system as the most obvious starting point for an E.E.C. scheme, bearing in mind the many problems of embracing the range of European cattle.

Unfortunately, by the time the E.E.C. project began (1979), several member states had well-established systems of their own. No one likes to change a working system, particularly as the E.E.C. needed a scheme for institutional purposes only (price reporting and intervention buying) whereas the member countries schemes had different objectives, for example their aim was to facilitate trade or to assist in informing producers of performance against market requirements.

Before examining the progress on the E.E.C. scheme, we shall refer to the methods that had already been developed in the major member states.

France

Dumont (105) laid the foundation for the development of beef carcase classification in France. He surveyed a large number of French livestock markets where various grade designations were used, following animals through to the abattoir. There were discrepancies between markets in the interpretations of the grade descriptions used, but he was able to show relations between indices of carcase muscling and fatness and live market valuations.

Various grading systems were used for price reporting purposes in both livestock and carcase meat markets. The organisation Société Interprofessionnelle du Bétail et des Viandes (S.I.B.E.V.) had the difficult task of maintaining consistency of application for price reporting purposes. In the early 1950s, they supplemented the so-called Catalogue FRANCE, used for live cattle price reports, with similar carcase descriptions. F corresponded to excellent conformation and E to the poorest cow. Older cattle (*Gros Bovins*) had a separate system to that for younger cattle (*Jeunes Bovins*), which are predominantly young bulls. Conformation variations are more easily distinguished on French cattle since they are less frequently distorted by fat deposition; nevertheless each class covered a wide range.

From 1974, this system was applied to an increasing proportion of beef carcases, the conformation classification being supplemented with fat classification from 1, very lean, to 5, very fat. The promotion and supervision of this scheme was eventually taken over by a new body with wider responsibilities, O.N.I.B.E.V., who changed the notation from FRANCE to EUROPA with the obvious intention of encouraging the scheme for wider use throughout the E.E.C. (360). The change of nomenclature was also made in the live market price reports in 1978.

At this time the classifications appeared to be little used in trading; indeed the translation of class names from A to R, E to A and F to E could only have been achieved without total confusion if practical use was minimal. While marking of carcases with the classifications became theoretically mandatory in 1974, observation suggests that application by the trade remains patchy and, where applied, little care is sometimes exercised in classification because of lack of trade interest. Indeed, at one stage, some traders appeared to seek to discredit the classifications by careless application. Some producer co-operatives, however, have used the scheme as the basis of deadweight purchase of finished cattle from their members.

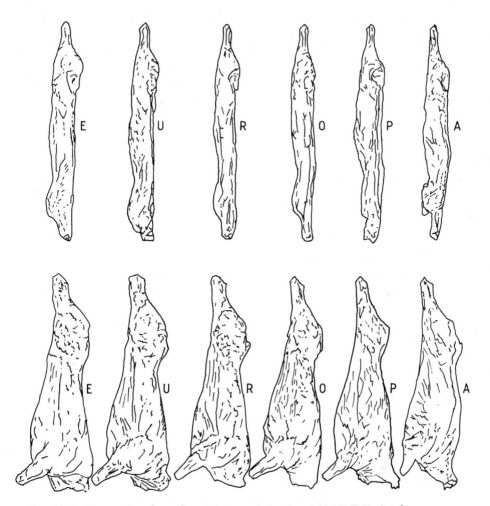

Fig. 13.4 The scale of conformation used in the O.N.I.B.E.V. beef carcase classification scheme (298)

While the French gravitated to the concept of a two-way grid for commercial classification about the same time as the idea was introduced in Great Britain (see below), their approach to the definition of conformation and fatness has been somewhat different. While photographs have been used to illustrate the conformation classes (outlines shown in fig. 13.4), there have been in addition extensive written descriptions (298) referring to the muscular development of individual parts and cuts, and utilising the concept of muscular 'profiles' (179). Fat class is defined in words but without any underlying objective basis of ranges of fat content or fat thickness.

An estimated distribution of French beef carcases classified according to the O.N.I.B.E.V. scheme is given in table 13.5; the shape of this distribution is of

Table 13.5 Estimated percentage of beef carcases in each fat and conformation class of the French O.N.I.B.E.V. beef carcase classification scheme (353)

Conformation Class	Fat class				
	1	2	3	4	5
E	0.5	2.0	0.5	—	—
U	—	3.5	9.5	3.0	—
R	—	5.0	17.5	12.0	1.0
O	—	3.0	14.0	15.5	1.0
P	0.5	2.0	5.5	1.5	0.5
A	0.5	1.0	0.5	—	—

interest and in contrast to the British distribution (see fig. 13.11). Despite the severe discrimination against fat in the French market, discounts against fat class 5 (compared with the average fat class 3) are of the order of 8 per cent, compared with a range of 40 per cent in price/kg between conformation classes U and A (353).

These figures relate to cows, which constitute about a third of the beef kill in France; it is of interest that at the same fatness and conformation, there is a very small price differential against cow carcases compared with steers and heifers (107).

West Germany

Grades for live slaughter cattle (steers, heifers, young bulls, older bulls and cows) and calves have been laid down since 1951 for price reporting purposes (376). Official carcase grades were laid down in 1969 to allow for a better organised meat market, to relate price quotations to slaughter value, to allow payment to producers to be made on carcase weight and grade, and to encourage the re-orientation of production towards market requirements.

As with pigs, the regulations stipulate that beef carcases may only be traded if identified with the official grade in the form (for example): F/I/m — a heifer with good flesh development in the higher valued cuts with an average amount of fat.

The definitions of the categories (table 13.6) provide a good example of the use of subtle changes in the degree of ossification of the cartilages to indicate age changes (336). (Elsewhere, there has been a good deal of scepticism of the validity of this procedure, for example, 257).

Table 13.6 Definitions of the sex/age categories used in the German beef grading scheme (336)

Category	Designation	Distinguishing characteristics	
		General	Maturity of the slaughter animals
Veal	KA	Meat of cattle with carcase weight up to 150 kg	Shows veal properties
Young cattle meat	J	Female and castrated male cattle	Sacral vertebrae still distinctly separated by joint cartilage; spinous-process caps of lumbar and thoracic vertebrae cartilaginous
Steer meat	O	Castrated male cattle	Sacrum and spinous-process caps of lumbar and thoracic vertebrae and manubrium sterni in various stages of ossification
Heifer meat	F	Female cattle that have not yet calved	As for steer meat
Young cow meat	JK	Female cattle that have calved	Spinous-process caps of lumbar vertebrae and thoracic vertebrae situated in the direction of the tail ossified; spinous-process caps of thoracic vertebrae situated in the direction of the head up to three-quarters ossified; manubrium sterni more than half ossified
Very young cow	SK	Female cattle slaughtered after first calving	Sacral vertebrae completely fused; spinous-process caps of lumbar vertebrae ossified but still distinguishable from spinous processes; spinous-process caps of thoracic vertebrae situated in the direction of the head up to one quarter and of those in the direction of the tail approximately half ossified; manubrium sterni half ossified.
Cow meat	K	Female cattle that have calved	Ossification of the skeleton further advanced than in the category young cow meat

Table 13.6 *contd*

Category	Designation	Distinguishing characteristics	
		General	Maturity of the slaughter animals
Young bull meat	JB	Uncastrated male cattle	Sacral vertebrae fused, separate joints still visible; spinous-process caps of lumbar vertebrae in advanced state of ossification; they are still visibly distinct from the spinous processes; spinous-process caps of thoracic vertebrae situated in the direction of the tail show incipient ossification, while those situated towards the head are still purely cartilaginous; manubrium sterni either pure cartilage or with incipient ossification
Bull meat	B	Uncastrated male cattle	Ossification of the skeleton further advanced than in the category young bull meat

Within categories, the basic classification is by conformation (E, I, II or III) (defined as the degrees of fleshiness, particularly in the higher valued cuts), with fat classification (into g, m or s) but the requirements for these fat classes appear to differ to a degree between categories. The middle class for fatness, m, refers to average fatness for the category. So an m class heifer is fatter than an m young bull; indeed it is of similar fatness to an s young bull. Such an arrangement may not be inappropriate when interpreting the classification applied to a particular carcase, or to price offers or price reports, but clearly it creates difficulty for the classifier when faced with a moving line of carcases of mixed category.

Table 13.7 shows the information published about the composition of the carcases of different grades which recognises the inevitability of a high degree of overlap between classes in the composition of individual carcases.

Republic of Ireland

The export of beef, particularly to the U.K., but more recently to continental Europe and other markets, is of vital importance to the agricultural economy of Eire. Nevertheless, the ability of the export meat trade to exploit the potentials has been inhibited to a degree by the quality of the beef available, and the traditional methods of procuring cattle. These involve purchase of live cattle at fairs or more recently auctions, or by flat rate pricing on a carcase weight basis for cattle straight off the farm.

Table 13.7 Composition of carcases of each fat and conformation class in the German beef grading system (336)

| | | Fat class | | |
		g (%)	m (%)	s (%)
Carcase fat percentage		<10	10-20	>20
Conformation class				
E	L*	72-80	65-73	55-66
	B**	18-22	16-20	15-19
I	L	70-78	63-71	55-64
	B	20-24	18-22	17-21
II	L	68-76	61-69	53-62
	B	22-26	20-24	19-23
III		More than 26% bone		

* Carcase muscle content
** Carcase bone content

The need for accurate communication between the exporter and his markets and between the export abattoirs and their producer suppliers, was recognised when the Irish Minister for Agriculture in 1970 established a Technical Study Group. The classification scheme they recommended to improve beef marketing was used as the basis for specifying intervention grades when Eire joined the E.E.C. and began to implement the Common Agricultural Policy in 1973.

The system embraced cows as well as clean cattle and involved sex, age, conformation (with seven classes from the best conformation I, through R, E, L, A, N, to D, the worst cow) based on a subjective judgement (using photographic reference scales and the weight/length ratio to aid standardisation), and fat (with seven categories from the least fat, 1, to the most fat, 7) again subjectively assessed with the aid of photographic reference standards. The conformation and fatness judgements have been made independently. A repeatability of 80 per cent has been reported for individual classifiers with a similar figure for the individual's class against those awarded by a supervisor or national panel (318).

The classification scheme became mandatory in all export plants, the application being carried out and the costs of operation met by the Department of Agriculture; pass-back of the information to producers was also to be obligatory but plants could continue to determine their own basis of payment to producers. Clearly the hope has been that it would be used to define grades that are priced differentially (327).

Saleable meat percentage from beef carcases has been shown to relate to subjective classification in a large sample of Irish cattle varying in yield from 57 per cent to 79 per cent (330). Through its relation to bone content in this sample, conformation class had a contribution to make to the prediction of saleable meat yield, but it was less important than fatness, as might be expected since the Irish cattle population is nearer to that of Great Britain than to continental Europe.

Table 13.8 The average weight, conformation and fat class of French, Irish and U.K. beef pistolas on Rungis market, Paris, in relation to wholesale price achieved in French francs per kg (297)

	French average	C of V	Irish average	C of V	U.K. average	C of V
Weight (kg)	98.4	22	77.5	10	82.6	7
Conformation*	5.9	27	4.7	10	5.0	4
Fat	2.2	17	3.5	26	4.2	18
Price (FF/kg)	22.1	22	18.1	17	18.8	2

*   For conformation X = 8, I = 7, D = 1
** C of V = Coefficient of variation

This classification scheme (extended by the addition of an extreme conformation class X) was used to measure the differences between Irish and British exported pistolas and the equivalent French beef being handled by the same wholesalers on Rungis market in Paris, and to explain the price differentials (table 13.8). The conformation difference between the French and the Irish beef accounted for 71 per cent of the price difference (with weight 94 per cent) and fatness only 6 per cent of the difference. This was despite the relatively greater impact of fatness on meat yield within the Irish cattle population, confirming that under French conditions good conformation appears to have a market value over and above any differential justified by its contribution to yield differences.

Other European schemes

There are, of course, grading or classification schemes in operation in some other European countries. In Denmark, there is a scheme (238) used in determining payment to farmers for cattle sold by carcase weight direct to the slaughterhouse. These constitute about half of the total marketed. In the Netherlands, a very detailed classification by fat cover and fleshiness has been used as the basis for intervention buying (95).

For many years, the Swedish system was unique in being based on a scorecard system which weighted together assessments of fleshing and lean meat qualities, the latter being made by assessment of hot intact sides rather than cold quartered sides as in the U.S.A. (157). However, this method has now been changed to what is, in effect, separate classification of fleshing and fatness within six categories (346).

Great Britain

THE BACKGROUND

As this review of schemes around the world has shown, the classification scheme devised is likely to be influenced greatly by the kind of beef that is to be classified. The beef sold in British retail shops is predominantly steer and heifer beef — with about two steers to every heifer. A high proportion of the mature bull and cow beef is diverted to manufacturing uses.

Cow beef production forms the smallest proportion of the total indigenous production of any E.E.C. country, because a high proportion of the progeny are reared to finished cattle weights as opposed to veal. A second difference between production in Britain and in continental Europe is that the production of young bulls for beef is not yet well established despite the advantages in leanness and feed efficiency.

Table 13.9 Production of beef in Great Britain (based on numbers of animals) from dairy cows, beef cows and imported store cattle (average for period 1978-80) (Source: estimates by J.B. Kilkenny, M.L.C.)

	Dairy cows 3.2 million			Beef (suckler) cows 1.5 million		Store cattle imported from Ireland
	Calves		Cull cows	Calves	Cull cows	
	Beef crosses	Friesian and Holstein				
Percentage of all home-produced beef	20	24	16	26	8	6
Percentage of home-produced clean beef*	26	32	—	34	—	8

* Contribution of calves from dairy cows make up 64 per cent of home-bred kill.

In Britain, there is one beef cow in the breeding herd for every two dairy cows (table 13.9). Crossing of dairy cows with bulls of beef breeds is widely practised and a high proportion of the pure-bred and cross-bred calves from these dairy cows are reared to beef. Because of the need to generate replace-ments, a significant part of beef production is from steers of the dairy breeds, predominantly Friesian but with an increasing proportion of Holstein blood.

Table 13.10 Percentage of clean beef production in Great Britain according to breed type (Source: estimates by J.B. Kilkenny, M.L.C.)

	Breed type of cow			
	Friesian/ Holstein	Beef X Friesian	Other beef type	Others
Breed type of bull:				
Friesian/Holstein	28	–	–	2
Charolais and other Continental breeds	12	9	9	1
Hereford and Angus	22	3	11	1
Others	–	–	–	2

Table 13.10 gives estimates of how British beef production from clean cattle is made up according to breed type.

The typical beef production system brings cattle to slaughter at eighteen months of age, but the average age at slaughter is probably rather more than that, with the small number of intensively fed cattle killed at about one year of age being matched by a rather higher proportion killed at two years of age and more. The feeding of grass through grazing or conservation is the basis of most production systems. The average carcase weight of steers is about 265 kg (ex KKCF), and of heifers 220 kg, with the average percentage of fat in the carcase about 23 per cent, much higher than in most of continental Europe.

Beef is sold to the consumer trimmed almost entirely of fat in countries like France and Belgium. This is not the case in Britain where the consumer is prepared to accept quite a large amount of fat in the beef purchased. The average over all the carcase beef sold across the retail counter (mostly without bone) is probably about 15 per cent separable fat (see fig. 2.4). This is tradi-tional and is fostered by many meat traders who continue to encourage house-wives in the belief that this level of fatness is essential to ensure good eating qualities despite much scientific research to the contrary. Nevertheless, the consumers' aversion to fat (brought about by price increases and the associated greater consciousness of waste, preferences for slimming foods, fear of saturated fats, etc.) is undoubtedly increasing in Britain, and bringing with it a stronger trade preference for leaner cattle.

Various attempts to establish national *grading* schemes for beef in Britain have always failed. The predominant reason was undoubtedly that trade require-ments showed sufficient variation from place to place to make the idea of a single 'top grade', 'select quality' or whatever, untenable. No trader could tolerate being forced into the situation that the type of beef he found most profitable to sell, taking into account local demand and price relationships, was categorised by someone else as 'second grade' or indeed anything but the best − it was the 'best' for him.

The principle of classification, as opposed to grading, having been established for pigs, a prime duty given to the M.L.C. when set up (174) was to devise 'a standard method of describing as fully as practicable those characteristics of a carcase which are the principal features of interest to persons trading in live-stock and carcases . . .'.

THE SCHEME

The M.L.C.'s beef carcase classification scheme was devised so that it:

(a) achieved a sensible balance of simplicity and precision;
(b) was capable of being applied to hot carcases on the killing-line;
(c) was as 'objective' as possible;
(d) sorted carcases according to criteria of tangible economic significance when cutting them up and merchandising beef;
(e) was capable of being turned into buying grades or specifications, through which traders could spell out their individual requirements and attach prices to them, although the scheme itself was to be purely descriptive.

Given these requirements, potential items for inclusion in a classification scheme may be sorted and many eliminated (160). The latter include *M. longissimus* area, texture and colour of the lean meat, breed type, colour of fat. Some of these can be added to a buyer's individual specification without difficulty, and others would not in any case provide information to producers on which they could act.

Classification in these circumstances is inevitably based on weight, sex, age, fatness and shape, all of which can make some contribution to predicting variations in the characteristics of the meat, the quantity of saleable meat and its distribution through the carcase.

Carcase weight posed no great problems of definition in Great Britain, since there has been a common specification for weight laid down by the government for the purpose of various support schemes for many years, although a variation whereby carcases may be dressed ex KKCF was introduced. Similarly definitions of bull, steer, heifer and cow were in existence. Age was a new problem; assessment of the degree of ossification, bone colour and so on was rejected in favour of the relatively crude but adequate measure of physiological age provided by dentition. In the British situation, however, among clean cattle the only need is to separate out the older cattle with four or more permanent incisors from the predominantly young group with calf teeth or two teeth up.

Fatness classification can be made as complex or as simple as one wishes. To the retailer cutting up beef carcases, there are three aspects to the amount of fat in beef carcases (as opposed to its quality):

(a) How much has to be trimmed off to make the beef cuts saleable? (This is influenced by the distribution of external fat as well as the total amount.)
(b) How fat will the trimmed cuts appear? (That is, how much fat is there in places where the retailer cannot easily trim?)
(c) Does the carcase have the amount of fat to provide, in his opinion, the right 'quality'? (Scientists' claims that lean meat quality is unrelated to fatness over much of its range of variation are academic, as long as traders continue to express preferences for a type of meat they *want* to sell.)

Sorting of carcases by *fat percentage* was the selected approach. Total carcase fat percentage is related to the amount of fat trimmed off commercially within a particular cutting and trimming method (see fig. 2.4). Taken in conjunction with carcase weight, fat percentage is reasonably closely related to fat cover (that is, the actual thickness of the external fat layer which is the basis of the E.A.A.P. fat classification, 98), and to the fat that will appear between the muscles on cut surfaces. It is also quite adequate for describing fat status for quality purposes.

The classification problem, therefore, is to sort carcases on the killing-line into ranges of fat percentage. Classes were defined objectively by ranges of external fat percentage (90), but the classification on the basis of external fat percentage was estimated by eye with the aid of photographic standards.

The main argument in favour of objective fat classification, that is measurement as opposed to eye judgement, is the greater degree of standardisation that should be possible from place to place. Such greater standardisation will be a waste of time, however, if the measurements are poorly related to what one wants to know or if they do not put the carcases into what the trade considers to be a realistic order.

Moreover, the distribution of external fat across the beef carcase is so uneven and variable that reliance on measurement at one or two points will lead, in a proportion of cases, to a fat classification that is clearly wrong to the trade. As we have seen, most beef grading schemes around the world get round this by allowing the grader to modify the fat measurement if the fat is distributed across the carcase in an unusual way. In effect this brings one back to an eye judgement.

Whether objective measurement or subjective assessment of fatness is used, it is usually necessary to operate in a series of 'boxes', or ranges of fatness. The lines of division set between the fat classes are essentially arbitrary and can be the subject of a good deal of argument. The British system attempted to operate with five classes (two for very extreme carcases with the bulk of the commercial kill in the central three), but in operation it became necessary to make subdivisions. The scheme also allowed for exceptional fat distribution by the addition to the fat class number of a P for patchy, U for exceptional cod or udder fat development in relation to external fat, or K for excessive KKCF fat development in those carcases where it had not been removed.

The M.L.C. system has defined conformation as shape, that is the thickness of muscle plus fat in relation to the size of the skeleton, rather than the 'muscularity' or 'fleshiness' preferred in continental Europe where cattle are at generally lower levels of fatness. The photographic reference scales used by the M.L.C. for conformation therefore include silhouettes, to emphasise that no distinction is made between the contributions of fat and lean to thickness (273).

Again five basic classes were chosen, from class 5 (good beef-type shape) through to 1 (poor shape), although a Z (very poor shape) had to be added to make the necessary distinctions among dairy types.

The essence of the M.L.C. scheme, therefore, was classification first by an assessment of external fat development, followed by classification by shape. The two figures (fatness always first) gave the basic description and the scheme was represented by a two-way grid as shown in table 13.11, together with the distribution of classified carcases reported in 1981 (280).

Table 13.11 The grid used in the M.L.C. beef carcase classification scheme* together with the percentage distribution of classified carcases reported in 1981 (280)

	Fat class						Overall
	1 (Leanest)	2	3L	3H	4	5 (Fattest)	
Conformation class							
5 (Best)	–	<0.5	1.0	2.0	1.0	<0.5	5.0
4	–	2.0	7.0	6.5	2.0	<0.5	18.5
3	<0.5	7.5	22.0	13.0	3.0	<0.5	46.0
2	<0.5	6.0	10.0	4.5	1.0	–	22.0
1	0.5	3.0	2.5	1.0	<0.5	–	7.5
Z (Worst)	<0.5	<0.5	–	–	–	–	1.0
Overall	1.5	20.0	42.0	27.0	8.0	1.5	100.0

* This is the former terminology subsequently altered in 1981 (see table 13.14).

Extensive dissections and cutting tests have shown the relation between these classifications and carcase composition. Table 13.12 shows the relative effects of fat class and conformation class on saleable meat yield, based on a large mixed sample of beef carcases in the M.L.C. data bank. In the centre of the range, fat variation has an effect on yield approximately twice that of conformation. However, records of prices paid for cattle purchased by deadweight suggest that conformation is, nevertheless, valued more highly than leanness in the current state of the British market.

Table 13.12 Typical saleable meat yields (as a percentage of carcase weight) from beef carcases falling into the different cells of the M.L.C. beef carcase classification grid (278)*

		Fat class					
		1	2	3L	3H	4	5
	5			72.4			
	4			71.7			
	3	74	72	71.0	70	69	67
Conformation	2			70.3			
	1			69.6			
	Z			68.9			
Fat trim (as a percentage of carcase weight) for carcases of average conformation		7	9	12	14	16	20

* This is the former terminology subsequently altered in 1981 (see table 13.14).

The results of the application of this scheme to some 40-45 per cent of the clean cattle slaughtered in Great Britain over the years 1973-76, generated information about the variation of weight/fatness/conformation according to time period/sex/region (222). Trends in the percentages of carcases classified into particular classes have been detected (162); it is not clear whether these were due to changes in the cattle population or to a drift in the classification standard. Although of considerable interest to those devising carcase classification schemes (and to those trying to measure the long-term effects of livestock improvement), trends over time have less significance to the trade who are concerned with comparisons over short periods and are looking mainly for a high consistency of application from place to place at the same time.

MARKETING IMPLICATIONS
Carcase classification, particularly of beef, has long been controversial in British meat industry politics; the reasons for this, together with an analysis of classification as a marketing tool, have been discussed at length elsewhere (161, 162). The M.L.C. scheme, applied by M.L.C. staff, was available to abattoir operators

from 1973, initially at no cost, but from 1978 it attracted a small charge per carcase classified. The percentage of the total kill classified fell, then rose again, to 20 per cent by 1981.

A number of medium-sized abattoir operators in Britain have formally expressed their buying grades in classification terms, although in some cases the arrangement only applied to particular sellers such as producer groups. There is no doubt that other traders who did not publicly acknowledge any involvement with classification, have used it informally within their businesses, for example, as an aid to their own grading, or as an assistance in sorting and allocation, or to check on the performance of different livestock buyers.

In the larger firms, of course, there is frequently dissension within the firm. Some headquarters managements see considerable advantages in using classification to define their grades, not only for the reasons given above but also to achieve greater internal management control; but procurement and abattoir managers may see their flexibility and initiative reduced. The answer to these pressures, of course, is that flexibility in pricing can still be retained even if classification is used to describe the carcase. Fixing the product description and manipulating the price is better in terms of information flow, rather than maintaining the price and manipulating the standards, as so often happens in day-to-day trading.

The practical application of beef carcase classification would have undoubtedly achieved a major advance in Britain if relevant government departments (in particular the Ministry of Agriculture, Fisheries and Food) had agreed to use the language of classification to define the standards of acceptance or rejection for the various statutory schemes (Beef Premium or Intervention) which also involve weight, fatness and conformation.

One of their reasons for not doing this was that classification was not sufficiently accepted by the wholesale meat trade. Unfortunately this was a 'chicken and egg' situation, because the trade clearly needed the encouragement that would arise from seeing the government express their confidence in the scheme by using it. Certification standards for the support schemes as laid down, suffered from many of the disadvantages attributed to vague wholesalers' buying graders; however they did not suffer from the same disadvantages in practical application, because they have been applied by independent third parties, and are the subject of many demonstrations and a national standardisation effort.

Market requirements do vary. If they did not, then a classification scheme would not have been necessary, and British traders could have accepted a national grading scheme. The danger is that, if large numbers of individual traders were to express their varying requirements in classification terms, and these proved to be very different in detail, then producers might be more confused than enlightened, particularly when it comes to long-term livestock improvement as opposed to short-term marketing considerations. Ideally, a body like M.L.C. would put all the wholesalers' requirements together (weighted by the price differentials) and deduce an average pattern to provide livestock improvement targets. Unfortunately, the trade was slow to spell out its requirements in terms of buying grades and related price differentials.

For livestock improvement purposes, therefore, we are thrown back on a generalised analysis of what carcase improvement means. Despite differing market requirements, few traders would disagree that the average beef carcase could benefit from having less bone and less excess fat, better thickness of flesh, and being somewhat heavier. In classification terms, this means increasing the percentage of carcases falling into the top left-hand corner of the classification grid (table 13.11). Such a 'target group' is too wide to be a trading specification, but it is reasonable to expect that when wholesalers do define their own top grades, most will fall into the target area.

The question of who applies carcase classification in practice is contentious. There are three possibilities:

(a) the abattoir operator's staff, unsupervised from outside;
(b) the abattoir operator's staff, supervised by some independent body;
(c) an independent third party.

The fact that weight is an aspect of classification is important in Britain since weight authentication in deadweight sales has been a by-product of various support schemes for fifty years; such authentication has been a major factor in building confidence in deadweight selling. So in Britain there is a strong producer preference for the third option, but of course the final decision will depend on cost considerations. There is no doubt that many meat wholesalers in Britain have been nervous of becoming locked into using carcase classification, feeling that their freedom of negotiation would be weakened, if and when a significant charge was proposed in order to finance the scheme in total.

The only technical point in this issue is the value of and need for independent application. One school of thought is that to generate adequate producer confidence in, or trade reliance on, classifications applied at a distant abattoir, they should be made by someone who is separate from and has no interest in the transaction, rather than by the buyer or seller himself; even if the costs are somewhat higher, the additional cost is to be seen as a reasonable insurance premium.

Further, to achieve the necessary standardisation to enable comparisons to be made between classifications applied at different places, at different times and at different states of the market (as would be needed by, for example, a multiple retailer buying meat from several abattoirs), a common workforce with integrated training and standardisation programmes is considered necessary. Especially when subjective judgements are involved, such a procedure would be altogether more demanding and susceptible of control than would be possible if the independent body merely supervised abattoir staff. Checking eye judgement classifications made by abattoir staff might possibly be easier to achieve than would a check on weights or measurements; but if supervision in terms of the percentage of carcases covered is to be more than cursory or symbolic, it is likely to have a total cost (the overt independent supervision cost plus the covert abattoir staff time costs) comparable with the cost of full independent application.

E.E.C.

The management of the beef market within the E.E.C. is achieved by a network of regulations concerning levies on beef imported into the Community, restitution payments on beef exported from it, and various support buying or premium (that is, deficiency payments) schemes in the individual member countries. On a day-to-day basis, decisions on these various market support arrangements are made by a Beef Management Committee of civil servants from member states. This committee receives information on prices prevailing in each member state and has to agree the implementation of appropriate market report measures in response to price movements.

Clearly the price reporting system is crucial to the efficient management of the market, as are the definitions of the types of beef taken into intervention in each state. For many years, price reports were for live cattle, the particular methods of collection and the categories embraced varying from country to country, as did the definitions of beef accepted into intervention. Various reports on the efficiency of the market management all argued for common price reporting methods (based on prices paid by abattoirs for cattle on a carcase weight basis) and for intervention across the Community to apply to the same classes of cattle. For these aims to be achieved, a common carcase classification system was seen to be essential.

The methods used in the countries of the E.E.C. for intervention buying have been compared (334) in an attempt to provide a basis for discussions about common systems. There had been a coming together of principle (separate classifications of fat and fleshiness, or conformation), but wide variations remained in the divisions applied across the spectrum of variation in these two characteristics.

Discussion began in 1979, culminating in the publication of Council Regulation 1208/81 giving the basis of the agreed scheme, followed by Commission Regulation 2930/81 giving more detailed definitions (set out in table 13.13).

In summary, the scheme is made up as follows:

(a) Separate classification of conformation and fat cover, in both cases in five classes (E, U, R, O and P for conformation, 1 to 5 for fat cover).
(b) In describing carcases, the conformation classification will be given first. This is in contrast to M.L.C. practice in Britain, where fatness variations have been quoted first because they have a bigger effect on carcase composition and saleable meat yield than do shape variations.
(c) For domestic purposes, member states may subdivide the basic classes.
(d) Conformation is defined by reference to 'profiles', with the muscular development criterion being an optional extra element (reflecting the different approaches to shape or muscularity assessment in Britain and

Table 13.13 The definitions of the classes of the E.E.C. beef carcase classification scheme as set out in Council Regulation 1208/81 and Commission Regulation 2930/81

Class	Description	Additional provisions
Conformation	Development of carcase profiles, in particular the essential parts (round, back, shoulder)	
E Excellent	All profiles convex to superconvex; exceptional muscle development	*Round*: very rounded *Back*: wide and very thick up to the shoulder *Shoulder*: very rounded *Topside*: spreads markedly over the symphysis *Rump*: very rounded
U Very good	Profiles on the whole convex; very good muscle development	*Round*: rounded *Back*: wide and thick up to the shoulder *Shoulder*: rounded *Topside*: spreads over the symphysis *Rump*: rounded
R Good	Profiles on the whole straight; good muscle development	*Round*: well developed *Back*: still thick but less wide at the shoulder *Shoulder*: fairly well developed *Topside*: slightly rounded *Rump*: slightly rounded
O Fair	Profiles straight to concave; average muscle development	*Round*: average development to lacking development *Back*: average thickness to lacking thickness *Shoulder*: average development to almost flat *Rump*: straight profile
P Poor	All profiles concave to very concave; poor muscle development	*Round*: poorly developed *Back*: narrow with bones visible *Shoulder*: flat with bones visible

Class	Description	Additional provisions
Fat cover	Amount of fat on the outside of the carcase and in the thoracic cavity.	
1 Low	None to low fat cover	No fat within the thoracic cavity
2 Slight	Slight fat cover, flesh visible almost everywhere	Within the thoracic cavity the muscle clearly visible between the ribs
3 Average	Flesh, with the exception of the round and shoulder, almost everywhere covered with fat, slight deposits of fat in the thoracic cavity	Within the thoracic cavity the muscle is still visible between the ribs
4 High	Flesh covered with fat, but on the round and shoulder still partly visible, some distinctive fat deposits in the thoracic cavity	The seams of fat on the round are prominent. Within the thoracic cavity the muscle between the ribs may be infiltrated with fat.
5 Very high	Entire carcase covered with fat; heavy fat deposits in the thoracic cavity	The round is almost completely covered with fat, so that the seams of fat are no longer visible. Within the thoracic cavity the muscle between the ribs is infiltrated with fat.

Ireland on the one hand, and continental Europe on the other).

(e) Fat classification includes reference to fat inside the thoracic cavity ('feathering' and 'overflow') as well as to external fat cover; traditionally this has been given a good deal of emphasis in French practice, but little in countries where the prevailing level of carcase fatness is higher — except the U.S.A., where it is seen as an indicator of marbling.

M.L.C. adopted the E.E.C. scheme for all beef carcase classification purposes in November 1981. This essentially involved a change of terminology and adoption of subdivisions for two E.E.C. fat and two E.E.C. conformation classes to preserve the degree of discrimination inherent in the long-standing M.L.C. scheme (see above). Table 13.14 shows the grid as subdivided for use in Great Britain.

The challenge of the 1980s in beef classification in Europe will be to achieve standardised application of this scheme. Photographic standards and/or international inspection teams will be used. But it is clear that the wording of the official scheme adopted is a 'committee-table' compromise of rather different national approaches and some problems in interpretation, as well as standardisation, can be expected.

Table 13.14 The grid of the E.E.C. beef carcase classification scheme, as subdivided for use in Great Britain

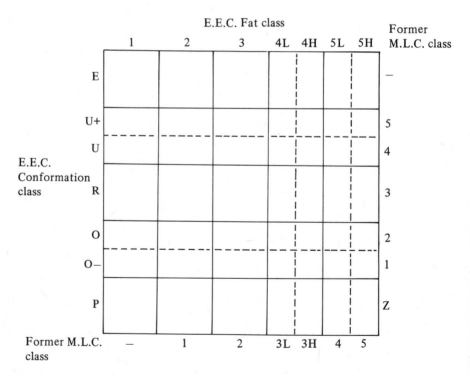

Livestock improvement schemes, population studies and experiments

14 Selection objectives

The choice of methods of carcase evaluation for use in livestock breeding schemes presents a different problem from classification or grading because carcase characteristics are not considered in isolation; they are linked directly with growth performance characteristics such as daily gain and feed conversion efficiency. Indeed, as was indicated earlier, these characteristics can sometimes provide more information about carcase composition than direct measures of the carcase.

Before considering the choice of techniques, we shall discuss the general features of animal breeding, in particular selection objectives and how they influence methods of selection.

GENETIC HISTORY

Man's direct involvement in the evolution of pigs, cattle and sheep began with domestication some six to ten thousand years ago when he would have sought docility, tractability and animals suited to draught purposes. Before domestication, animals developed in the wild, moulded only by pressures acting to ensure good survival and reproduction.

With the advent of the industrial revolution in Europe there began to develop more intensive systems of livestock production for milk, wool and meat. One consequence of this was the selection of nuclei of outstanding animals from local populations to form the basis of groups which eventually became formalised as breeds. This phase of development led to a new emphasis in selection with uniformity of colour, shape and size becoming important to distinguish the breed.

From those early years to the present day, the show ring has had a major role in moulding breeds, selection being dominated by appearance. While the act of judging has often become an end in itself with only lip service being given to commercial traits such as meat yield and quality, it would be wrong to belittle the changes which were brought about by the simple methods of breeders in the eighteenth and nineteenth centuries. There is no doubting the beneficial effect they had on the performance of farm livestock.

During the last thirty years, there have been major developments in the selection methods used, in the size of populations available for selection and in the ease of collecting, sorting and analysing large numbers of performance records.

The appearance of an animal on the farm or in the show ring still influences whether it will be chosen to be a parent in the next generation, but its commercial performance, and that of its close relations, is now of overriding importance in pig improvement in most developed countries, and is increasingly influencing the selection of cattle and sheep. An animal with high performance will be used as a parent if it also has a good appearance, but an animal with poor performance is likely to be culled, however good its appearance.

While selection has been achieving gradual changes within breeds, dramatic changes have been brought about in the structure of national livestock populations around the world by breed substitution and the upgrading of native stock by improved breeds. In particular, there was a major flow of beef genes from Europe to America and Australia in the nineteenth century; in the past decade there has been a reverse flow of North American Holstein genes to upgrade European black and white strains of Friesian cattle for milk production. Major pig breeding companies, backed up by ten or twenty years of selection in European countries, are now competing with one another to upgrade native stocks in less developed countries.

Developments in large-scale transfer of semen and stock has speeded up the process, making it possible, for example, to replace cattle populations almost completely in ten to fifteen years. The importance of breed substitution to the future of livestock breeding has been discussed by Land (241).

The first part of this section is concerned with carcase evaluation for selection within breeds. Breed substitution follows the comparison of breeds in population studies, the carcase evaluation aspects of which will be examined later.

STRUCTURE OF ANIMAL BREEDING PROGRAMMES

For many years, animal breeding was the concern only of individual herd owners whereas now several other types of organisation are involved. These include government organisations, breed co-operatives and breeding companies. Large-scale breeding organisations have major economies of scale and are likely to gain ground from smaller individual breeders. The cost of testing and culling animals in order to apply worthwhile selection pressure is high in relation to the cost of production, and the larger the population under selection, the greater the chance of success.

Modern breeding programmes depend on fast data processing equipment, technical advice and continuing access to new genetic developments; all of these are expensive and their costs need to be spread over as large an output as possible. The cost of the programme has to be more than recouped if the breeder is to remain in business and the time, from the start of the selection programme to the establishment of benefits in terms of improved animal performance and the sale of stock to commercial producers, may be many years. The more progeny produced from improved stock, the lower the cost of the programme as a charge on each animal produced.

All these factors favour the largest organisations for animal breeding, but there is also pressure from commercial producers for consistent breeding stock to meet increasingly tight production and market requirements. The numbers and quality required can only be supplied by breeders whose multiplication procedures can offer, for example, thousands of gilts per year of closely similar breeding. Factors affecting the economic efficiency of pig breeding schemes have been reviewed by Bichard (33).

Also, the larger breeding organisations have the power to influence the meat industry by advertising their product and by vertical integration with wholesalers and retailers. They can, therefore, become initiators of change rather than simply producing breeding stock in response to weak signals from a traditional trade.

Their power will increase because of their ability to market carcases of similar type. If the product of the breeding stock of different organisations or companies becomes recognised nationally as an identifiable type, it will be indicative of certain carcase qualities and become as much a factor in the prediction of carcase composition as breed or sex. The source of stock may become a factor in classification and grading schemes if the normal measurements taken do not adequately identify commercial value. The impact of the development of pig breeding companies on marketing and carcase evaluation will be referred to later.

Objectives

The first decision to make in initiating a selection programme concerns the objectives, that is the characteristics to be improved. This can be more difficult than it might appear because selection programmes take time before they can have much effect on commercial production. Emphasis has to be given to factors which will be important in ten or fifteen years time. Setting goals is a major problem for breeders and changing the goals from one year to another has been the downfall of many operations.

The carcase characteristics to be improved will be only part of an overall package including reproductive and growth performance traits. They may be a small part and have only a minor effect on breeding decisions, particularly when population structures are complex as they are in cattle. This is well illustrated by table 14.1, adapted from Cunningham (86), showing the relative importance of different beef traits to different participants in the production system.

To the dairy farmer, calving ease, gestation length and the effect on the dam's milk yield are most important. Breeders of suckler beef cows are concerned primarily with calving ease and calf production. Calf rearers are concerned with traits such as growth rate and hardiness and, only to a lesser extent, with the conformation of the live animal as they may not be rearing the animal through to finished beef. Store cattle rearers are mainly concerned with growth rate and conformation, with hardiness being rather less important. Beef finishers have similar requirements, but are also concerned with rate of maturity.

The requirements of the meat trade are very different from those of producers, except that their raw material needs to be produced as cheaply as possible. Their major concern is with yields of higher valued product (determined

Table 14.1 Relative importance of different beef traits to different participants in the production/marketing chain (modified from Cunningham, 86)

Trait	Breeder (dairy)	Breeder (suckler)	Calf rearer	Store rearer	Fattener	Wholesaler or meat trader	Meat processor	Consumer
Calving ease	***	***						
Gestation length	***	*						
Effect of dam's milk yield	***	*						
Growth rate	*	*	***	***	***			
Hardiness	*	*	***	**	*			
Live conformation	*	*	**	***	**			
Rate of maturity (ease of fattening)					***			
Carcase conformation (meat to bone ratio)					**	***	***	
Carcase fatness (fat to lean ratio)					**	***	***	***
Carcase weight at given level of fatness					**	**		
Proportion of higher-priced cuts						*		
Muscle thickness						*		*
Meat quality (processing)							**	
Eating quality						*	*	***

* = low importance; ** = medium importance; *** = very important

by killing-out percentage, fatness, muscle to bone ratio and proportion of more valuable cuts) and with meat quality. The conflicts which can occur in objectives at different points in the marketing chain have been discussed by Harris (168) and Miller and Pearson (284). The latter also discuss in detail the economic aspects of selection and review the literature on the subject.

In planning a selection programme, the possible range of farm production systems and market requirements in which the animals will be used also has to be determined. Will different selection schemes be needed to breed strains for each system? Selection will normally be carried out under the system giving maximum expression to the character being selected. Strains of livestock are generally extremely adaptable to a range of conditions. Only if extreme environments or very different market circumstances occur will it be necessary to contemplate more than one selection programme. Eliminating the extremes of environment by altering the commercial production system is usually simpler and more profitable than multiplying the number of selection programmes.

In the context of carcase evaluation, specific market requirements for weight or structural characteristics such as length and blockiness may be of concern. Rigid and specific requirements by markets can place considerable constraints and added costs on breeding schemes and careful thought should be given to whether the market requirement is dictated by habit or by tradition, rather than sound economic considerations.

There are many, and sometimes conflicting, objectives for improvement. In addition particular problems exist in the improvement of carcase characteristics as follows:

(a) They are more difficult and costly to measure than growth performance characteristics. Growth rate can be measured easily, relatively accurately and cheaply; efficiency of feed conversion into live weight gain is more difficult because of the need to measure feed eaten, but recent developments in electronically-controlled feeding troughs, or gates which give individual access, have made this easier for cattle and pig improvement programmes.

(b) The meat trade and consumers are concerned with the phenotype and not the genotype. Genetic differences for meat quality characteristics can be modified by production environment, transport and lairage conditions and, of course, by differences in meat handling and processing methods. A high proportion of the variation observed in these characteristics is due to environmental differences, in particular the way animals are handled prior to slaughter or the way the carcases are handled post mortem. For example, pale soft exudative (P.S.E.) meat in pigs is particularly sensitive to the way the animals are handled before slaughter. Faced with the choice of including meat quality factors in selection indexes (which will reduce selection pressure in other characteristics) or devoting more resources to lairage and slaughterhouse improvements, the latter course may be the better one although more difficult to implement on a national basis.

(c) A whole range of characteristics is involved in meat quality and consumer appreciation, most of which are subjective. Little information is available on their economic importance and there may be differences between markets with regard to their requirements; good eating characteristics may not be compatible with good processing characteristics. Determination of economic weights for such characteristics is, therefore, difficult.

(d) Breeders are naturally reluctant to do anything about characteristics which are not of immediate financial benefit to producers, particularly if they are expensive to measure. More can be done in this respect within a national testing scheme, directed towards all sections of the industry, with the consumer ultimately in mind. But in several countries, Britain included, responsibility for breeding is moving into the hands of breeding companies.

Given these constraints on selection for carcase characteristics, it is hardly surprising that improvement in livestock has centred on growth rate and, to a lesser extent, on feed conversion efficiency.

Nevertheless, quite a lot is known about genetic parameters for carcase characteristics and many breeding programmes, particularly those for pigs, include some direct pressure to improve these.

The main carcase characteristics for genetic improvement (in addition to carcase weight) are as follows:

(a) lean to fat ratio;
(b) lean to bone ratio;
(c) proportion of total lean occurring in the higher-priced cuts;
(d) fat partition and distribution;
(e) meat quality.

It is simpler to deal with carcase lean content in terms of its ratios with fat and bone because these two ratios appear in many breeding populations to be influenced by different genes. In other words, genetic change can be brought about in one of the ratios without significantly changing the other.

Under some circumstances carcase lean content is combined with growth rate to form a single objective for selection — lean tissue growth rate (or rate of lean tissue gain) — or with efficiency of feed conversion to form lean tissue feed conversion (or efficiency of lean meat gain).

Principles of selection

The principles of genetic selection will be outlined briefly and some of the factors which influence the rate of response defined.

The response to selection (R) in a particular character to be improved depends on several factors:

$$R = ih\sigma_A$$

where i is the intensity of the selection, i.e. a measure of the proportion of the tested animals which are selected for use in later generations; and h is the square root of the heritability of the characteristic (h^2 is the proportion of the variation observed in the population which is attributable to genetic differences). The latter is important as it determines the prospects for genetic improvement; most carcase characteristics have moderate to high heritabilities ($h^2 = 0.3$ to 0.6) and are easy to improve provided that they can be measured accurately in practical breeding programmes. σ_A is the standard deviation of the breeding values of the individual animals tested. The breeding value of an individual is the value of that animal, as judged by the mean value of its progeny. If an individual is mated to a number of individuals taken at random from the population, then its breeding value is twice the average difference of the progeny from the population mean.

When selection is aimed at the improvement of the economic value of animals, several characteristics are simultaneously involved. Consideration is then given to an aggregate breeding value which includes the individual's merit in all the characteristics, with each weighted according to its economic value.

The most rapid improvement of overall economic value is expected from selection applied simultaneously to all the component characteristics (termed index selection), appropriate weight being given to each character according to its relative economic importance, its heritability and the correlations between the different characters (170). The use of economic weights and values for different characteristics was discussed by Niebel and others (296).

All objectives cannot be included in the aggregate breeding value for various reasons. Carcase and meat quality characteristics are often omitted because of a lack of reliable genetic parameters and difficulties associated with their measurement. Satisfactory economic weights are also difficult to determine. When there is a problem about including a particular characteristic in selection indexes, such characteristics, particularly those associated with meat quality, are often recorded separately and animals excluded from selection if they fall below a prescribed level.

When the characteristic for improvement cannot be measured directly, correlated characteristics are measured and used to provide an indirect improvement. This essentially involves a simple prediction — the variable with the highest correlation to the characteristic providing the highest response. The expected response is reduced in proportion to the level of correlation and it is important to identify the most precise predicting variables. In index selection, all correlated variables in the index can be used to improve the estimation of overall economic value.

Just as one variable can be used to improve another through the correlation, so the improvement of a given characteristic will lead to correlated changes in other characteristics which are genetically correlated with it. This correlated response to selection can be particularly important in the case of carcase meat quality characteristics, and changes in such characteristics must be monitored in case they are undesirable. Improvements in overall carcase lean content might for example reduce eating quality or lead to a correlated increase in adult body size.

For a fuller account of the principles of selection the reader should refer to Falconer (119). A detailed account of the construction of selection indexes has been published by Lerner (247).

Performance or progeny testing?

With progeny groups of sufficient size, progeny testing can give a more precise estimate of breeding value than performance testing in which all measurements are made on the live individuals from which the next generation will be selected. However, in terms of overall genetic progress, the advantages are small for traits such as growth rate and feed conversion efficiency which can be measured in the live animal and have reasonably high heritabilities. Characteristics with high heritability can normally be improved via selection on the basis of the individual animal's performance.

Progeny testing is necessary when the characteristics have low heritability. Progeny testing requires more facilities than performance testing to test the same number of sires, and the generation interval is markedly increased. Compared with performance testing it is, therefore, slow and expensive. Normally, it can only be justified for sires where small differences in performance become important when they are multiplied by large numbers of matings. Where bulls are used for artificial insemination (A.I.) on large numbers of females, progeny testing may be justified even though bulls have already been selected after a performance test.

Although pigs lend themselves to progeny and sib testing, for cattle and sheep, progeny testing is the only option for the improvement of carcase characteristics which cannot be measured on the live animal. Progeny testing also has the advantage over performance testing that it can be related more directly to commercial production systems. Indeed, the progeny test should evaluate animals in the main system or systems of production in which the commercial progeny will be reared, and with slaughter at end points which relate directly to market requirements. Ideally the test should terminate with slaughter at the optimum carcase weight for market requirements, or at the optimum fatness if it can be defined.

Selection for lean to fat ratio

In breeding programmes, selection for increased lean to fat ratio is often brought about as a correlated response to selection for growth rate and efficiency of live weight gain (both of which can be measured directly) with some additional selection pressure against fat thickness measured by ultrasonics. Under such circumstances, selection is effectively for later-maturing animals of large adult body size. When slaughtered at a given weight or age such animals are leaner (see chapter 3).

The relationship between efficiency and size has been the subject of much debate, particularly in relation to cattle breeding. Concern has been expressed that such selection may not be in the best interest of overall efficiency because of the costs of maintaining adult breeding stock of large mature size. Is it valuable to improve growth efficiency at the expense of overall maintenance requirements?

This raises the question of what is an optimum size? Klosterman (234) reviewing early work on the topic argued that a single optimum may be a mistake since there will be swings in selection objectives as production and market situations change. These dangers have been expressed in the change from large to earlier-maturing cattle, because of the need to finish on forages, and now back again in response to consumer demand for lean beef. Theoretically a more sensible approach is to develop and maintain specific lines for specific purposes and not waste valuable resources on genetic improvement, which could be brought about more easily by substituting one breed for another.

Once an optimum size has been established, efforts could be directed towards improving growth and efficiency within this. As discussed earlier (chapter 3), size at any age can be divided into two components, one measuring the effect of proportionality to adult body size (the normal growth pattern) and the other measuring the extent of deviations from this basic relationship (the extent to which there is variation in the growth pattern for animals of the same adult body size). Differences in mature size are unlikely to be associated with important differences in biological efficiency to the same carcase composition, whereas differences in the shape of the curve (deviations from the normal pattern) are likely to be so (35, 363). From the point of view of improving overall efficiency, the latter is the more important. The key is to correct differences in rate of maturity or growth rate for adult body size.

The same situation applies to sheep improvement and Bradford (36) has examined the possible effects of selection for relative growth rate. Figure 14.1 illustrates how the growth curve of a preferred animal compares with that of an animal selected for growth without regard to size at maturity. Bradford and Spurlock (37) recommended that weaning at sixty days of age or younger, feeding for rapid growth and measuring weight for age at five or six months of age, should provide a good indication of a ram's genetic potential for early growth.

The extent to which such improvement is possible without increasing size was discussed by Fitzhugh and Taylor (126). They concluded that selection on relative growth rate is effective in reducing the correlated increase in mature weight (and also birth weight), but there is a significant reduction in growth rate as compared with selection carried out ignoring changes in adult body size (125).

In conclusion, selection for lean to fat ratio in cattle and sheep is readily achieved by selection for growth rate if an increase in adult body size is accepted. If selection for lean to fat ratio via relative growth rate is attempted, responses may be less satisfactory.

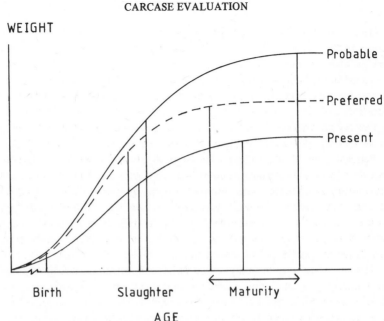

Fig. 14.1 Growth curves for animals selected for overall growth rate without adjustment for adult body size (probable) and selection for early growth rate (preferred) (36)

Selection for lean to bone ratio

Among animals of the same adult body size and with the same lean to fat ratio, there is substantial variation in lean to bone ratio. In many populations, individuals with high lean to bone ratios tend to have higher killing-out percentages, thicker muscles and are generally shorter and blockier (28, 302). There may also be small associated differences in joint proportions.

These various characteristics have been shown in pigs to be associated in some circumstances with a recessive gene, the halothane gene (see chapter 15).

Unlike the lean to fat ratio which can be improved through its association with growth rate and feed efficiency, the identification of animals with high lean to bone ratios normally requires some form of direct carcase assessment by visual scoring for shape, measurement of muscle areas or by tissue separation. This is straightforward in progeny tests but difficulties do exist in performance tests. Ultrasonic measurements of *M. longissimus* area of cattle have been used with some success in Denmark (26). The main alternative is a visual assessment of muscling but the accuracy of this is not clear because such assessments on the live animal can easily be confused with fatness.

Selection for lean tissue distribution

Although, as indicated earlier, variation in lean distribution between cuts is limited, some variation exists which could possibly be exploited in breeding programmes where small genetic differences can be multiplied up by penetration to large numbers of commercial progeny.

There are several studies which provide an indication of the genetic parameters involved. Berg *et al.* (32) quote Danish results which show a phenotypic standard deviation for percentage total lean in the pistol joint in cattle of two percentage units and a heritability of 0.29. A detailed study in British sheep by Wolf *et al.* (392) gave a higher heritability of 0.65.

Perhaps more thought should be given to possible predictors for estimating lean distribution. In particular, consideration should be given as to whether lean distribution can be predicted from the weights of joints without any trimming or dissection, as this would considerably reduce the cost of evaluation procedures. Several workers have demonstrated that lean, bone and fat follow the same general pattern of development between the various regions of the carcase and simple jointing may be found to be adequate for prediction purposes.

There is some reason to believe that improvement in tissue distribution in the higher-priced cuts will be brought about anyway as a correlated response to selection for faster growth rate associated with increased adult body size. Such selection is expected to reduce the degree of maturity of livestock at a fixed live weight and this will increase the proportion of the total lean found in the higher-priced cuts, and in the hind leg in particular which is an earlier maturing joint. This is supported by the results of the previously quoted Danish work in which a genetic correlation between growth rate and percentage lean in the higher-priced joints of 0.24 in beef cattle was reported. Wolf *et al.* (392) found a similar figure of 0.17 for sheep.

Finally, on the subject of lean distribution, it is important to recognise an increase in the higher-priced cuts is not always the best economic objective. By increasing the lean content of lower-priced cuts, the increase in actual retail realisation value may be more than that obtained for a similar increase in the proportion of lean content of the higher-priced cuts. For example, in bacon production in Great Britain, some carcases which have a satisfactory thickness of fat over the *M. longissimus* (and thus grade well), have an unsightly wedge of fat in the streak beside the muscle which seriously reduces their value. The condition is due to lack of muscle, and an increase in the lean in this part of the carcase, even at the expense of higher-priced lean, would result in a considerable increase in value — much more than that obtained by increasing the amount of lean in the ham joint, or increasing the size of the *M. longissimus*.

Selection for fat partition and distribution

Little attention has been paid to the possibility of selecting for favourable fat partition and distribution, although this could potentially be important particularly if fat could be shifted away from the internal body cavity to the carcase where it is more valuable, or if the proportion of total fat deposited intramuscularly could be increased (250).

Pigs have received the most attention from the point of view of within-breed genetic parameters. Duniec, Kielanowski and Osińska (109), analysing data from Polish progeny testing stations, found the heritability of chemical fat content in the loin muscle to be 0.50 and that of the fatty tissue in the carcase to be 0.69. The genetic correlation between these characteristics was low (0.11) and they concluded that different genetic factors are responsible for the deposition of fat in different depots.

If there is a poor genetic relationship between the growth of different depots, selection based on one depot is unlikely to provide an effective reduction in others. There is some evidence, albeit limited, to support this proposition. Chadwick (62), analysing data from the M.L.C.-sponsored selection experiment at Newcastle University, found that selection based on growth rate, food conversion efficiency and reduced back fat thickness appeared to have effected little reduction in intermuscular fat.

Apart from these observations, there is little evidence on genetic aspects of fat partition within breeds. The effects of fat partition and distribution have also been omitted in most genetic studies with laboratory animals, although effects of selection for weight on the relative rate of fat deposition has been well documented. An exception is the study of Allen (5), who found that two-way selection for body weight in mice changed the developmental pattern of fat deposition. Not only were the relative rates of fat deposition and the level of fat at low weights altered by selection, but the relationships between individual depots were also affected, resulting in differences in distribution at common weights. If confirmed with meat animals, the practical implication of Allen's results is that a breeder selecting to change body weight must be aware not only of correlated responses in overall fatness, but also of simultaneous changes in fat distribution.

Information has been accumulating on the genetic relationships between eating quality (tenderness, juiciness and flavour) and intramuscular fat in pigs. The results as a whole suggest that meat with more intramuscular fat has better eating quality but the correlations are low and the samples include considerable variation in fatness (309).

Monitoring genetic change

Direct selection for meat quality, other than simple characteristics such as colour and pH, is difficult because expensive measuring techniques are necessary. Consequently most of the changes in these characteristics come about indirectly as correlated responses to selection for growth rate, efficiency of live weight gain, lean to fat ratio and conformation.

In view of this, some means of monitoring such characteristics in breeding programmes is essential. This work is particularly important in pigs because of the known genetic correlations between characteristics which are the basis of selection and deleterious conditions such as pale soft exudative muscle (P.S.E.) (see chapter 15). If there were, for example, an increase in muscle weight loss, due to drip from pig carcases associated with P.S.E., of one percentage unit, this would cost the British meat industry £4 million per annum at the whole-sale level.

There is increasing interest in the maintenance of control herds because of the uncontrolled deteriorations which have occurred in the meat quality character-istics of pigs in several European countries. Meat quality characteristics are very sensitive to the environment and the only method of measuring genetic change which is entirely satisfactory is to use genetic controls maintained in herds with random mating. In Britain the possibility of operating control herds by using frozen semen from a panel of boars is being considered. Frozen semen can be used to breed each successive generation so that the control is continually re-bred, with exactly the same genetic make-up on the male side in each succes-sive generation.

Monitoring changes in carcase characteristics is equally important for picking up unwanted changes in, for example, joint proportions or the appearance of cross-sections. M.L.C. has operated a comparative test of the breeding stock offered for sale by the major breeding companies, which has been invaluable as a means of examining carcase relationships in the national population. Besides its obvious role of monitoring trends and variation, such a test additionally focusses attention on characteristics such as meat quality and tissue distribu-tion which do not influence producer returns directly at the moment but which may be important in the future.

A continuous test of this type also provides the means of refining the relationships between predicting measurements and composition used in classi-fication and grading schemes. This is important because genetic improvement is slowed down if the market does not adequately identify and pay for improved stock. Breeding companies are unlikely to invest in the improvement of charac-teristics unless these improvements provide clear benefits for the producers who purchase their stock.

15 Pig improvement schemes

Testing methods and the carcase evaluation techniques used in pig breeding are more advanced than those for cattle and sheep in most countries.

Discussion among breeders and scientists involved in these schemes rightly concerns objectives rather than techniques and we shall approach the subject of carcase evaluation in pig breeding from this position, drawing particularly on our experience from involvement in the national pig improvement scheme operated in Great Britain by M.L.C. The situation is similar in several ways to that in other countries and cross-reference will be made where appropriate.

In response to consumer demand for lean meat at reasonable prices, pig breeding programmes in Great Britain have concentrated on selection for improved growth rate, feed conversion efficiency and carcase lean content.

In the M.L.C.'s central testing scheme, selection has also been made for *M. longissimus* area and trimming percentage (sides prepared for curing as a percentage of carcase weight) but there has been no direct selection for improved meat quality or for detailed carcase characteristics such as fat distribution or muscle to bone ratio.

Breeding companies, which since the early 1970s have taken an increasing share of the British market for breeding stock, have paid little direct attention to carcase and meat quality characteristics. Some of them have tested under the M.L.C. umbrella with limited carcase evaluation, whereas others have concentrated almost entirely on performance testing with ultrasonic fat thickness measurements being the only direct measures of carcase characteristics.

This policy of ignoring detailed carcase and meat quality characteristics has met with little comment from the meat industry in the 1970s and there have been few problems with meat quality (197). The industry has certainly been aware of variation in meat quality, but this variation has been small in comparison with improvements in carcase lean content which have been well recognised by the meat trade. Further, poor meat quality, where sufficiently pronounced to cause concern, has often been traced to environmental factors rather than to genetic defects.

Selection programmes have been successful in improving carcase lean content, and this genetic improvement, together with environmental and marketing changes (particularly the development of grade and deadweight selling), has produced a significant reduction in the fatness of the national slaughter population. Table 15.1 shows the estimated response to selection in comparison with genetic control herds. However, the 1980s have seen an increase in concern that greater leanness is bringing with it some associated problems and more attention is being focussed on carcase and meat quality by some of the major whole-salers and retailers. Increases in the use of entire males, the level of which was 15 per cent of the national slaughter population in 1981, has added to the attention, because they are significantly leaner than castrates (199, 275).

Table 15.1 Rate of genetic response of pigs in M.L.C.'s central testing scheme between 1970 and 1980. Change per annum of test pigs compared with genetic control. (D.W. Jones, unpublished data)

	Large White	Landrace
Feed conversion ratio (kg feed/ kg live weight gain)	−0.02	−0.02
C fat thickness over M. longissimus (mm)	−0.49	−0.49
M. longissimus area (cm^2)	0.40	0.14
Killing-out percentage	0.10	0.18
Lean in rumpback joint (%)	0.46	0.87

The meat trade in Britain has begun to think in terms of a requirement for a minimum level of fatness for their pigs as it does for cattle, and to a lesser extent for sheep. This is expressed via resistance to young boars, penalties for ultra-lean carcases in some bacon pig contracts, and concern about a possible shortage of fat for the processing industry.

The situation is not yet serious and selection for further reductions in fatness is necessary because the variation in fatness at a given weight remains sub-stantial. But the reaction of the meat trade to the increasing percentage of very lean pigs does raise several questions about carcase objectives. What is the mini-mum fat requirement? Should breeders continue to select for lean to fat ratio and leave it to the producer to modify fatness levels by nutritional changes or by slaughtering at heavier carcase weights? Should more emphasis be placed on lean to bone ratio rather than lean to fat ratio? These questions are fundamental to what happens to the pig industry in Britain and many other countries which now have pig populations approaching the minimum level of fatness required at a given carcase weight.

The possibility of increasing carcase weight to achieve an optimum level of fatness as selection for leanness continues, is particularly important in the British context because there is a significant market for light pigs for fresh pork (in the carcase weight range 40-55 kg) and the overall average carcase weight at 65 kg is low in comparison with that in most other developed countries. As indicated earlier (chapter 1), lightweight pigs are inefficient to produce in terms of the overall efficiency of lean meat production and there may be a movement away from them in the long term, although we have detected little change in carcase weights since 1970.

Until now, selection for pig improvement has been facilitated because the changes required in growth rate, efficiency and leanness have all been in the right direction. This is in contrast to the confusion which exists in cattle breeding, for example, where ability to fatten and achieve a minimum level of fatness within the target weight range may be an important selection criterion. With pigs, geneticists have been able to select for a single basic objective (efficiency of lean meat production) and leave it to the producer to provide the environment to get the most out of the improved genotype. In the future, it may prove desirable to define an optimum production environment (in terms of nutrition, housing and weight at slaughter) and select for the pig which best suits this. Determination of an optimum production environment would in fact solve some of the problems which now beset decisions on the most suitable selection environment for breeding schemes.

Debate has continued over the years about whether a restricted feeding or *ad libitum* feeding system should be employed in selection programmes. The arguments have led to the concept of the biological alternative to the selection index whereby selection is directly for overall objectives such as lean tissue food conversion or lean tissue growth rate, rather than indirectly for these characters through indexes where a number of characters are given economic weightings. The various arguments are set out by Fowler, Bichard and Pease (131).

The argument for the biological model becomes somewhat simplistic against a need for optimum lean to fat ratio and when improvement in more detailed carcase and meat quality characteristics is necessary. In these circumstances, the economic/index model is essential. The biological model as presented also revolves around the balance between fat and lean, no attention being given to other carcase components. Once an optimum fat to lean ratio is achieved, the best way (indeed the only way) of improving carcase lean percentage is to select for a reduction in the weights of head, feet and bone. Fowler *et al* (131) argued that there can be little scope for reduction of these components, yet there are differences between pig breeds in lean to bone ratio and head weights.

The meat industry's attitudes towards its raw material will influence the extent to which the basic approach of selection for leanness in association with a moving optimum slaughter weight is acceptable. If the meat industry accepts that maximum efficiency will be achieved by using pigs which produce lean meat at minimum cost, this approach will be favoured. If, on the other hand, the trade expects breeding and production to tailor pig carcases closely to its specific weight requirements, then progress is likely to be much slower.

The most effective way to increase carcase lean content at the same level of fatness is to improve lean to bone ratio which inevitably brings the relationships between carcase conformation, lean to bone ratio, and meat quality into consideration. The pig industry in Britain is dominated by the British Large White and British Landrace breeds which are long and show limited variation in carcase shape or length in comparison with the populations of other countries — short carcases with heavily developed hams which are common in Belgium, Germany and the Netherlands are rare in Britain. Although there are other reasons for the differences between countries, a major factor in this has been the central importance of the Wiltshire cure (whole side bacon curing) which has a minimum length requirement in its pig buying specification (see chapter 11). Curers — both British and Danish — have used the length requirement to safeguard themselves against an increase in variability of bacon pigs.

Although the reduction of variation has been of value to the bacon sector, the industry as a whole has not been served so well because blockier pigs selected for conformation can have important carcase advantages. Continental carcases of this type have superior muscling, higher lean to bone ratios, and generally kill-out better (77, 337). The lack of a strong home-market demand for blockier pigs has also limited the development of these types of pigs by British breeders and breeding companies, some of which have found it difficult to compete in overseas markets. Veterinary restriction on pig imports has also made it difficult for Britain to compete with countries which have a greater facility to select from the world's gene-pool.

However, restrictions on the movement of breeding stock within the E.E.C. are gradually being relaxed so that there is now more emphasis on conformation and the development of muscular sire lines, based on continental breeds, by British commercial breeding companies.

The purity of the British Large White breed and the general policy of selecting for lean to fat ratio rather than selecting for conformation and lean to bone ratio has, however, protected the British pig population against meat quality problems associated with blockier types of pig. Research in many pig populations now indicates a genetic association between muscularity and meat quality.

Pig meat quality

Pale soft exudative muscle (P.S.E.) is the major meat quality problem in pigmeat today. P.S.E. meat loses more weight as drip between cutting and consumption; it is unsatisfactory for manufacturers because it gives rise to increased weight losses during processing and cooking, and is responsible for defects in the colour and texture of products. A further important quality problem is dark firm dry muscle (D.F.D.) which results in abnormal colour in fresh and cured products and in reduced keeping quality.

P.S.E. occurs when there is an abnormally rapid increase in the acidity of muscle after slaughter. It is brought about by physiological changes caused by stress before or at the time of slaughter. Some types of pig are more stress-sensitive than others and show a higher incidence of P.S.E.

P.S.E. is reflected in a variety of physical effects which are used as indicators of the condition. Colour (measured objectively or visually) of the fresh or cured meat, water-holding capacity, and pH (acidity) at forty-five minutes after slaughter (known as pH_1) are some of the criteria most frequently used to indicate P.S.E. in a carcase. Colour and pH at 24 hours after slaughter (known as ultimate pH, pH_u or pH_2) are the most commonly used indicators of D.F.D.

Genetic studies on the inheritance of meat quality in many breeds, using a range of criteria related to P.S.E., generally agree on a moderate heritability of about 0.3 (for reviews see 265 and 356). Studies on traits related to D.F.D. are less numerous, but also indicate a moderate heritability (for example, 361). Genetic improvements in meat quality traits can, therefore, be achieved through selection.

While it appears that meat quality is not generally associated with growth rate and that selection for lean growth rate (i.e. minimum fat and maximum growth) will not compromise quality (355), there is now strong evidence that pigs with high lean content associated with high muscle to bone ratio and well developed hams, are more likely to develop P.S.E. meat (261, 378). Selection for leanness and muscular development without regard to meat quality could lead to an increase in the incidence of quality problems. However, in breeds where the incidence of meat quality problems is extremely low, these relationships are weak and often non-significant as in the British Large White and Landrace breeds (115).

A review of pig breeding in Europe (251) shows that several countries now include colour or some quality criterion in formal indexing procedures in their improvement programmes, while many countries include it as an 'additional trait' in their selection objectives. In a theoretical study on the effect of including meat quality in a progeny test index, Malmfors (263) showed that this trait can be held constant or even slightly improved, without much reduction in the rates of change in live weight gain and in other performance traits.

THE HALOTHANE GENE

The detection of P.S.E. and the porcine stress syndrome (P.S.S.) has been facilitated by the finding that pigs prone to these conditions can be detected by halothane testing (112, 380). The test consists of administering halothane to young pigs for three to five minutes. Pigs which develop muscular rigidity, typified by a rigid extension of the limbs and often accompanied by a rapid rise in body temperature, are considered reactors or stress susceptible. Pigs which remain perfectly relaxed under anaesthesia are termed non-reactors or stress resistant. The repeatability of the test has been found to be very high and the chance of mis-classifying an animal is about 5 per cent (380).

The halothane test is simple to carry out and to interpret, and the result is immediately known. In most cases the test is not fatal. It can be carried out on the young boar, which means that a decision can be made on its breeding potential before it takes up costly performance test space. So this test has great potential as a tool for bringing about genetic improvement in stress susceptibility and meat quality in populations where these have a high incidence. There are however, medical reservations about the widespread use of anaesthetics under field conditions.

The inheritance of the reaction has been found to be controlled by a single recessive gene. This is more common in Continental breeds of pig, particularly those influenced by the Pietrain, and is apparently responsible for their advantages in leanness and muscling. Reported incidence of the positive reaction to halothane range from 0 per cent to 6 per cent in Large Whites, 5 per cent to 86 per cent in Landrace, and 31 per cent to 94 per cent in Pietrains (379). The frequency of 11 per cent in British Landrace is relatively low compared with some other world strains, but greater than in the Irish, Australian, Norwegian and Danish Landrace breeds.

Selection of lines to increase the incidence of the gene confirms that it has considerable carcase advantages (302). All trials report that pigs with the gene have a higher lean content, averaging about 2.5 per cent of carcase weight. In some trials, but not all, this is accompanied by an increase in ham proportions, improved *M. longissimus* area and better killing-out percentage. The halothane gene is, therefore, a contributor to the relationship between conformation, meat to bone ratio and meat quality observed in many breed populations and the range of incidence between them may explain why the genetic parameters differ so much between populations. The culling of reactors will tend to discriminate against individuals with high lean content and well-developed hams which would otherwise be favoured.

Research is now being carried out at A.B.R.O., Edinburgh, and at other research centres to determine the potential of the gene and to see whether, sensibly used, it has advantages in commercial pig populations, or whether the disadvantages are such that action should be taken to reduce its frequency. If used, it is likely to be confined to sire lines in order to confer heterozygote advantage in leanness on commercial crosses.

OTHER METHODS OF IDENTIFYING P.S.E. AND P.S.S.
There are several other techniques available for identifying pigs prone to P.S.E. and P.S.S. Assay of the serum enzyme creatinine phosphokinase can be used to identify muscle disorders associated with the porcine stress syndrome. This test is used in breeding programmes in Germany (40). Other techniques include chromosomal markers (9) and the efflux of calcium ions from mitochondria (70). Such techniques have been reviewed by McGloughlin (270). The report of an international symposium held in Norway provides a detailed account (331).

Carcase evaluation and testing procedures

The organisation of pig testing differs between and within countries. Sometimes it is in the hands of national or state governments, sometimes in the hands of industry-funded development organisations, and sometimes under the control of private or public companies or individual breeders. The types of testing applied and the extent of evaluation for carcase and meat quality characteristics also differ. Many countries carry out progeny testing, but the popularity of performance testing has grown, both on farms and in testing stations.

We shall review briefly the procedures operating in a selection of countries

Table 15.2 Characteristics measured on slaughtered sibs or progeny in central pig testing schemes in different countries (251)

	Belgium	Denmark	West Germany	Finland	France	Great Britain	Ireland	Netherlands	Norway	Poland	Sweden	Switzerland	Austria
Daily gain	*	*	*	*	*	*	*	*	*	*	*	*	*
Feed conversion ratio	*	*	*	*	*	*	*	*	*	*	*	*	*
Higher-priced cuts in carcase (%)	*			*	*							*	
Lean in carcase (%)		*				*					*		
M. longissimus area		*				*	*		*	*	*		*
Ham in carcase (%)								*	*		*		*
Loin in carcase (%)								*	*				
Meat in ham (%)										*			
Fat to lean ratio in back		*											*
Fat thickness	*	*		*	*	*	*	*	*		*		*
Fat in carcase (%)				*									
Flare fat (%)					*								
Trimming (%)[1]						*							
Killing-out (%)						*							
Meat quality		*	*		*	*		*	*	*		*	*
Halothane				*				*			*	*	
Carcase length		*				*	*				*		*

[1] Side trimmed for Wiltshire cure as a percentage of untrimmed side weight.

where there are interesting differences of approach to pig testing, with particular reference to the carcase evaluation methods applied. In the case of European countries, E.A.A.P. has carried out several surveys of testing methods, the latest of which were reported by Lindhé et al. (251) and Smith (348). Table 15.2 summarises the measurements taken on slaughtered sibs in thirteen European countries as part of station testing.

The survey of Smith (348) indicated that on-farm testing schemes of all the countries examined included backfat thickness measured by ultrasonic machine.

Denmark

The Danes were the first to introduce a major programme of pig testing, stimulated by the requirements of the export market for bacon to Great Britain (71). The Danish system, which has been used as a model in many countries, is based on testing the progeny of potential sires and involves groups of two castrated males and two gilts. The test period is over a fixed live weight range (25-90 kg) on *ad libitum* and group feeding. Standardisation of pre-slaughter handling is regarded as important in Denmark and after slaughter carcases are evaluated at a purpose-built centre.

A range of carcase measurements is taken, including fat thickness, carcase length and area of *M. longissimus*, followed by jointing of one side and removal of subcutaneous fat from the back and ham joints. Total separation of a sample of carcases is performed periodically to provide a basis for multiple regression equations to predict carcase lean content. By combining the variables routinely assessed, some 90 per cent of the total variation in lean percentage can be explained (7). A modified Danish system of carcase evaluation with subcutaneous fat separation is applied in the Swedish pig improvement scheme.

Only minor attention has been paid to the visual assessment of carcases in predicting carcase composition. Pedersen and Busk (311), in agreement with many others, concluded that visual judgements should be disregarded in the context of pig testing.

Meat quality estimation forms an important part of the evaluation of Danish pigs. From 1954 to 1972, a visual scoring system for meat colour was used, but in 1972 a comprehensive meat quality index based on objective measurements taken in the loin and ham was introduced, combining various meat quality traits related particularly to bacon production. The meat quality index (KK) is a selection index combining colour of fresh *M. biceps femoris* and colour of raw, cured *M. longissimus*, with ultimate pH (24 hours post mortem) measured in the *M. biceps femoris*, *M. longissimus* and *M. semispinalis capitis*.

The decline in meat quality of Danish pigs observed until 1972 was halted following the introduction of the KK index, presumably at the expense of selection for other characteristics. Meat quality has since shown a substantial improvement as judged by phenotypic trends.

Growth performance and carcase evaluation results are reported to breeders, who make their own judgement about the weighting to attach to different factors.

Performance testing of the boars themselves is carried out on both stations and farms. The Danscanner ultrasonic machine is used to measure fat thickness and *M. longissimus* area.

Similar procedures are applied in other countries for on-farm testing, although A-mode ultrasonic machines are normally used. Denmark is unique in measuring *M. longissimus* areas in national performance testing.

Great Britain

Until the mid-1960s, pig testing in Britain followed quite closely the system of progeny testing applied in Denmark. However, concern was expressed in Britain about the slow rate of genetic progress towards more efficient lean meat production, and a critical review of alternatives led to the introduction of a combined test. This takes the form of performance testing on stations run by M.L.C. of two boars, one castrate male and one gilt from the same litter, with feeding to appetite over a fixed weight range (27-90 kg). The castrate and gilt are slaughtered to provide carcase information to supplement the estimate of boar leanness provided by ultrasonic fat depths and growth performance characters. Selection is essentially for the efficiency of lean tissue gain.

Evaluation of the slaughtered sibs of the boars includes a range of fat thickness measurements and *M. longissimus* area. Until 1978, a sample joint (the rumpback) was separated into its component tissues and used together with other characteristics to predict lean content (88). Following a review of M.L.C. expenditure on central testing in terms of the contribution made to rate of genetic progress by the different measured characters, the separation of the sample joint was omitted. The loss due to failure to measure percentage lean in the sample joint was estimated to be only 1 per cent of the total progress possible in the overall economic objective. This was considered small in relation to the cost of the sample joint dissection.

As indicated earlier, a feature of pig breeding in Britain has been the growth of pig breeding companies. The influence of the British-based companies has extended abroad through the export of breeding stock, through the establishment of subsidiary companies in other countries and through the stimulus provided for the establishment of native companies. Although the attention paid to carcase and meat quality characteristics has been on the whole low, some of the companies have been more concerned about carcase quality and used M.L.C. services of carcase evaluation.

Because of the increasingly important role of these companies in influencing the British pig industry and the need for producers to have independent evidence on the merits of pigs from the different companies, M.L.C. established a comparative test known as Commercial Pig Evaluation (279). Several other countries have since introduced similar forms of test.

The assessment of carcase and meat quality has been an important part of the evaluation of pigs from the breeding companies in the M.L.C. comparative test. Carcases have been assessed using the procedure indicated above for combined testing, except that the hand joint was separated and used in combination with fat thickness measurements in the loin to predict overall lean content. This combination was cheaper to measure and as precise as separation of the rump back. In view of the wide cross-section of genotypes represented across the companies, the full separation of one side of one-third of all test carcases was considered important in the early years of the test, with hand joint separation being applied to the remaining two-thirds. However, as information accumulated, the extent of detailed carcase work could be substantially reduced. Results from these tests are considered in more detail in chapter 19.

The Netherlands

Combined testing is an important feature of pig improvement in the Netherlands. The system is broadly similar to that described above, but the Netherlands was in the forefront of European countries in the use of halothane testing as a way of identifying the genetic predisposition of nucleus pigs to produce P.S.E. meat. This is applied in the Netherlands to all male pigs on the testing stations and the result influences the way in which tested boars are used. For example only those boars with a high index score, very good conformation and which are not halothane positive are sold for use at A.I. Finland, Switzerland and Sweden are other countries where the halothane test is applied to all central test boars (251).

Canada

A national progeny testing programme similar to that developed in Denmark was introduced in the 1930s in Canada. Though sound in concept, the programme did not produce any measurable genetic improvement (134). The advent of back fat probing of live pigs (171) and the subsequent development of ultrasonic techniques led to the introduction of performance testing in 1966. Both on-farm and station testing are applied, but unlike some of the European schemes, testing of sibs to provide carcase information to supplement the fat measurements taken on the boars has not been adopted as a routine. The Canadian government has supported research work to examine ways of improving the precision of estimating lean content in performance test stock (136), but none has proved an effective replacement for the combination of growth rate, feed conversion efficiency and back fat thickness.

U.S.A.

Unlike Canada and most European countries, the U.S.A. does not have a unified national pig breeding programme. Instead, extension services in several states offer fat probing, ultrasonic measurements and advice, and there are a number of central performance testing stations operated either by the state or by individual breed organisations. Breeding companies are fewer with relatively less influence on the industry than in Europe, and their selection methods are less sophisticated. Among private pure-bred breeders, there appears to be less emphasis on performance testing with selection largely on type.

In contrast to the intensity of carcase and meat quality evaluation work applied in a number of European schemes, the Americans have been less interested in identifying and using those sires with the highest lean tissue growth rate or lean tissue food conversion. This apparent lack of concern may reflect the abundance of cheap corn for animal feed and a readiness to trim any excess fat before retail sale. However, attitudes have begun to change as feed becomes scarcer and European pig breeding companies start to spread their sphere of influence to North America. These companies are marketing more efficient and leaner breeding stock than that commonly found in the U.S.A.

16 Beef improvement schemes

Progeny testing is much more expensive for beef cattle than for pigs, particularly if detailed carcase evaluation is to be carried out after slaughter. Breeding objectives are also less clearly defined for beef cattle, reflecting the range of production environments in which cattle have to perform commercially and the range of market requirements which exist.

Most beef cattle improvement schemes are based, therefore, on bull performance tests with some associated progeny testing where this is cost-effective. Where bulls are used in artificial insemination (A.I.) on large numbers of females, progeny testing may be justified even though bulls have already been selected after a performance test.

The methods of performance and progeny testing used with bulls in Europe are well documented. In 1971, an E.A.A.P. Working Group found that central bull performance testing had a widespread application in European cattle breeding (240) but substantial differences in the testing techniques adopted were observed; the group made some general recommendations for testing methods.

Since the early 1970s, bull performance testing has become a key element in breeding programmes for both beef and dairy/dual purpose breeds in Europe. In addition, more experimental knowledge has been obtained about the potential traits for testing and selection, and more advanced techniques have been developed, so increasing the scope of central performance testing. As a consequence, an E.E.C./ E.A.A.P. Working Group was formed in 1979 with the task of establishing new recommendations for performance testing of bulls before their selection and use in A.I. (28).

The group took as their overall selection objective the efficiency of lean meat production, including the cost of feed, invested capital, buildings and use of labour. Carcase quality was taken to be expressed by three main variables — killing-out percentage, muscle to fat ratio, and muscle to bone ratio. Morphological characteristics such as fleshiness, conformation and visually assessed fatness were thought to be of sufficient importance commercially for inclusion, but visual assessments were in most cases not sufficiently reliable for use in selection programmes. They agreed that efforts should be focussed on establishing objective methods for the assessment of body composition and on improvements in the accuracy of ultrasonic machines, which are used in some performance tests.

Results discussed in chapter 6 indicate that ultrasonic measurements of the subcutaneous fat layer give the best estimate of the lean content and these are therefore commonly used. Fat areas are better than fat thickness measurements and the more complex scanning machines are better than simple A-mode and B-mode machines. The Danscanner is used routinely in the Danish performance tests of young bulls of dual purpose and beef breeds: all the animals are measured over the *M. longissimus* at the first lumbar vertebra (45). The Scano-gram is used for performance testing bulls in Britain, fat areas being measured over the *M. longissimus* at the tenth and thirteenth ribs and at the level of the third/fourth lumbar vertebrae.

Selection for decreased fat thickness is likely to have a very different effect from that of selection for increased *M. longissimus* area. Selection for muscle area may tend to increase lean to bone ratio and killing-out percentage, whereas selection for fat thickness measurements will tend to influence the fatness and maturity type of the animals. There is little published information on the relationships between ultrasonic measurements and carcase composition in groups of cattle from breeding programmes. Some Danish results obtained with the S.V.C. scanner (a complex B-mode scanner) are shown in table 16.1 (26).

The Working Group in its 1981 report made three recommendations relating to carcase evaluation:

(a) Subjective classification systems for muscle development should be related to photographic or descriptive standards and based on linear scales. Such systems need to be based on within-breed standards and should not be confused with scoring associated with breed differences.
(b) Ultrasonic measurements of subcutaneous fat and *M. longissimus* area must be well organised and controlled, and interpreted by skilled operators. Repeated measurements at four week intervals in the last part of the test period are recommended. Fat thickness and muscle area should be adjusted to a constant live weight basis.
(c) Body measurements should be taken according to the E.A.A.P. recom-mendations (98).

Performance testing of beef bulls can be carried out in one of three ways. The first, known as time-constant testing, involves measuring the animals' growth rate over a certain time period, say 150 or 200 days, irrespective of the age and weight of the individual animals at the start of the test. The second method, weight-constant testing, involves the measurement of the time it takes for animals to achieve a specified weight increase, for example from 250 to 400 kg. The third method, age-constant testing, involves the measurement of the weight gain of animals over a specified age range, such as 150 to 400 days of age.

In Great Britain, bull performance tests are operated by the M.L.C. at five stations accommodating in total about 400 bulls each year. Growth rate and

Table 16.1 Correlations between carcase composition and live body measurements taken by S.V.C. ultrasonic scanner on 295 young bulls distributed in 50 progeny groups from the EGTVED test station (26)

Carcase composition	Ultrasonic muscle area (cm²)			Ultrasonic muscle area/fat area			Carcase muscle area (cm²)**		
	r_P	Residual s.d.	r_G	r_P	Residual s.d.	r_G	r_P	Residual s.d.	r_G
Pistola lean (%)*	0.37	0.9	0.52	0.55	0.8	0.79	0.49	0.8	0.70
Lean (%)	0.31	1.6	0.29	0.53	1.3	0.57	0.42	1.5	0.46
Fat (%)	-0.16	1.7	-0.02	-0.47	1.4	-0.50	-0.26	1.7	-0.20
Bone (%)	-0.32	0.8	-0.55	0.12	0.9	-0.03	-0.33	0.8	-0.50
Lean to bone ratio	0.40	0.21	0.62	0.32	0.23	0.30	0.45	0.21	0.66
Average measurement	54.3			3.98			61.3		
s.d.	7.1			0.52			5.7		
h^2	0.49 ± 0.21			0.46 ± 0.21			0.69 ± 0.23		

Animals were scanned at the constant live weight of 450 kg and slaughtered the next day. Measurements of fat and M. longissimus areas were taken at the first and fifth lumbar vertebrae.
* Pistola lean (%) = amount of lean in the pistola as a percentage of the total carcase weight.
r_P = phenotypic correlation
r_G = genetic correlation
** M. longissimus area on the carcase included for comparison.

feed intake of individual bulls are measured using age-constant testing for a period from about 150 to 400 days of age. The whole period of the test is considered to be an equilibrating period during which the effects of different farm treatments before weaning and the start of the test are steadily reduced.

In the U.S.A., time-constant testing is commonly used in which bull calves are taken at weaning from their dams, and under uniform conditions of feeding, rate of gain and feed consumption are measured for 140, 196 and 240 days.

At the end of the M.L.C. test, the bulls are visually assessed for conformation and a withers height measurement is taken in addition to the ultrasonic fat areas over the *M. longissimus* referred to earlier.

Tradition has favoured selection based on tests in a high nutrition environment, on the theory that this will allow the better bulls to show their full potential. In the E.A.A.P. survey of methods used in Europe, the most commonly used feeding system was roughage *ad libitum* and concentrates restricted; this is appropriate when selection is for lean tissue growth rate and appetite, if roughage feeding is normal in commercial practice where the improved stock are to be used.

Under range conditions where feeding is often poor after weaning, little progress is apparent from breeding except in weaning weight, and such areas import bulls regularly to keep up the beef qualities of their stock. These bulls are produced in stud farms under conditions of unlimited nutrition, nurse cows frequently being used until they are about eighteen months old, so that selection can be made of bulls which show the greatest development of beef qualities. One disadvantage of this system is that the bulls which grow best under conditions of intensive feeding are not necessarily the ones whose progeny grow best under more extensive conditions. In the U.K., performance tests of bulls on a high concentrate ration are probably satisfactory because their progeny, though on pasture, can also experience a high plane of feeding during part of their commercial growth. But bulls selected in this way will probably not give the progeny best adapted to dry tropical conditions.

The main British programme of progeny testing is carried out by the Milk Marketing Board (England and Wales) (M.M.B.) of its beef bulls used for A.I., the progeny being reared and finished at a central station. The M.M.B. supplements this by additional tests carried out in beef suckler herds. The M.L.C. uses the records from its farm beef recording service to progeny-test other bulls already in use in A.I.

The progeny test is easier to apply in beef than in dairy cattle, for beef qualities are expressed in both sexes and at all ages, so that beef bulls can be proven at a much earlier age than dairy bulls. In progeny testing for beef, at least twenty steers or young bulls by each beef bull under test are taken at weaning from beef cows, or as calves in the case of dairy cows, and reared preferably by individual feeding under similar conditions. A simple linear measurement and visual appraisal is made after slaughter.

In these tests, the usual question arises, should the steers be killed when they have reached a certain degree of finish, a certain age, or a certain weight? The first criterion is difficult to estimate and the second is easy to operate but may give some carcases which are too fat (or heavy) and some that are too lean (or light). The last has the advantage that carcase measurements can be compared directly, as is the case with pig progeny testing. The M.M.B. use the latter type of progeny test, which involves visual assessments for fatness and conformation and several measurements on the cut surface of the carcases at the tenth rib.

In the Danish national progeny testing scheme, groups of ten bull calves by different sires are slaughtered at a live weight of 300 kg and detailed carcase evaluation carried out following closely standardised handling procedures. This involves the dissection of the hind leg and assessments of meat toughness from the sixth/seventh rib cut.

A summary of genetic parameters for beef characters is shown in table 16.2.

Table 16.2 Summary of genetic parameters for beef cattle: heritabilities (on the diagonal) and genetic correlations (28)

	BW	DG	W_{12}	FC	FC/G	MW	L/B	L/F	DP
BW	0.44	0.40	0.64		−0.46	0.89	−0.04	0.55	−0.05
DG		0.54	0.98	0.64	−0.95	0.40	−0.34	0.52	−0.61
W_{12}			0.42						
FC				0.64					
FC/G					0.36		0.27	−0.53	0.46
MW						0.57	0.05		
L/B							0.52	0.25	0.56
L/F								0.50	−0.12
DP									0.58

BW = birth weight; DG = daily gain; W_{12} = weight at 12 months; FC = feed consumed; FC/G = feed consumed/kg gain; MW = mature weight; L/B = lean/bone ratio; L/F = lean/fat ratio; DP = dressing percentage

BEEF CHARACTERISTICS IN DAIRY CATTLE

Beef coming as a by-product from the dairy herd makes a major contribution to overall beef production in many countries. In Britain, as we have seen, as much as two-thirds of the home produced beef carries at least some Friesian blood. There is a general trend to the upgrading of native European Friesians with Canadian Holsteins, the extent of which has been reviewed by Cunningham (87). This is causing concern among beef producers and in the meat trade because of the relatively poor beefing characteristics of Holsteins compared with British Friesians and other European black and white strains. The Holsteins have considerably poorer conformation and lower lean to bone ratios than the native Friesian breeds that they are replacing, so interest in improving these characteristics has intensified.

In Britain, the M.M.B. in collaboration with M.L.C. has developed a system of visual appraisal of dairy heifers which, it is hoped, will enable distinctions to be drawn between Friesian bulls in terms of the suitability of their male calves for beef. All the heifers of M.M.B. Friesian bulls used in A.I. are being assessed for muscularity. The results will not be used in the selection of sires to return to the stud for extensive use; the intention is rather to provide information on beef shape in addition to that already given on dairy production and dairy conformation, to enable those farmers who wish to do so to take this characteristic into account when selecting appropriate sires.

The visual assessment of muscularity is simple and cheap. Moreover, used in the way indicated, the degree of selection that can be applied for dairy characteristics in the choice of young bulls for progeny testing is not reduced. The technique has yet to be evaluated; meanwhile there is no intention of culling bulls for poor beef merit. This can only be a holding position and the question of selection objectives, testing methods and selection intensity remains. A progeny test of Friesian steers by bulls selected on the basis of their heifer progeny's conformation scores was begun in 1980 to determine the effect of this work on beef carcase characteristics.

Dual testing for milk and beef is routine over much of Europe. The usual approach is to precede the progeny test by a beef performance test. In these tests, carcase traits are usually given low weighting because so many other characteristics have to be considered and because market differentials are low in several countries (151). Dual testing of this type has not been adopted in Britain but a fresh discussion of the possibilities has been prompted by the effects of the Holsteins imported from Canada.

A beef performance test of Friesian bulls has been rejected in Britain on the grounds of cost, and a fall in the dairy merit of bull mothers if more contract matings took place to allow culling of the young bulls which were unsatisfactory for beef. Cost-benefit analyses show that genetic gains for milk are very sensitive to the intensity with which bull mothers are selected and that the financial value in terms of milk yield response is greater than that of response in terms of improved beef production. Moreover, selection objectives for beef are not clear and there is concern that selection for live weight gain may increase cow size and reduce the efficiency of milk production.

17 Sheep improvement schemes

The development of breeding programmes for sheep is far less advanced than those for pigs and cattle, few countries having a national programme for selection within breeds. Where programmes do exist they are normally based on performance testing, with no direct measures of carcase characteristics. They rely on improvements associated with selection for growth rate.

The problem of how best to make improvements in sheep carcase quality is particularly important for the sheep industries in many countries, since a high proportion of the carcases produced are too fat for modern consumer requirements. Over-fatness, together with the difficulty of using sheep meat in processed meat products, are believed to have been important factors in the decline in the demand for lamb in Britain relative to other meats.

Sheep graze for most of their life, so feed conversion is relatively unimportant commercially except in areas of very intensive grazing where stocking rate may be significant. Taken as an overall economic objective, selection for rate of lean tissue gain (lean tissue gain/day) is probably most important. As with cattle, this can be achieved by selection for growth rate with a correlated increase in adult body size. There is a problem in discriminating between rams with a high rate of live weight gain with significant fat deposition, and those with a high rate of lean tissue gain.

If the concern is with an optimum weight and level of fatness, there would be considerable advantages in changing the growth curve so that growth rate is increased to market weight, but not thereafter (see fig. 14.1).

A useful review concerning the improvement of carcase merit in meat sire breeds was published by Bradford (36). Although the cost of progeny testing is usually likely to be prohibitive, this could be justified in a small number of flocks at the top of the breeding pyramid. Bradford gives examples of the numbers required; the number of sheep in flocks engaged in progeny testing need not exceed 20 per cent of the total terminal sire breed population or 0.2 per cent of the total population. Rams should be performance tested as lambs, selected and used in pure-bred flocks at one year of age and replaced annually from the best of the next crop of rams, progeny tested as lambs, so permitting their selection on the basis of a progeny test at the yearling age. Use of artificial insemination in commercial flocks would permit much more widespread use of the best progeny tested rams, rather than one or two generations removed.

Selection programmes for sheep have been limited in the United Kingdom, but in New Zealand and Australia more comprehensive schemes have been developed for selection for growth, wool characters and number of lambs born. In Australia where large populations on any one farm are available for selection, even larger populations have been obtained by the organisation of nucleus breeding schemes. Several breeders collaborate and select their best animals for transfer to an elite nucleus flock where greater selection intensity is practised. Young males are supplied from the nucleus for progeny testing in the collaborating flocks and the best are returned to the nucleus to breed more young males for testing. In some cases, the best females from the collaborator flocks are also supplied to the nucleus, but many of the nucleus flock female replacements are bred in the flock from the very best progeny-tested males mated to nucleus flock females. However, even in these countries surprisingly little direct attention is paid to carcase characteristics; several key publications on sheep improvement there fail to mention carcase traits.

Progeny testing provides the most accurate method of selection for carcase characteristics, and indeed at present it is the only means of selecting for the detailed carcase characteristics. (The level of precision achieved for the prediction of carcase lean percentage with different carcase measurements was shown in chapter 8).

However, as with other species, progeny testing places serious constraints on the implementation of large-scale sheep breeding programmes and considerable advantages are to be gained from performance testing involving the estimation of body composition of live rams. However, ultrasonic techniques, which are at present the most useful live animal assessment procedure for pig and beef breeding programmes, are less valuable with sheep. The degree of precision is low in relation to the capital and operating costs of the Scanogram or Danscanner, and their proposed use in a particular breeding scheme would need to be examined carefully from a cost-benefit point of view.

Results from published studies (chapter 6) indicate that scan measurements of fat area at the twelfth rib can be used to identify differences in carcase composition of lambs of the same breed, sex and live weight when significant variation exists, although even then with low precision. It is debatable whether the predictions are precise enough for practical application. At best they may be useful in selection programmes within nucleus flocks of the more important meat sire breeds, where there is the opportunity to multiply any small genetic advantage by large numbers of lambs at the slaughter population level, or as an aid in differentiating between animals of widely different carcase composition in experiments.

A comparison of different predicting measurements, including ultrasonics, within nucleus Suffolk flocks in Britain failed to show that the measurements were of any value. The weight for age of lambs adjusted for their birth rearing type (born and reared as singles or twins), gave the most precise indication of rate of lean tissue gain, and none of the measurements examined reduced the residual s.d. significantly (table 17.1). There was limited variation in carcase

Table 17.1 Residual s.d. for the prediction of rate of lean gain and percentage lean in carcase from different measurements. (Based on 20 Suffolk ram lambs within each of two nucleus flocks). (Unpublished M.L.C. results)

| | Flock 1 | | Flock 2 | |
	Lean gain (g/day)	Lean in carcase (%)	Lean gain (g/day)	Lean in carcase (%)
Mean	85.0	64.5	74.2	59.9
Standard deviation	11.8	2.69	9.3	2.46
Prediction from:				
Final live weight (W) + age at final weighing (A)	3.8	1.42	4.2	1.92
$W + A$ + best linear body measurement	3.8	1.34	4.1	1.92
$W + A$ + best ultrasonic measurement taken by Scanogram*	3.8	1.35	4.0	1.91
$W + A$ + best ultrasonic measurement taken by Danscanner*	3.7	1.34	NM	NM

* Measurements were taken on cross-sectional photographs at the twelfth rib.
NM Not measured

lean percentage in these flocks at equal weight for age and this may not prove to be a general finding. It does, however, underline that it is important to determine whether the technique is successful (by carrying out some dissection) before money is committed to expensive ultrasonic work on a routine basis.

There have been several studies in the U.S.A. to examine the effects of selection for growth rate on carcase composition in lamb (for example, 303). In general the results confirm a relationship between growth rate and increased carcase lean content at a given slaughter weight. In a large-scale British study of genetic parameters in cross-bred lambs (392), average daily gain from birth to slaughter had a genetic correlation of 0.95 with lean weight growth per day of age. Other genetic correlations among carcase traits were favourable in terms of the selection objective of higher carcase lean percentage at a fixed carcase weight although this would be associated with a decreased lean to bone ratio.

Without an effective live animal assessment of fatness, the visual identification of the blockier sires with better muscling and higher muscle to bone ratios is difficult. That is because, as indicated earlier, conformation assessments, which are the main method of identifying muscularity, are normally confounded with fatness (see chapter 9). Very skilled assessors would be required to pick up the small conformation-related differences in composition. With less skilled operators, the relationships could easily slip away to nothing, or selection on conformation might even lead to the selection of fatter carcases. If conformation is to play an important role as a measured character in sheep breeding schemes, it would be advisable to carry out carcase dissection of progeny at several stages in the selection programme to compare selected and non-selected lines and determine whether differences in carcase composition are being realised and, if so, what the direction of the improvement is.

We believe that in practice it would be better to ignore conformation completely in sheep because of the difficulties of accurate fatness assessment. The minor differences which are found between British sheep breeds in carcase lean content at equal fatness, despite their selection over a long period for different conformation types (212), together with the poor relationships found within breeds, suggest that selection based on conformation is unlikely to be successful in increasing leanness.

The use of progeny testing coupled with selection for more detailed carcase characteristics may be appropriate given the right breed structure.

Carcase quality of market lambs will be improved if the lambs are slaughtered at the appropriate degree of maturity, which can be estimated from knowledge of adult body size (see chapter 6). Improved recommendations on optimum slaughter weight would be made if reports of testing programmes with sheep routinely included mature weights of adult breeding animals.

18 Carcase evaluation in population studies and experiments

Carcase evaluation is the final stage in animal population studies and experiments and is an essential element if the study is to be comprehensive. Although the final stage, the techniques used affect the experimental design, particularly the numbers of animals involved and the choice of end point, and careful thought needs to be given to them *before* the experiment begins. In our experience from providing a carcase evaluation service to universities and research institutes, all too often the techniques are not considered in detail until the trial is under way and the animals are approaching slaughter. Indeed, experiments are sometimes planned and costed without building in the necessary costs of carcase evaluations.

Optimum efficiency in one part of the production and distribution chain may not lead to optimum efficiency overall, so it is important when designing experiments to take a view of all the factors which bear on the efficiency of production, processing and marketing right through to the consumer. For example, several trials were carried out in Britain which showed major advantages for entire male pigs over castrates in the efficiency of production. But these trials did not include a full evaluation of the suitability of entire males for the meat industry, in particular for bacon curing. When this information was eventually obtained, the balance of advantage was reduced substantially although it remained in favour of entire males (199, 275).

The cost of carcase evaluation must also be seen in relation to the overall cost of the experiment. The latter is often equated to the value of the animal at slaughter, and carcase evaluation costs expressed as a proportion of this. However, experimental production is often much more expensive than commercial production, allowing for the salaries of the personnel involved, the cost of experimental land, buildings, equipment and overheads, and the additional cost of experimental production techniques over those of optimum commercial production. Carroll (61) put the costs of beef experiments at as much as ten times the commercial cost. In relation to the real experimental production cost, therefore, carcase evaluation may represent a small percentage increase in overall cost and so be more easily justified. Expensively acquired experimental material should not be wasted because costs are not looked at in a realistic way, particularly if the experiment has to be repeated at a later date to provide carcase information.

A central dissection facility operated independently or by co-operating research centres (linked to, but isolated from, a commercial abattoir) can reduce significantly the unit cost of carcase evaluation work. The expensive overhead represented by the maintenance of such facilities can be spread over a large number of animals, and there are also considerable advantages in having a permanent staff of skilled assessors, technicians and dissectors. To make the most of experiments from the carcase point of view, some such facility is necessary. Concentrating effort in this way also provides material for the quick and efficient testing of new prediction techniques. The creation of large files of carcase evaluation data allows the techniques to be examined over a wide range of carcase types.

There is not space here to go into details of experimental procedures and methodology. There are, however, several useful publications which include such information. The British Society of Animal Production (B.S.A.P.) held a symposium on cattle experiments in 1975, the proceedings of which have been published (394). The important point is made that the ultimate object of any investigation, at whatever level, is to enable someone somewhere to make a decision. The success of an experiment is, therefore, not to be measured by the numerical result achieved, but by the weight of evidence provided by the experimenter in favour of that numerical result. This consideration is particularly important for carcase evaluation work where it is often necessary to rely on predicting measurements which may weaken the results.

The E.A.A.P. set up a working party to survey cattle breed comparisons and crossbreeding trials in Europe. Their report (21) includes recommendations on methodology for future experiments. Among other things, the importance of greater uniformity in dissection methods is emphasised.

The following questions need to be asked when considering carcase evaluation in population studies and experiments:

(a) What end point is most appropriate? Should the group of animals being compared be slaughtered at the same age, the same weight or on some other basis?
(b) Should the animals be slaughtered serially or all at the same point?
(c) Which characteristics should be examined and what size of differences need to be identified statistically?
(d) Is evaluation of the live animal appropriate and, if so, what methods should be employed?
(e) How should carcase composition be predicted? What measurements should be taken and what is the best approach to prediction?
(f) How will the results be analysed and presented, and how will economic differences be calculated?

Each of these questions will be considered in turn.

Choice of end point

Slaughter of experimental groups can be arranged on a number of bases:

- — at the same live weight
- — at the same age
- — at the same level of fatness
- — at the same degree of maturity
- — after the same time on test or after a fixed amount of food has been eaten.

All the animals in each group may be slaughtered at a single point or selected in advance to be slaughtered serially over a range of end points.

SAME LIVE WEIGHT

Slaughtering at a predetermined live weight entails frequent weighing and the experimenter has only limited warning of the date of slaughter. The animals are likely to differ considerably in the level of fatness at slaughter if there are important differences in the mature size of the breed populations tested (see chapter 3) or if very different feeding planes are compared. Slaughter at fixed live weight has been most commonly used in pig research, because market requirements for pig carcases are defined closely in weight terms in many countries, less frequently with cattle and rarely in sheep research.

SAME AGE

This has two important attractions: no error is involved in the determination and the date of slaughter is known well in advance to assist planning. Slaughtering at the same age can, however, cause problems in experiments where growth rates are unpredictable because of poor environmental control, as for example with grazing animals. Under such conditions the animals may not have grown to a sufficient weight or level of fatness at the set age for a proper commercial evaluation of the results.

SAME FATNESS

Selection of animals for slaughter at the same predetermined level of fatness is more difficult and can introduce bias into the comparison of treatments or populations if the selection at fixed fatness is not successful. In an early attempt at slaughtering at fixed fatness in a large-scale breed comparison in Britain (249) some breeds were slaughtered at lower levels of fatness than expected, and satisfactory adjustment of the data to allow statistical comparisons at equal fatness proved impossible.

Live animal evaluation techniques can be used to improve precision. The Scanogram was used, for example, in the M.L.C. beef breed evaluation programme to select cattle for slaughter at a given carcase subcutaneous fat percentage (226). Fat areas over the *M. longissimus* at the 10th and 13th rib positions were used to predict carcase subcutaneous fat percentage. A residual s.d. of 1.18% subcutaneous fat was obtained when the data were pooled within year, breed and system of production. The equivalent residual s.d. for leanness would be about 2% of carcase weight.

Slaughter on an equal fatness basis can be useful in trials involving breeds differing widely in mature size because it approximates to equal maturity (269). Further, in commercial practice, cattle tend to be slaughtered at similar levels of fatness over quite wide ranges of age and weight.

When comparing treatments or populations at a fixed level of fatness, the chosen level needs careful definition. Should the animals be compared, for example, at the same fat thickness, at the same level of external fat cover or at the same dissectible fat content in the carcase? There are important differences between breeds in fat partition (chapter 3) which can cause comparisons made on different definitions of equal fatness to give different results. In M.L.C. beef and sheep breed comparison trials we have used a fixed carcase subcutaneous fat percentage (83, 210). This was chosen in preference to total fat because it has more commercial relevance at the producer/wholesaler level: producers select cattle and sheep for slaughter largely on the basis of estimated subcutaneous fat cover, while a visual assessment of subcutaneous fat cover is the basis of wholesalers' selection of carcases for alternative uses or buyers in Britain.

SAME DEGREE OF MATURITY

Slaughter at the same degree of maturity is likely to be most valuable in basic growth studies or in trials carried out to characterise breed populations. This may be defined, for example, in terms of live weight as a proportion of adult body weight or the more readily obtained birth weight.

SAME TEST PERIOD

Slaughter after a fixed period on test or after a given amount of food has been eaten is used in nutritional studies, particularly those concerned with the efficiency of nutrient retention in the animal body.

Serial slaughtering

End points which satisfy all experimental requirements are rarely possible; indeed there is often an interaction between treatment and slaughter point (that is the effect of the treatment varies with the end point chosen). Because of this, slaughtering animals serially may be considered to allow the interactions to be measured and results for different points identified. Serial slaughtering also allows the construction of growth curves and the determination of optimum slaughter points, for example the point at which animals convert feed into lean meat most efficiently. For ease of operation, slaughter at a series of predetermined ages is probably the most satisfactory procedure and is commonly used in beef and sheep population studies (for example, 236 and 393). In the final phase of the M.L.C. beef breed evaluation programme, serial slaughter at three levels of fatness was attempted, the level chosen for each breed depending on its adult body size. The effectiveness of this procedure has yet to be determined.

A problem with serial slaughtering is to decide on the emphasis to be given to the detection of interactions. When no interactions occur, comparison at a single point can be made by regression, information from all the points contributing to the comparison. Because of this no large increase in numbers should be necessary to achieve a similar degree of precision for the main comparison. However, if important interactions do occur, and there is a need to measure them as accurately as the main differences, a considerable increase in the numbers will be necessary. The art is to have some idea beforehand of the likelihood of interactions with the treatments applied. If there is uncertainty about their importance, numbers are needed to establish the facts; the issue cannot be avoided by going for one end point only.

In some population studies and experiments, when only the last part of the lifetime performance of the animals is studied, a group of animals may be slaughtered at the start of the experiment to provide base data for the calculation of characteristics such as rate of lean tissue gain or efficiency of lean meat gain from start to finish of test. Carcase evaluation in pre-experimental slaughter groups is efficient because the same animals provide information for each of the treatments involved.

Choice of characteristics

Experiments and population studies may have various biological objectives or economic goals and potentially a large number of characteristics could be considered. However, carcase evaluation is often carried out in a limited way since:

(a) Production experiments are rarely made to describe the overall situation; while production characteristics may be examined in detail, often the experiment is not designed to extend 'beyond the farm gate'.
(b) Assessment of some of the more detailed carcase characteristics is expensive, time consuming and too complex for most research workers to carry out as a routine.

The choice of characteristics to be studied is important and can have a big impact on the cost of carcase evaluation in a particular trial. The question to ask is: 'Are we interested only in the lean content of the carcase, which is the prime determinant of commercial value, or are other base-line characteristics such as the proportion of lean in the higher-priced joints, the distribution and partition of fat between depots and the eating quality of meat also important in the context of the trial?'

The more base-line characteristics that must be included in the trial, the less choice there will be in the carcase evaluation techniques which can be used for a given cost. Inclusion of the lean meat distribution between joints, for example, normally requires some whole side evaluation, so ruling out sample joint dissection as the main method of evaluation. If it is decided to ignore tissue distribution, then the choice becomes simpler; this may well be a sensible decision in nutritional or other environmental studies where differences in distribution are not expected.

Detailed meat quality characteristics, if included, can also complicate the experimental design in some cases if there is a need to slaughter animals from different treatments or populations at the same time so that meat samples from their carcases can be handled contemporaneously. Failure to do this can introduce uncontrolled variation into comparisons because of the influence of post mortem treatment on meat quality. When such a procedure would conflict with the optimum trial design, our advice would be to set aside a subset of carcases for special treatment for meat quality assessment rather than to compromise the design.

Besides considerations of base-line characteristics, certain simple measurements may be important in their own right and necessary for a full economic appraisal of the results. Of particular importance can be the measurements used in the classification and grading schemes of the countries where the results are to be applied (these measurements may or may not be related to the ultimate value of the carcases in terms of meat yield). Such information is cheap and easy to obtain, yet the results of many studies surprisingly have been published without it. Their incorporation can also lead to the refinement of the techniques used in the classification and grading schemes. The involvement of research workers in this way may also lead to a greater understanding of the practical application of carcase evaluation techniques and to more commercially orientated research.

Numbers required

Determination of the numbers of carcases necessary to identify specified differences between treatments when different predicting measurements are used was considered in detail by Timon and Bichard (365). They showed that the numbers required are a function of the specified difference, the level of statistical confidence required in its estimation and the precision of the predicting measurements involved.

The relationship is not a simple one; those interested in using it should refer to the original paper, which includes a table (table 18.1) showing the numbers of carcases required to provide the same confidence in detecting differences of various magnitudes between two treatments when predicting measurements with different precision are used.

Information from live animals

The possibility of carrying out live animal assessment in experiments and population studies involving carcase evaluation is often overlooked. Such information can, however, increase the precision of the study considerably.

Consider, for example, a study to compare the carcase lean percentage of

Table 18.1 Number of sheep carcases per treatment required to detect a significant difference* (δ^1)** of different orders of magnitude between two treatments in carcase lean percentage (365)

Methods of carcase evaluation	Number of animals required for different δ^1		
	1.0	0.5	0.25
Side dissection	11	37	143
Lean in leg and loin (%)	12	41	154
Lean in loin (%)	12	43	162
Specific gravity	14	48	193
Combination of linear measurements	15	53	201
Visual fat scores	17	62	239

* Probability of detecting a real difference = 0.75; probability of detecting a chance difference as real = 0.05.
** δ^1 = minimum detectable difference in standard units (δ/s.d.y.).

two lines of pigs from a selection experiment or breeding programme with (say) 100 pigs available for measurement. Some full dissection is considered necessary but only a small sub-sample of the animals can be slaughtered and dissected because of cost. The problem here is one of sampling error: how does one ensure that the sub-samples selected are representative of the two lines and that the information obtained from them is used as effectively as possible? Ultrasonic measurements of fat thickness may be taken on all the pigs and this information used to refine the estimates of carcase lean percentage obtained from the sub-sample slaughtered and dissected (see the discussion of sub-sampling with regression later).

Consider, as a second example, an experiment in which all the animals are to be compared at a fixed level of fatness. In the normal course of events, adjustment of measurements made to constant fatness would be based on the between animal regression on some measure of fatness taken on the carcases after slaughter. However, the precision of such adjustments may be improved if ultrasonic measurements are taken on all animals at fixed points over the growth period, and the within-animal regression of the character studied on ultrasonic measurements used to adjust the data. Under some circumstances this could provide a much better approximation of the growth of the animals.

Periodic live animal assessment can also be valuable where serial slaughter is desirable but not possible. In life-time performance trials, this would apply when there is a change in diet or feeding level as, for example, at the beginning and end of different feeding periods (for example, the store period) in beef production trials. The information can be used to examine changes in carcase composition over short periods of the trial and estimate the importance, for example, of compensatory growth.

Choice of predictors

The selection of the most suitable predictors for use in population studies and experiments presents a more complex problem than in commercial classification and grading or in breeding schemes: there is normally a wider range of potential predictors available and more flexibility in the ways they can be used. Further in contrast to the classification situation, details of genotypes, feeding regimen, fattening conditions and so on are normally available to improve the prediction.

Factors involved in the selection of predictors are:

(a) the precision of estimates obtained using the predictors
(b) the cost of taking the predicting measurements
(c) the stability of prediction equations between the populations or experimental treatments being compared.

The precision of a predictor, or combination of predictors, is defined by the residual s.d. about the regression line used for prediction, the proportionate reduction in the standard deviation being taken as a measure of the success of the predictor. Precision in relation to the cost of different predictors was considered in chapter 8.

However, as has been mentioned several times earlier in this book, regression relationships can vary between carcases differing, for example, in breed type, sex or feeding regimen and so introduce biases into the comparison of populations or experimental treatments. (A graphic representation of this was shown in chapter 4). In many circumstances, such biases may be of more practical importance than the precision of prediction within population or treatment.

The number of animals per treatment in an experiment will be determined by the experimental design and the level of precision required in detecting a given difference at a particular level of statistical significance. Consequently, the use of poorer predictors (which are likely to be less costly) can be counterbalanced by the use of the extra animals required to absorb this increase in variance due to errors of prediction. Timon and Bichard (365) found that a relatively small increase in the numbers of animals per treatment is sufficient to absorb a substantial amount of error variance in prediction. For example, they found that 164 sheep carcases, evaluated using simple linear measurements, gave the same precision as 100 side-dissected carcases in predicting lean content. The comparable number required if the dissection of the loin joint was used as predictor was 116.

But increasing the number of animals per treatment will not alter the extent of any bias resulting from different regression relationships between treatments. So an important object of carcase evaluation research is to find unbiased predictors.

The importance of variation in the intercept and slope parameters of the prediction equation depends both on the type of population comparison or experiment and on the method of prediction used. The possible methods of prediction are of two basic types:

(a) There is no base line dissection; predicting measurements only are taken on the carcases. These measurements are used to estimate population or treatment differences using regression parameters obtained elesewhere.

(b) A subsample of the carcases from each treatment or population is fully dissected and a predicting measurement taken on the whole sample. Regression equations derived from the dissected subsample are used to obtain estimates of population or treatment differences in carcase composition based on the whole sample.

The former procedure depends for its validity on the assumption that regression equations for the predicting measurements and carcase composition are stable and can be applied from one situation to another. Some confidence can be placed in the use of predictors which have been shown to have stable equations over a range of conditions, but there is no certainty that they will apply under all new circumstances and hence no guarantee that the estimates of carcase composition will not be biased to some extent. Also actual application of a regression equation is not necessary to occasion a bias; an equation is effectively being applied when the assumption is made that the ranking and the relative differences in carcase composition between treatments are the same as for the predicting measurements.

Although there are many reports of analyses to compare predictors in a single group of animals, examination of the same predictors over a series of different treatments or populations to determine the stability of prediction equations has been rare: sample sizes have generally been too small, or the data insufficiently variable in origin, to do this.

Stability of prediction equations for pigs

For many years, prediction relationships have been known to differ between sexes and breeds. Attention was drawn to the problem by Harrington (156) and early results on the subject were reviewed by Osinska (305), but only recently has the problem been brought into focus in practical applications.

Evidence on the existence of important population differences in prediction relationships is now available from a co-ordinated study of carcase evaluation techniques in E.E.C. countries (77). At the same fat thickness measurement, there was a range of three to six percentage units (depending on the particular fat measurement) in carcase lean content between extreme populations (fig. 18.1). The different populations in the trial were not grown, slaughtered or measured contemporaneously so the reason for the biases is not certain. However, the extreme populations were, on the one hand British and Danish, and on the other Belgian Landrace and Belgian Pietrain, which are known to differ markedly in muscle to bone ratio and to some extent in tissue distribution. The bias might, therefore, be expected to have an important genetic component.

Despite these differences between populations in carcase lean content at equal fatness, there was some consistency in the relative precision of different

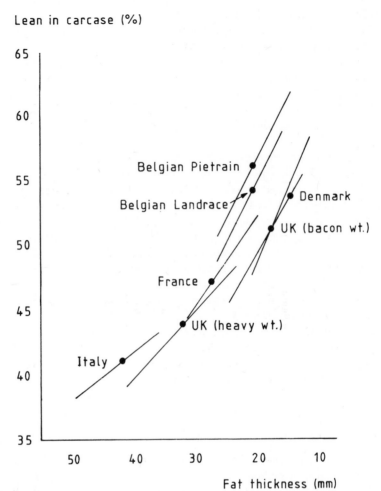

Fig. 18.1 Carcase lean percentage against fat thickness for different populations of European pigs (77)

'Fat thickness' is the average of three fat thickness measurements taken by the Danish MFA: over *M. gluteus*, third lumbar (8 cm) and third/fourth last rib (6 cm).

predictors. In particular, the Danish grading equation was consistently more precise than the basic E.E.C. technique (involving mid-line fat thickness and conformation type as in the original six member states) in predicting carcase lean content. de Boer *et al.* (99) recorded the same result in a trial carried out in the Netherlands (table 18.2). The bias between populations was also reduced to some extent when the Danish equation was used, suggesting that there may be value in using a range of measurements when there is concern about bias.

The M.L.C.'s comparison of commercial hybrid pigs from different breeding companies in Great Britain (known as Commercial Pig Evaluation) indicated

Table 18.2 Residual s.d. for the prediction of pig carcase lean percentage (defined in the same way for each country) from different combinations of predictors

	Denmark	U.K. (Bacon)	Belgium Pietrain	Belgium Landrace	France	U.K. (Heavy)	Italy	De Boer and others (99) Netherlands
				CEC (77)				
Mean carcase weight (kg)	65.2	68.7	80.3	82.6	84.4	93.8	130.3	84.9
Number of carcases	36	36	36	36	34	30	32	104
Standard deviation of carcase lean percentage	5.37	5.22	5.92	5.76	4.92	5.46	3.41	5.13
Residual s.d. for								
E.E.C. max. fat thickness	2.84	3.13	2.88	3.55	3.16	3.02	2.46	2.91
E.E.C. max. + type class	2.88	2.64	2.53	2.91	2.85	2.78	2.48	2.50
Fat thickness at 3rd/4th last rib by M.F.A. probe (3/4F)*	1.88	2.46	2.15	3.23	2.98	3.28	2.74	2.60
3/4F + type class	1.76	2.10	1.96	2.94	2.29	2.85	2.74	2.25
Combination of measurements as in the Danish technique (311)	1.73	2.16	1.93	2.39	1.89	2.38	2.04	2.09

* Fat thickness over the M. longissimus, 6 cm from the dorsal mid-line.

Table 18.3 Composition of pig carcases from the breeding companies involved in M.L.C.'s commercial pig evaluation, compared at the same carcase weight and P_2 fat thickness (221)*. Results are shown as deviations from the overall mean: company mean minus overall mean

	Number of carcases	Lean in carcase (%)	Separable fat in carcase (%)	Lean to bone ratio
Overall mean		49.1	26.4	5.78
Company means				
A	140	0	−0.2	−0.04
B	106	−1.6	1.5	−0.20
C	148	1.5	−1.5	0.02
D	141	−0.9	0.3	−0.15
E	129	0.7	−0.4	0.17
F	107	1.1	−0.6	0.19
G	142	−0.1	0	0.01
H**	94	0.2	−0.3	−0.01
I	103	−1.2	1.0	−0.13
J	105	0.1	−0.1	0.08
K	71	0.1	0.1	0
L	34	0	0.2	0.02
M	33	0.6	0	0.19
N	32	−0.2	0.4	−0.08

* Data were analysed using a model which included effects for year, sex and feeding regimen.
** Pure-bred Large White.

significant differences with a range of up to three percentage units in carcase lean content between pigs from different breeding companies at equal carcase weight and P_2 fat thickness (116, 221). Using the company of origin of the pigs as a predictor, together with carcase weight and P_2, reduced the residual s.d. of carcase lean percentage from 2.45 to 2.30. There was little difference between pigs from different companies in lean to bone ratio, the bias in this case being due essentially to differences in carcase fat percentage at equal weight and P_2 thickness (table 18.3). A detailed examination of company differences in tissue distribution using multivariate statistical techniques indicated, among other things, that the companies with a higher lean content than would have been predicted had more subcutaneous fat in the back and less in the streak (belly) than companies with low lean content at equal P_2 and weight (117).

The evidence so far available indicates that the bias is not eliminated by any of the conventional mid-line or probe fat thickness measurements, by *M. longissimus* depth or by conformation score. Fat thickness measurements taken by probe in the streak have, therefore, been examined and preliminary results suggest that elimination of the bias will be difficult without recourse to techniques which directly measure muscle content.

Our work shows that the use of sample joint dissections is not immune from prediction bias. Evans and Kempster (116) examined differences between commercial companies, feeding regimens (*ad libitum* and restricted feeding) and sexes (castrated males and gilts) in the relationships between carcase lean percentage and the lean percentage of sample joints. Fat thickness at P_2 was included as an independent variate because such measurements are readily obtainable at little extra cost and, as indicated in chapter 8, the inclusion of P_2 in multiple regression significantly improves the prediction of carcase leanness from some sample joints.

Table 18.4 Regression of percentage lean in pig carcase on percentage lean in joints and P_2 fat thickness: statistical significance of intercept differences for pig breeding companies[1], sexes and feeding regimens, and deviations from the average intercept for each factor (116). Based on 384 bacon weight pigs from M.L.C.'s commercial pig evaluation

	Average intercept	P^2	*Companies* Deviation[3] H	L	P^2	*Sexes* Deviation castrated males	P^2	*Feeding regimens* Deviation Restricted-fed
Sample joint:								
Ham	7.73	NS			***	−0.26	***	+0.23
Rump back[4]								
Restricted	25.73	***	+1.03	−0.99	NS			
Ad libitum	12.74	**	+0.60	−0.79	NS			
Rib back	27.49	*	+0.29	−0.59	NS		NS	
Streak (belly)	29.85	**	+0.57	−0.60	***	−0.81	*	+0.17
Collar	34.57	***	+0.58	−1.18	NS		NS	
Hand	29.37	**	+0.56	−0.73	***	−0.18	NS	

[1] Commercial breeding company from which the pigs came.
[2] Significance of intercept differences: NS = not significant $(P > 0.05)$, * = $P < 0.05$, ** = $P < 0.01$, *** = $P < 0.001$.
[3] Companies H and L denote companies with highest and lowest intercepts respectively.
[4] Regressions were computed using common regression slopes for all groups where slopes did not differ significantly. There was a difference in slope between feeding regimens for the rump back joint, so the intercept differences for these were considered separately.

The slopes of the prediction equations were the same for different factors except in the case of the rump back joint for which they differed between feeding regimens. Differences in intercept are shown in table 18.4. The ham joint was most sensitive to differences in feeding regimen and therefore likely to be a poor choice in nutritional experiments where some base-line dissection is impossible. This joint was, however, the most stable for measuring differences between genetic populations and would be recommended for use in M.L.C.'s commercial pig evaluation. It would not necessarily be suitable for use in comparisons with wider genetic differences, in particular between breeds which are known to differ significantly in joint proportions. The results of the study only give an indication of the differences which might be found in other situations.

The occurrence of sample joints with unstable prediction equations is of particular concern because sample joints are primarily research tools and used in trials where small treatment or genetic differences may be of critical interest. So in such trials, some full dissection may be essential and the use of sample joints may not represent an optimal use of resources: dissection of a subset of carcases coupled with simple measurements on the remainder may be more cost-effective.

Stability of prediction equations for beef

Research into the stability of prediction equations for beef has been concerned mainly with the complications introduced by the important differences known to exist between breeds in fat partition (see chapter 3), and with the bias which may be introduced into experiments by the use of sample joints. The latter give cause for concern because they often make up a smaller proportion of the carcase than in the case of pigs and sheep, where the cost of sample joint per animal evaluated is lower.

The occurrence of variation in fat partition between depots provides a complication when predicting overall composition from measurements taken on a single depot, for example when carcase composition is predicted from subcutaneous fat depths or areas. Pomeroy and Williams (314) drew attention to the problems by demonstrating the differences which would occur between predicted and actual fat content if it were assumed that beef and dairy-type cattle have the same relationship between total dissectible fat and subcutaneous fat in the carcase. They found that the degree of bias was reduced when KKCF and subcutaneous fat were used together as predictors, and these findings were subsequently confirmed in a large body of dissection data covering a wide range of British breed types (214). When breed means for carcase fat percentage, derived from the overall regression of carcase fat percentage on carcase subcutaneous fat percentage, were compared with the actual breed means, the differences ranged from −3.6 to + 4.2 per cent fat in carcase.

The occurrence of breed differences in carcase fat content at the same fat thickness (reflecting these differences in fat partition) was demonstrated by Charles and Johnson (69). With Hereford as base, Aberdeen Angus, Charolais crosses and Friesians had respectively 0.9, 3.4 and 4.9 percentage units more fat in the carcase with the same fat thickness over the *M. longissimus* at the twelfth rib. Preliminary studies of M.L.C. beef breed evaluation data suggest a similar degree of bias using fat thickness at the twelfth rib.

These findings show that fat thickness measurements or measurements of one depot should not be relied on in beef breed evaluations; supplementation with information on KKCF percentage may be helpful but even the combination of fat thickness and KKCF percentage is unlikely to be adequate.

As with pigs, important differences also exist between breeds in carcase lean content at equal fatness reflecting differences in lean to bone ratio. Consequently, a full evaluation of carcase fatness may not give an unbiased estimate of breed differences in carcase leanness unless it is supplemented with some estimates of lean to bone ratio.

The potential dangers of using prediction equations for beef sample joint dissections in circumstances other than for those in which they were constructed have been pointed out, but few trials have been carried out to test the stability of equations in different situations. Ledger and Hutchison (245) found that the prediction of total fat in the carcase was improved by the use of separate prediction equations for steer and cow carcases. Williams *et al.* (385) examined the stability of regression equations between different breed groups of carcases by comparing predicted values with actual values; but their three groups differed in dissection procedure, so it is not possible to distinguish the effects of these various factors.

Table 18.5 Estimates of bias in the prediction of beef carcase lean percentage from the percentage of lean in various sample joints, on the assumption that prediction equations are the same for all breed groups (224). Based on a total of 753 steer carcases comprising 17 breed-type X feeding system groups

Sample joint	Cost of dissection as a percentage of side dissection cost [+]	Average bias*
Shin	3	1.86
Coast	12	0.43
Clod + sticking	8	0.65
Fore rib	9	0.63
Pony	20	0.54
Leg	3	1.79
Thin flank	5	0.92
Rump	10	0.39
Sirloin	12	0.64
Wing rib	6	0.68
Top piece	15	0.48

[+] Under the conditions of M.L.C.'s Carcase Evaluation Unit.
* Difference between the predicted mean (obtained from the overall regression equation) and the actual mean for each breed-type group, averaged over all groups ignoring the sign of the difference.

Our own work on this subject is summarised in table 18.5 (based on the same sample of carcases which was used to examine differences in precision and in the method of constructing the prediction equation, see chapter 8). The bias associated with the use of different joints is related to their size and cost, the smaller and cheaper joints, particularly the shin and leg, showing considerable bias in predicted composition. These results give substance to the fears expressed by others about the use of smaller sample joints and indicate that these joints should be avoided in trials when base-line dissection is impossible. Among the joints tested the wing rib appears to offer the best compromise between accuracy and cost.

Stability of prediction equations for sheep

Although there are many reports of analyses to compare the precision of different predictors in a single group of lambs, few have examined the same predictors over a series of groups; sample sizes have generally been too small or the data insufficiently variable in origin to do this. Several trials have provided indirect evidence of instability in prediction relationships. In particular, there appears to be an advantage in using different prediction equations for each sex when estimating the yield of retail cuts of lamb (58, 301).

Kempster *et al.* (204) found substantial instability in regression equations between seven breed-type groups, particularly for simple linear measurements and visual scores. However, this trial was designed specifically to examine predictors for use in sheep carcase classification, the groups being drawn at random from commercial abattoirs; so it was not suitable for drawing firm conclusions about predictors in the context of breeding schemes, population studies or experiments where the lambs would be grown contemporaneously.

More specific indicators emerged from a large-scale breed comparison trial carried out in Britain by the Animal Breeding Research Organisation (A.B.R.O.), Edinburgh, in collaboration with M.L.C. This involved the dissection of 894 cross-bred lambs out of two dam types by Dorset Down, Ile de France, Oldenburg, Oxford Down, Suffolk and Texel sires. Analysis of the carcase data indicated that bias between breeds can still be a problem even when breeds are compared within flock and year (table 18.6). The Texel crosses appeared quite different from the other breeds in several of the prediction relationships; they had significantly higher carcase lean percentages than would be predicted, due largely to their high lean to bone ratio and low KKCF percentage. The more precise predictors tended to be among the more stable, although some of the sample joints were exceptions to this rule.

On the basis of these results, dissection of the shoulder joint would be recommended for use in breed comparison trials when the full dissection of some carcases is impossible. Trials involving the Texel or similar breeds require special attention when selecting predictors.

Table 18.6 Estimate of bias in the prediction of sheep carcase lean percentage from a range of predictors on the assumption that prediction equations are the same for all breeds*

| | | Predictors | | | | | |
| | Number of carcases | Visual score | | Fat thickness | Percentage lean in sample joint | | | |
		external fat cover	KKCF development		best-end neck	shoulder	loin	leg
Kempster et al. (203)								
Breed-type group:								
Welsh Mountain	77	+1.5	+0.8	+1.3	+0.6	+0.9	+0.6	+0.7
Blackfaced Mountain	73	−1.2	−1.0	−0.8	+0.4	0.0	−0.1	−1.6
Longwool crosses	72	−2.1	−1.7	−1.9	−0.6	0.0	−1.4	−0.3
Suffolk crosses	62	+0.5	+0.4	+0.9	+0.1	−0.3	+0.6	−1.1
Intermediate**	49	−0.6	−0.4	−0.3	−0.6	−0.3	−0.3	+0.5
Southdown crosses	53	+2.1	+1.6	+0.9	+0.3	−0.4	+0.4	+2.2
Lowland Longwool	35	+0.3	+1.3	−0.1	−1.0	−0.4	+0.5	+0.9
*Kempster and Jones*** (unpublished results)*								
Sire breed:								
Dorset Down	154	+1.7	+2.0	+1.6	+0.7	+0.6	+1.0	+0.9
Ile de France	165	+0.7	+0.8	+0.6	−0.1	0.0	−0.1	+0.9
Oldenburg	138	−0.4	−0.2	−0.4	0.0	+0.1	−0.4	−0.8
Oxford Down	156	+0.7	+0.7	+0.3	+0.4	+0.1	+0.2	−0.3
Suffolk	158	+0.6	+0.4	+0.6	+0.4	+0.1	+0.4	−0.4
Texel	190	−3.3	−3.7	−2.8	−2.0	−0.7	−1.3	−0.5

* Predicted minus actual carcase lean percentage, with prediction based on a common regression line computed over all data.

** Intermediate-type lambs by Dorset Down or Hampshire Down sires.

*** Based on data from the A.R.C. Animal Breeding Research Organisation trial (393). The analysis was balanced for year, dam breed and sex effects.

Subsampling with regression

Subsampling of carcases for detailed evaluation, in combination with a simple measurement taken on all carcases, is a technique known as subsampling with regression. It is an excellent tool for overcoming, or at least minimising, the problem of bias brought about by the use of predictors with unstable regression equations.

The statistical methodology for the technique was developed by Conniffe and Moran (79). All the information available is amalgamated to provide the best estimates of treatment or population differences. The method assumes common regression slopes (or planes) for all treatments or populations, but makes no assumptions about intercept differences which are estimated directly by the method. Conniffe (78) found that the tests of treatment differences using subsampling with regression were robust to moderate variations in the slopes between treatments, and pointed out that, in any case, estimates of treatment differences were unbiased.

The principle of the technique is illustrated in fig. 18.2 using the example of predicting lean content in pig carcases from P_2 measurements. Consider two treatments with N pigs on each, with P_2 fat thickness measurements taken on all carcases after slaughter. A subsample of n pigs per treatment is also taken for side dissection. The subsample allows two positions (A and B) on the plot of carcase lean percentage on P_2 (fig. 18.2) to be pinpointed and the slope of the regression of carcase lean percentage on P_2 to be calculated pooled within treatment. Lines with this slope are drawn through A and B. The procedure is then simply to slide the position of the treatment means along the slopes to the positions corresponding to the average P_2 determined on all N pigs in each treatment (X_1 and X_2) to obtain the estimated treatment means for carcase lean content (Y_1 and Y_2).

Evans and Kempster (116) examined the use of the subsampling technique with regression in a large sample of dissected pig carcases to determine the optimum use of the technique with several predictors differing in precision and cost.

Fig. 18.3 shows the precision of an estimated treatment mean plotted against the total cost of the predicting measurements for different values of N and n. Precision is scaled in units of standard error (σ), while cost is given in terms relative to the cost of full side dissections. Line A is the precision achieved for different levels of cost when all the carcases per treatment are dissected; lines B, C and D give the same information for different options of subsampling with regression. B is subsampling with regression on P_2 fat thickness only; C and D are subsampling on percentage lean in the hand joint and ham joint, respectively, both with P_2 included in multiple regression. (The relative cost and precision of the different joints used in the calculations was as shown in table 8.3).

The advantage in terms of cost per unit of precision of using subsampling with regression instead of the full dissection of all animals within each treatment is clearly demonstrated. When compared with full dissection of all animals

Lean in carcase (%)

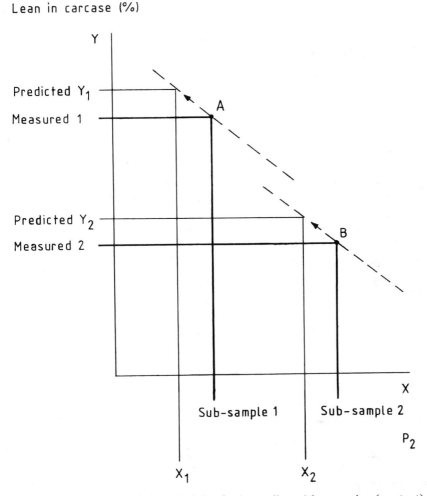

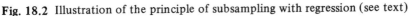

Fig. 18.2 Illustration of the principle of subsampling with regression (see text)

involved, an improvement in precision of about 0.05σ would be obtained on average using subsampling with regression on P_2 only.

If the aim were moderate precision, the use of P_2 only (line B) would cost about the same (per unit precision) as subsampling involving percentage lean in the ham joint and P_2, but if the standard error were required more precisely, say to less than 0.20σ, then estimation based on ham joint and P_2 would be cheaper than estimations based on P_2 only.

In practice, the number of carcases which can be involved in an experiment is likely to be limited, so full dissection of the proportion of carcases which is optimum for a particular set of circumstances may not be possible. However, the subsampling with regression technique should still give more precise comparisons for a given cost than full dissection of a single sample. Since the optimum

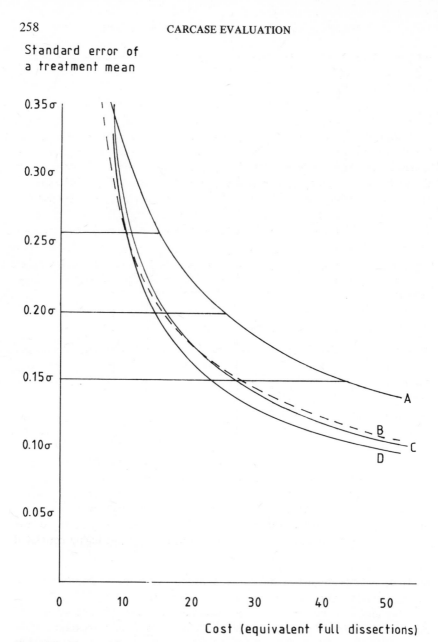

Fig. 18.3 Standard error of an estimated treatment mean for percentage lean in carcase against total cost in full dissection units for A, full dissection of a single sample, B, subsampling with regression on P_2 only, C, subsampling with regression on percentage lean in hand and P_2 and D, subsampling with regression on percentage lean in ham and P_2 (116)

ratio N/n is larger for P_2 alone than for percentage lean in sample joint with P_2, a limitation on numbers will have more effect on prediction from P_2 than on prediction from sample joint and P_2.

As an example, consider an experiment in which the number of animals is limited to 50 per treatment, and the precision of an estimated treatment mean is required to be 0.20σ. An optimum proportion of $\frac{1}{6}$ fully dissected would mean 8 full dissections and 42 ham joint dissections. This would give an estimated standard error 0.209σ, which almost meets the requirement. With 9 full dissections and 41 ham joint dissections, the standard error would be 0.198σ and the total cost 15.7 full dissection units. If, on the other hand, only auxiliary P_2 measurements were used, 16 carcases would have to be dissected fully to achieve the required precision (with P_2 measurements again taken on all 50 carcases). The standard error of an estimated treatment mean would be 0.198σ and the cost 21.7 full dissection units. Both methods would be cheaper than the full dissection of a single sample of 25 carcases which would be needed for the same precision.

Economic appraisal of results

Results from population studies and experiments have to be evaluated in monetary terms before they can be applied in practice in the livestock and meat industries. To what extent should this be done in scientific papers and how much detail should be given?

Research workers should certainly attempt to predict the overall carcase composition of their experimental animals in base-line terms and report the results, rather than reporting simply on the predicting measurements. This may be difficult because of the inadequacy of the carcase evaluation techniques used, but the author will always be better placed than the reader to interpret the results of his predicting measurements. Many have been content to take a whole battery of measurements and report the significance of treatment differences for each of them. The measurements are rarely independent of one another; a better procedure is to select those which are most highly correlated

Notes to Fig. 18.3
The three standard errors indicated have costs and numbers as follows:

	Predictor	Standard error		
		0.26	0.20	0.15
Cost (equivalent full dissections)	A	15	25	44
	B	10	15	27
	C	10	16	27
	D	10	14	22
Number of fully dissected sides (n)	A	15	25	44
	B	9	14	25
	C	7	11	18
	D	6	9	14
Total number of carcases evaluated (N)	A	15	25	44
	B	90	140	250
	C	35	55	90
	D	36	54	84

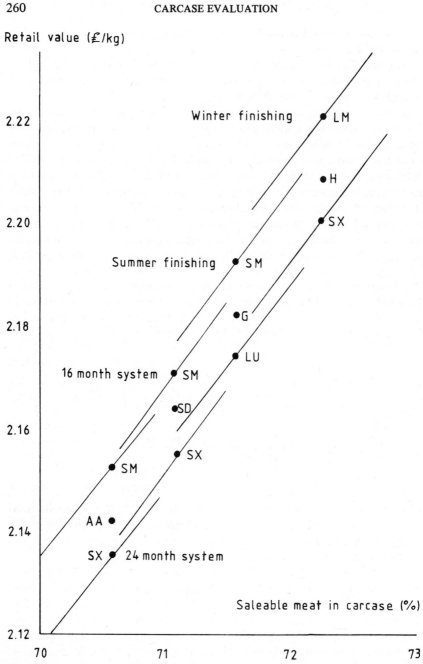

Fig. 18.4 Retail value (£ per kg) against carcase saleable meat percentage for different beef crosses (209). Only extreme and average breeds are shown

Sire breed codes
AA Aberdeen Angus; G Galloway; H Hereford; LM Limousin; LU Luing; SD South Devon; SM Simmental; SX Sussex

with carcase composition and to report treatment differences in these and in estimated carcase composition.

This policy of encouraging research workers to report predicted carcase lean content (for example) would focus attention on the importance of selecting the most suitable predicting measurements.

Interest in commercial valuation of carcases of different types from population studies and experiments was revived by Harries, Williams and Pomeroy (153, 154), who put forward a comparative measure of retail value for beef carcases that takes account of the fat sold as part of the saleable meat, and the distribution of lean among different joints. This was not a new approach. Others have calculated commercial value based on the weights of untrimmed joints (118, 166) or reported the calculation of the retail value, allowing for fat trimming (167). However, unlike the earlier authors, Harries et al. argued strongly that the calculation of retail value was necessary because overall carcase lean and fat content do not provide a sufficiently accurate assessment of commercial value 'since much depends on how these tissues, especially lean, are distributed'.

Subsequently, Abraham and co-workers (3) examined a retail value index in 280 beef carcases of different sexes selected to cover the normal variation in commercial packing plants in the U.S.A. They found a very high correlation of 0.99 between retail value index and yield of boneless, closely trimmed retail cuts.

Our own work based on sire breed differences in the M.L.C. beef breed evaluation programme showed an equally close relationship (209); fig. 18.4 shows the relationship found between retail value, computed by pricing the saleable meat in each cut, against total saleable meat in carcase. The largest difference recorded between sire breeds at the same carcase meat yield was equivalent to 0.92 per cent of carcase retail value (the pooled within-breed residual s.d. was 0.65 per cent of retail value). When further adjustment of the data was made to equal percentage of higher priced cuts, the ranges between breeds and the residual s.d. were halved.

In view of these close relationships, the publication of retail value indexes among the results of trials seems unnecessary; for most purposes, saleable meat percentage is quite adequate, supported by evidence on the proportion of this saleable meat that is found in the higher priced cuts where it is thought that this might have a significant influence on retail value.

Further, the specific calculation of retail value has little commercial significance. The results of most experiments and population studies are applied some years after publication when the relative prices of cuts are likely to have changed. The way carcases are jointed and the various cuts utilised also shows considerable variation throughout the meat trade. Other factors can influence retail value (among carcases of similar saleable meat yield) more than tissue distribution, such as colour of fat, muscle quality and possibly muscle thickness. The importance of these will depend on the experiment. Only the individual research workers can ensure that all factors which might seriously influence value are measured.

SECTION 5
Strategy

19 A strategy for carcase evaluation research

The discussion contained in the preceding sections shows that when choosing prediction methods the following need to be considered:

(a) Wherever possible develop prediction equations, or at least the appropriate intercepts, within the breeding programme or trial where they are to be used. Initial work to develop prediction equations should involve several predicting measurements, so that a choice of the most suitable can be made.
(b) Find a balance between the numbers of animals subjected to side dissection (or similar base-line technique) and the numbers on which only the predicting measurements are taken, which is most cost-effective, even if this involves taking only the simplest measurements on some carcases.
(c) When full dissection is impossible:
    (i) use predictors which have been shown to have the most stable regression equations over the type of comparison concerned;
    (ii) use two or more predictors which are based on the measurement of different characteristics in the animal body; and
    (iii) change the prediction measurements from time to time, for example in different replicates of the same experiment or population study. Such a policy may be particularly important in different generations of breeding schemes since reliance on a single predictor might lead to slower progress than expected in the overall improvement in carcase composition.

When results are prepared for publication, attempts should always be made to estimate overall carcase composition in terms of the base-line technique; but economic assessment by calculation of value by pricing individual joints is unlikely to add much information.

Requirements for future R. and D.

Since no carcase measurements or sample joint dissections have yet been found which are of outstanding value in relation to their cost, such a biological panacea is unlikely to exist. The allocation of valuable resources in haphazard attempts to find it is probably futile.

More important is the examination of the underlying features of growth and development in relation to the prediction problem. Why are some predictors more precise than others? Why do some predictors have more stable regression relationships? The kind of questions that need to be asked are these:

(a) What makes a particular fat thickness measurement good for prediction purposes? Is it its absolute thickness relative to other fat thicknesses which is important, or its position relative to the structure of underlying muscles, or the rate at which it changes with overall composition?
(b) What constitutes a good sample joint? Is it its size, its location in the animal body or the relative proportion of the different tissues which is important?
(c) How do treatment, breed and sex differences in tissue growth and development lead to biases when attempting to predict composition from a simple index?

The answers to these questions would lead towards an overall strategy for prediction work and away from the current piecemeal approach.

If we knew, for example, that the best fat thickness measurements are those which increase most with overall fatness over the relevant growth period, or that the relative precision of sample joints depends on their proportions of lean, fat and bone, then the most suitable predictors could be selected for particular applications without the need to test all possibilities. Similarly if we knew, for example, that differences in KKCF percentage in the carcase are mainly responsible for breed differences in carcase lean percentage in particular circumstances, predictors related to this characteristic would be used and the likelihood of serious biases reduced.

In view of the importance of breed differences in the relationships between simple predictors and base-line carcase characteristics, the results obtained from a particular study of predictors will depend critically on the sample of breeds involved. Relationships established using samples including only extreme breed types are unlikely to give results which are applicable to populations of intermediate types. The assumption that relationships established in the breed population of a particular country will apply equally to those of other countries may also prove wrong. The only safe approach is to examine predictors in the sample of breeds for which their use is intended and, indeed, in broadly the relevant breed mix.

EXPLAINING BIAS

The practical significance of prediction bias and the need for detailed analyses of underlying characteristics is well illustrated by breed bias in carcase classification and grading. The factors involved in such schemes are necessarily simple because of operational difficulties under commercial abattoir conditions. So pig carcase schemes are based essentially on carcase weight and fat thickness measurements taken in the mid-line or over the *M. longissimus* at the last rib. Beef and sheep schemes are normally based on carcase weight and visual appraisals of external fat cover and overall conformation. Alternative measuring systems are continually being explored but at present there are none which offer significant improvements in the precision of lean prediction and which are suitable for practical application.

By implication, in such schemes a given classification is taken to indicate the same meat yield and commercial value irrespective of breed and production environment. Data from national breed comparison trials in Britain have been used to test this assumption, indicating that significant breed biases do exist, i.e. the carcase meat yield of some breeds is over-estimated and that of others under-estimated.

Table 19.1 Importance of conformation and breed as predictors of carcase lean or saleable meat percentage (summary from tables 9.1, 9.2, 9.3)

	M.L.C. commercial pig evaluation		M.L.C. beef breed evaluation		Ram breed comparisons A.B.R.O./M.L.C.		M.L.C.	
	R.s.d. *	*(%)*	*R.s.d.*	*(%)*	*R.s.d.*	*(%)*	*R.s.d.*	*(%)*
Prediction from:								
Carcase weight (W)								
and fat class or P_2 (F)	2.45		1.81		3.29		2.97	
$W + F$ + conformation	2.44	1	1.68	14	3.29	0	2.96	1
$W + F$ + breed	2.31	11	1.45	36	2.96	19	2.88	6
$W + F$ + conformation								
+ breed	2.30	12	1.41	39	2.96	19	2.88	6

*   R.s.d. = Residual s.d.

% = Proportion of the variation among carcases of equal W and F which is explained by conformation and breed.

Table 19.1 shows the increase in precision achieved from knowledge of breed in the different species when carcase weight, P_2 fat thickness (pigs) or fat class (cattle and sheep), and conformation class are known. Figs. 19.1 and 19.3 illustrate the relationships between saleable meat or separable lean percentage in the carcase and conformation class (in both cases at the same fat assessment) among breeds or crosses.

Conformation, it can be argued, can play the role of breed indicator in beef classification schemes. Results from the M.L.C. beef breed evaluation (fig. 19.1) indicate a range of up to one and a half percentage units between sire breeds when they have the same carcase fat assessment and conformation. A comparable figure for the M.L.C. ram breed comparison (fig. 19.2) is three to four percentage units due largely to the difference between the Texel and traditional British sire breeds. A range of two to three percentage units has been recorded between the pigs

Saleable meat in carcase (%)

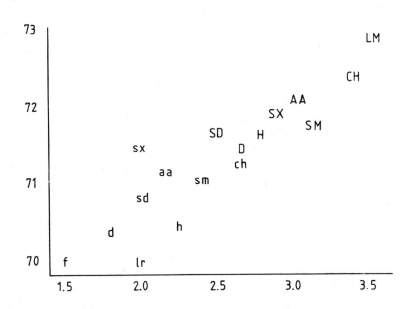

Conformation (6-point scale)

Fig. 19.1 Sire breed means for percentage saleable meat in carcase against conformation score at equal fat class. (Based on M.L.C.'s beef breed evaluation trials) (210, 211)

Dairy-bred cattle are indicated by lower case codes and suckler-bred cattle by upper case codes. The two groups should be considered separately.

Sire breed
AA Aberdeen Angus; Ch Charolais; D Devon; F Friesian; H Hereford; LM Limousin; LR Lincoln Red; SD South Devon; SX Sussex

from different breeding companies in M.L.C.'s commercial pig evaluation programme.

Examination of the bias indicates that, in the case of beef and sheep, it is associated largely with the inability of conformation to identify accurately the differences which exist between breeds in muscle to bone ratio.

In the case of differences between pigs from various breeding companies, on the other hand, the bias is due almost entirely to differences in fat partition and distribution. P_2 is not providing a sufficiently accurate indication of the variation between companies in carcase fat content. There appears to be little variation in lean to bone ratio between the pig breeding companies' output up to 1980, which contrasts with the extreme differences within the pig populations in other E.E.C. countries.

These biases between breeds will almost certainly be reduced to some extent

Lean in carcase (%)

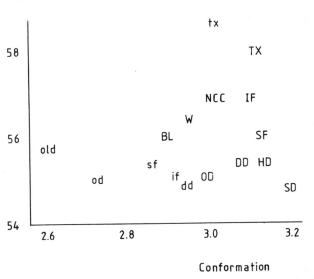

Conformation

(4 and 5-point scales)

Fig. 19.2 Sire breed means for percentage lean in carcase against conformation score at equal fat class (Based on M.L.C.'s ram breed comparison and a three year A.B.R.O./M.L.C. trial, 212).

M.L.C. ram breed comparison lambs are indicated by upper case codes and A.B.R.O./M.L.C. lambs by lower case codes. The two sets of results should be considered separately.

Sire breed
BL Border Leicester; DD Dorset Down; HD Hampshire Down; IF Ile de France; NCC North Country Cheviot; OLD Oldenburg; OD Oxford Down; SD Southdown; SF Suffolk; TX Texel; W Wensleydale

by improving measuring techniques. But the fact that they are caused by basic differences in tissue structure and distribution suggests that it will be difficult to eliminate them without recourse to techniques which provide a direct measure of muscle content.

We have examined the problem of bias among pigs from different company sources using the multivariate technique involving canonical variates (117). The object was to identify the carcase characteristics which discriminate most effectively between company pigs. Weights of tissues in each joint and of other components of carcase weight were included in the analysis.

The positions of different companies for the first two canonical variates (that is those which explained most of the variation between companies) are shown in fig. 19.4. The first canonical variate (CV1) explained 39 per cent of the variation. It had a high positive loading on weight of feet, bone in ham,

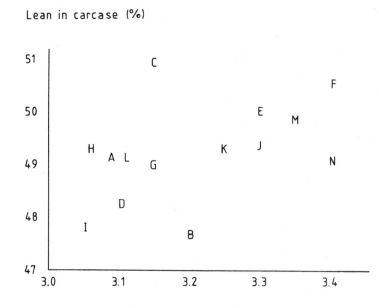

Fig. 19.3 Pig breeding company means for percentage lean in carcase against conformation score at equal weight and P_2 fat thickness. (Based on years 3 to 6 of M.L.C.'s commercial pig evaluation, 221).

Companies are coded A to N; H is the pure-bred Large White control

lean in shoulder and back and subcutaneous fat in the streak. High negative loadings were recorded for bone in the shoulder, lean in the streak, subcutaneous fat in the back and lean in the ham. This first variate, therefore, essentially contrasts on the one hand, lean in the shoulder and back, and on the other, lean in the ham and streak. The relative position of the companies for CV1 was very similar to their relative position for the bias arising in the prediction of percentage lean from P_2; companies with positive weights (more lean in the shoulder and back) having less lean at the same P_2 (see fig. 19.3).

The second canonical variate (CV2) which explained a further 26 per cent of the variation, was essentially a measure of the overall ratio of fat to lean.

This analysis illustrates the complex nature of tissue distribution which can lead to differences in prediction relationships. It also shows that, when discriminating between breeding companies or breeds, basic differences in tissue distribution may be more important than the overall level of leanness.

CO-ORDINATION OF RESEARCH

Obviously there are many areas of research in carcase evaluation and related topics which will be pressed forward wherever research workers seek to improve methods of fat and lean estimation of live animals and carcases.

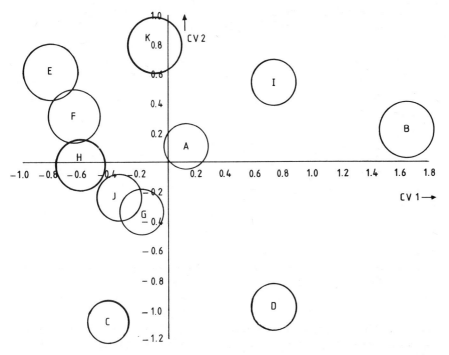

Fig. 19.4 Positions of pigs from different breeding companies for the first two canonical variates: CV1 related to differences in tissue distribution between joints and CV2 related to the overall ratio of lean to fat in the carcase (117).

Companies are coded A to K as in Fig. 19.3

In the longer term, physiological predictors of composition may become increasingly important; they may be used for prediction of genetic advantage or alternatively to manipulate the genetic types of animals we already have.

There is a need to re-assess continually the information being accumulated on hormonal and other factors controlling growth and carcase quality, in the light of possible application in the early and more precise quantitative selection of breeding stock.

In terms of practical experimentation and the application of common classification and breeding schemes, the most important areas concern:

(a) the standardisation of base-line techniques;
(b) co-operative research in the comparison of breeds reared on various regimens to various weights, in particular a close study of the variation in meat to bone ratio and its relationship with conformation between breeds;
(c) the relationship between morphological characteristics and wholesale and retail trade valuation among carcases differing in weight and composition.

At the very outset we criticised the lack of practical consideration in carcase research and a number of reasons were given for this. In our view, a critical step to overcome this is to establish a clear link between the data collected in experiments and population studies on the one hand, and the terms of commercial classification on the other. In M.L.C. work in Britain, this has been provided very simply by:

(a) the relationship between visually assessed subcutaneous fat percentage in cattle and sheep and actual carcase subcutaneous fat percentage obtained by dissection;

(b) the standard use in pig carcase classification of a single fat thickness measurement, around which all other measures including tissue separation and carcase lean percentage revolve.

This link has been a major factor in solving or elucidating a number of industry problems.

For example, the information has been available to provide the links in the chain from chemical composition through tissue percentages to fat thickness measurements and then grading results, which were needed in the construction of the computer model pig (382). Such models are now used extensively by advisory organisations to guide producers on methods of improving efficiency and profitability.

Similarly, we have also been able to provide information on the differences in meat yield which are to be expected between Canadian Holstein and British Friesian cattle. The British meat industry has tended to over-react to the poorer conformation of Holsteins, penalising them more than is justified by the yield differences. The provision of yield results in relation to commercial classification results has helped to set the right balance.

A third example of the importance of the link between experimentation and classification is provided by the analysis of commercial pig evaluation data to examine the differences in carcase lean content and in predicting measurements between pigs from various breeding companies. Where the differences in lean content occurs has been identified, and the value of the variation in composition between companies at the same P_2 fat thickness has been calculated.

So efforts should always be made to forge the link between classification or grading, and experimentation and detailed carcase evaluation work. Efforts should also be made to obtain as much information on prediction relationships as possible from detailed carcase evaluation in experiments and population studies. This implies the need for an overall strategy in carcase evaluation, with a common approach to the use of control breeds, to the use of regressor variables and to methods of analysis. The collection of information on basic characteristics such as muscle and bone dimensions would also be valuable as a routine in breed evaluation trials, and many different predicting measurements should be collected as routine.

Another important factor is the development of standard assessment procedures, which cover all the main aspects of the carcase, backed up by photographic records and the development of data banks. Detailed tissue separation is extremely expensive and as many other carcase observations as possible should be done alongside this, even if the measurements and photographs do not have immediate relevance. As new problems emerge, they can sometimes be solved by existing data in a very cost-effective way. But of course, the correct balance must be found. Large numbers of repeated measurements may not be useful and photographs covering areas of the carcase which can subsequently be measured in detail if required, are more reliable. With the development of automatic recording equipment, this problem will become less important.

To achieve effective standardisation of base-line techniques between countries and research centres within a country, the technique must not be too complicated and expensive; the cheaper the method, the more likely it is to be used. There may also be disadvantages in the standardisation of predicting measurements between experiments. If certain measurements are biased in a particular way, and if all centres used the same measurements, all experimental results on a particular subject may become biased. Some common measurements may be used, but most should be different. If standardisation is necessary, then it is the base-line technique which requires standardisation.

But the need for standardisation of base-line techniques between countries — particularly techniques of meticulous dissection — is frequently not strong. The point of co-ordinated experiments is to determine whether results are repeatable across a range of environmental circumstances — and the dissection method is only one of many environmental factors which will vary. The aim should be a sufficient similarity of base-line techniques to allow sensible comparison of results. However, there are clearly situations where standardisation is essential — for example, where a common classification or grading scheme is being developed.

Realism is particularly important in the context of equipment testing. Since predictors change in their relative precision, and have regression equations which differ between different populations of animals, so the relative value of different pieces of equipment and the particular measuring sites at which they are found to be most accurate, will vary according to the sample of live animals or carcases upon which they are tested. It is much more important, therefore, to compare machines over a range of samples, than to go into considerable depth in terms of repeatabilities, detailed multivariate prediction equations, etc. on a single population of carcases.

The one thing which will stand out clearly for readers of this book is that all carcase evaluation work (research, development or commercial application) is a compromise. No panaceas exist and all things cannot be covered in all experiments. Ultimately choice depends on a balance between cost and accuracy. For those selecting a particular carcase evaluation technique or approach, the message is a simple one: think flexibly, consider all the options, and try to achieve the greatest value for money.

References

References

1. Abraham, H.C. (1976) 'Estimating beef carcase cutability.' *Proc. Amer. Soc. Anim. Sci.* August 1976.
2. Abraham, H.C. (1977) 'Grades of fed beef carcases, Nov. '73 to Oct. '74'. *U.S.D.A. Marketing Research Report* no. 1073.
3. Abraham, H.C., Murphey, C.E., Cross, H.R., Smith, G.C. and Franks, Jr. W.J. (1980) 'Factors affecting beef carcase cutability: an evaluation of the U.S.D.A. yield grades for beef" *J. Anim. Sci.* **50**, 841-51.
4. Allen, D.M. (1966) 'The relationship of some linear and physical measurements to beef carcase composition'. Ph.D. thesis, Michigan State University, East Lansing, Michigan.
5. Allen, P. (1977) 'Experimental studies of genetical variation in the pattern of fat deposition of mice and sheep'. Ph.D. thesis, National University of Ireland, Dublin.
6. Alliston, J.C., Kempster, A.J., Owen, M.G. and Ellis, M. (1982) 'An evaluation of three ultrasonic machines for predicting the body composition of live pigs of the same breed, sex and live weight.' *Anim. Prod.* (in press).
7. Andersson, K. (1977) 'Slaktkroppskontroll i svinstam Kontrollen'. *Konsulentavdelningens stencilserie*, Almant 8, Lantbrukshögskolan, 750 07 Uppsala.
8. Andersson, O. and Hansson, I. (1980) 'Swedish lamb carcase classification'. *31st Annual Meeting of the European Association for Animal Production*, Munich, 1980.
9. Andresen, E., Barton-Gade, P., Hyldgaard-Jensen, J., Jørgensen, P.F., Nielsen, P.B. and Moussgaard, J. (1979) 'Selection for improved meat quality with the aid of genetic markers in pigs of Danish Landrace breed'. *Acta. Agric. Scand.* **29**, 291-4.
10. Andrew, E.R. (1980) 'N.m.r. imaging of intact biological systems'. *Phil. Trans. R. Soc. Lond. B* **289**, 471-81.
11. Andrews, A.H. (1975) *The ageing of cattle by their dentition*. Royal Smithfield Club, Bath.
12. Andrews, F.N. and Whaley, R.M. (1955) 'Measure fat and muscle in live animal and carcase'. *Rep. Ind. Agric. Exp. Sta.* no. 68, 27-9.
13. Anon. (1978) 'Tipificaçao de carcaça, método para valorizar a carne bovina e a suina'. *Lavoura-Pecuaria.* **7**, 31-4.
14. Anon. (1978) 'U.S.D.A. grade, label proposals hit'. *The National Provisioner.* 25 March 1978, 26-30.

15. Anon. (1981) 'How and why the grades have changed'. *Meat Industry*. May 1981, 20, 21, 94; and *Meat Industry*. May 1981, 22, 23, 25, 26, 86.

16. Anon. (1981) 'Hot boning. Is it really the beef industry's future?' *Meat Industry*. September 1981, 34-40.

17. Arndt, G. (1981) 'A state-of-the-art survey of the application and development of the F.D.I. and H.G.P.' *32nd Annual Meeting of the European Association for Animal Production*. Zagreb, 1981.

18. Association of Official Analytical Chemists. (1975) 'Official methods of analysis of the Association of Official Analytical Chemists'. 12th edn. Washington.

19. Australian Meat Board (1971) 'Australian beef carcase appraisal system'. Leaflet.

20. Bach, H. and Schön, L. (1973) 'Trade grades for pig carcases in wholesale meat markets. The problem − conduct of classification'. *Schweinezucht und Schweinemast*, no. 5, May 1973.

21. Baker, H.K., Andersen, B.B., Colleau, J., Langholz, H., Legoshin, G. and Southgate, J. (1976) 'Cattle breed comparison and crossbreeding trials in Europe; a survey prepared by a Working Party of the European Association for Animal Production'. *Livest. Prod. Sci.* 3, 1-12.

22. Barton, R.A. (1967) 'The relation between live animal conformation and the carcase of cattle'. *Anim. Breed. Abstr.* 35, 1-22.

23. Barton, R.A. (1978) 'The grading or classification of ovine and bovine carcases in New Zealand and Australia'. *Symposium on problems related to carcase classification of ovines and bovines*, Zaragoza, May 1978.

24. Barton, R.A. and Philips, T.O. (1950) 'Type of Southdown sire in relation to fat-lamb carcase quality'. *Sheepfmg. Ann. Massey Agric. Coll.* 3, 27-29, 31-39.

25. Bass, J.J., Colomer-Rocher, F., Johnson, D.L. and Binks, G. (1980) 'The relationship between carcase conformation and carcase composition in cattle'. *J. Agric. Sci. Camb.* 97, 37-44.

26. Bech Andersen, B. (1975) 'Recent experimental development in ultrasonic measurement of cattle'. *Livest. Prod. Sci.* 2, 137-146.

27. Bech Andersen, B., Busk, H., Chadwick, J.P., Cuthbertson, A., Fursey, G.A.J., Jones, D.W., Lewin, P., Miles, C.A. and Owen, M.G. (1981) *Ultrasonic techniques for describing carcase characteristics in live cattle*. C.E.C. Luxembourg (EUR 7640).

28. Bech Andersen, B., De Baerdemaeker, A., Bittante, G., Bonaiti, B., Colleau, J.J., Fimland, E., Jansen, J., Lewis, W.H.E., Politiek, R.D., Seeland, G., Teehan, T.J. and Werkmeister, F. (1981) 'Performance testing of bulls in A.I.: Report of a working group of the Commission on Cattle Production'. *Livest. Prod. Sci.* 8, 101-10.

29. Bech Andersen, B., Liboriussen, T., Kousgaard, K. and Buchter, L. (1977) 'Crossbreeding experiment with beef and dual-purpose sire breeds on Danish dairy cows. III. Daily gain, feed conversion and carcase quality of intensively-fed young bulls'. *Livest. Prod. Sci.* 4, 19-29.

30. Berg, R.T. and Bunnage, R.J. (1968) 'Predicting cutability in beef carcases'. *Univ. of Alberta, Dept. of Animal Science, 47th Annual Feeders' Day Report*, 19-23.

31. Berg, R.T. and Butterfield, R.M. (1976) *New Concepts of Cattle Growth*.

Sydney University Press.

32. Berg, R.T., Bech Andersen, B. and Liboriussen, T. (1978) 'Growth of bovine tissues. 2. Genetic influences on muscle growth and distribution in young bulls'. *Anim. Prod.* **27**, 51-61.

33. Bichard, M. (1977) 'Economic efficiency of pig breeding schemes: a breeding company view'. *Livest. Prod. Sci.* **4**, 245-54.

34. Biggs, A.P. (1975) 'Beef carcase classification. Current research and implications for marketing'. *Quart. Rev. Agric. Econ.* **28**, no. 2, April 1975, 67-79.

35. Blaxter, K. (1968) 'The effect of dietary energy supply on growth'. In Lodge, G.A. and Lamming, G.E. *eds. Growth and development of mammals*, Proc. 14th Easter School of Agricultural Science, University of Nottingham, 1967, 329-44.

36. Bradford, G.E. (1974) 'Breeding plans for improvement of meat production and carcase merit in the meat breeds of sheep'. *1st World Congress on Genetics applied to Livestock Production*, 1. Plenary Sessions, 725-38, Editorial Garsi, Madrid.

37. Bradford, G.E. and Spurlock, G.M. (1972) 'Selection for meat production in sheep – results of a progeny test'. *J. Anim. Sci.* **34**, 737-45.

38. Bratzler, L.J. (1958) 'Fifty years of progress in meat research'. *J. Anim. Sci.* **17**, 1079-87.

39. Brayshaw, G.H. and DeLoach, D.B. (1963) 'Economic considerations concerning comprehensive uniform grades for beef and lamb'. *Dept. of Agric. Econ., Univ. of Newcastle.* Report no. 158G.

40. Bickhardt, K., Flock, D.K. and Richter, I. (1977) 'Creatine-kinase test (C.K. test) as a selection criterion to estimate stress resistance and meat quality in pigs'. *Vet. Sci. Comm.* **1**, 225-33.

41. British Society of Animal Production (1973) 'Size of animal in relation to productivity with special reference to the ruminant'. (Symposium). *Proc. Br. Soc. Anim. Prod.* **2**, 9-44.

42. Brough, O.L. and Shepherd, G. (1955) 'Objective grade specifications for slaughter barrow and gilt carcases'. *Res. Bull. Ia agric. Exp. Sta.* no. 421.

43. Brown, A.J., Coates, H.E. and Speight, B.S. (1978) *A photographic guide to the muscular and skeletal anatomy of the beef carcase*. Meat Research Institute, Bristol.

44. Brownlie, L.E. (1975) 'Progress in the development of a practical beef carcase classification'. *Wool Tech. and Sheep Breeding*, **21**, no. 11, 21-6.

45. Busk, H. (1980) 'New technique for measuring body composition on live animals'. *31st Annual Meeting of the European Association for Animal Production*, Munich, 1980.

46. Butler, O.D. (1957) 'The relation of conformation to carcase traits'. *J. Anim. Sci.* **16**, 227-33.

47. Butterfield, R.M. (1962) 'Prediction of muscle content of steer carcases'. *Nature*, **195**, 193-4.

48. Butterfield, R.M. (1963) 'Relative growth of the musculature of the ox'. In Tribe, D.E. *ed. Carcass composition and appraisal of meat animals*. C.S.I.R.O., Melbourne.

49. Butterfield, R.M. (1965) 'The relationship of carcase measurements and

dissection data to beef carcase composition'. *Res. vet. Sci.* **6**, 24-32.

50. Butterfield, R.M., Pinchbeck, Y., Zamora, J. and Gardner, I. (1977) 'The estimation of the composition of lamb carcases by use of an image analyser 'Classimat' on multiple cross-sections'. *Livest. Prod. Sci.* **4**, 283-90.

51. Butterfield, R.M. and May, N.D.S. (1966) *Muscles of the ox.* University of Queensland Press, Brisbane.

52. Callow, E.H. (1962) 'The relationship between the weight of tissue in a single joint and the total weight of the tissue in a side of beef'. *Anim. Prod.* **4**, 37.

53. Campion, D.R. and Harrison, V.L. (1976) 'The new beef carcase quality grade standards: What the changes mean'. *U.S.D.A. Econ. Res. Service*, LMS-208, April 1976.

54. Canada Department of Agriculture (1961) 'Office consolidation of the hog carcase grading regulations'. P.C. 1958-1202 as amended, Queen's Printer, Ottawa.

55. Canada Department of Agriculture (1969) 'Canada's new hog carcase valuation system'. Leaflet.

56. Canada Department of Agriculture (1976) 'Canada's beef grading system'. *Pub. Agriculture Canada.* no. 1579.

57. Canadian Swine Council and Meat Packers Council of Canada (1968) 'A proposal for revision of the hog grading system presented to the Canada Department of Agriculture'. Mimeo.

58. Carpenter, Z.L., King, G.T., Shelton, M. and Butler, O.D. (1969) 'Indices for estimating cutability of wether, ram and ewe lamb carcases'. *J. Anim. Sci.* **28**, 180-86.

59. Carpenter, Z.L., Smith, G.C. and Farr, W.D. (1977) 'Reflections on the beef grade changes'. *Proc. Meat Ind. Res. Conf.* March 1977, 121-6, American Meat Institute Foundation, Arlington, Va.

60. Carr, T.R., Walters, L.E. and Whiteman, J.V. (1978) 'Relation of ^{40}K count and probe to carcase composition changes in growing and finishing swine'. *J. Anim. Sci.* **46**, 651-7.

61. Carroll, M.A. (1976) 'The impact of carcase and meat aspects of experimental design, particularly in relation to feeding levels and time of slaughter'. *Criteria and methods for assessment of carcase and meat characteristics in beef production experiments.* 17-24. C.E.C. Luxembourg (EUR 5489).

62. Chadwick, J.P. (1977) 'Selection for economy of production and carcase lean content in Large White pigs and its influence on meat quality characteristics'. Ph.D. thesis, University of Newcastle-upon-Tyne.

63. Chadwick, J.P. and Kempster, A.J. (1980) 'Trends in the carcase characteristics of the British pig population and considerations of optimum slaughter weight'. *Anim. Prod.* **30**, 495 (Abstract).

64. Chadwick, J.P. and Kempster, A.J. (1982) 'Prediction of beef carcase composition. 1. From fat measurements taken on the intact side using different probing instruments'. *J. Agric. Sci., Camb.* (in press).

65. Charles, D.D. (1964) 'Classifying trade beef by specifications'. *Aust. Vet. J.* **40**, 27-31.

66. Charles, D.D. (1967) 'The marketing of beef'. University of Queensland, leaflet.

67. Charles, D.D. (1974) 'A method of estimating carcase components in cattle'. *Res. Vet. Sci.* **16**, 89-94.

68. Charles, D.D., Butterfield, R.M. and Francis, J. (1965) 'Marketing beef by specifications'. Mimeo.

69. Charles, D.D. and Johnson, E.R. (1976) 'Breed differences in amount and distribution of bovine carcase dissectible fat'. *J. Anim. Sci.* **42**, 332-41.

70. Cheah, K.S. and Cheah, A.M. (1979) 'Mitochondrial calcium efflux and porcine stress syndrome'. *30th Annual Meeting of the European Association for Animal Production.* Harrogate, 1979.

71. Clausen, H., Nørtoft Thompson, R. and Pedersen, O.K. (1968) *56. Beretning om Sammenlignende Forsøg med Svin fra Statsanerkendte Avlscentre.* 364 Beretning fra Forsøgslaboratoriet, København.

72. Clifton, E.S. and Shepherd, G. (1953) 'Objective grade specifications for slaughter steer carcases'. *Res. Bull. Ia Agric. Exp. Sta.* no. 402.

73. Codex Alimentarius Commission (1974) 'Draft system for the description of carcases of bovine and porcine species'. Codex Committee on Meat, Alinorm 74/17, Mimeo.

74. Cold Storage Commission (1978) 'The beef carcase classification scheme'. *Supplement to the Rhodesian Government Gazette* 29 Dec. 1978, Salisbury.

75. Cole, J.W., Orme, L.E. and Kincaid, C.M. (1960) 'Relationships of loin eye area, separable lean of various beef cuts and carcase measurements to total carcase lean in beef'. *J. Anim. Sci.* **19**, 89-100.

76. Colomer-Rocher, F., Bass, J.J. and Johnson, D.L. (1980) 'Beef carcase conformation and some relationships with carcase composition and muscle dimensions'. *J. Agric. Sci., Camb.* **94**, 697-708.

77. Commission of the European Communities (1979) 'Development of uniform methods of pig carcase classification in the E.C.' *Information on Agriculture Series.* no. 70, Brussels-Luxembourg, C.E.C.

78. Conniffe, D. (1975) 'Double sampling with regression − extension to the case of unequal regression coefficients'. *The Statistician* **24**, 259-66.

79. Conniffe, D. and Moran, M.A. (1972) 'Double sampling with regression in comparative studies of carcase composition'. *Biometrics* **28**, 1011-23.

80. Cross, H.R., Douglass, L.W., Linderman, E.D., Murphey, C.E., Savell, J.W., Smith, G.C. and Stiffler, D.M. (1980) 'An evaluation of the accuracy and uniformity of the U.S.D.A. beef quality and yield grading system'. Report to Office of Inspector General, U.S.D.A.

81. Cross, H.R., Smith, G.C. and Carpenter, Z.L. (1973) 'Pork carcase cutability equations incorporating some new indices of muscling and fatness'. *J. Anim. Sci.* **37**, 423-9.

82. Cross, R.L., Carpenter, J.W. and Palmer, A.Z. (1970) 'Pork carcase muscling: fat, lean and bone ratios'. *J. Anim. Sci.* **30**, 866-71.

83. Croston, D., Jones, D.W. and Kempster, A.J. (1979) 'A comparison of the performance and carcase characteristics of lambs by nine sire breeds'. *Anim. Prod.* **28**, 456-7 (Abstr.).

84. Crouse, J.D. and Dikeman, M.E. (1976) 'Determinates of retail product of carcase beef'. *J. Anim. Sci.* **42**, 584-91.

85. Crouse, J.D., Dikeman, M.E., Koch, R.M. and Murphey, C.E. (1975) 'Evaluation of traits in the U.S.D.A. yield grade equation for predicting

beef carcase cutability in breed groups differing in growth and fattening characteristics'. *J. Anim. Sci.* **41**, 548-53.

86. Cunningham, E.P. (1981) 'Beef breeding today and in the year 2000'. *5th World Limousin Beef Cattle Conference*, National Agriculture Centre, Stoneleigh, England, 1981.

87. Cunningham, E.P. (1979) 'Trends in cattle production and breeding in Western Europe'. *Optimum methods of cattle breeding for increasing meat and dairy production.* Proc. of a Symposium held at the Warsaw Agricultural University, Poland, June 1978.

88. Cuthbertson, A. (1968) 'P.I.D.A. dissection techniques'. *Symposium on methods of carcase evaluation.* E.A.A.P. Dublin, 1968.

89. Cuthbertson, A., Harrington, G. and Smith, R.J. (1972) 'Tissue separation – to assess beef and lamb variation'. *Proc. Br. Soc. Anim. Prod. (New series)* **1**, 113-22.

90. Cuthbertson, A. and Harrington, G. (1973) 'Development of beef classification in Great Britain'. *World Rev. Anim. Prod.* **9**, 65-75.

91. Cuthbertson, A. and Harrington, G. (1976) 'The M.L.C. sheep carcase classification scheme'. *Proc. of the Carcase Classification Symposium.* Adelaide, May 1976, Australian Meat Board.

92. Davis, W.C., McCarthy, B.F. and Burgess, J.A. (1933) 'Market classes and grades of pork carcases and fresh pork cuts'. *Circ. U.S. Dep. Agric.* no. 288.

93. Davis, W.C. and Whalin, C.V. (1924) 'Market classes and grades of dressed beef'. *U.S.D.A. Bull.* no. 1246.

94. de Boer, H. (Discussion leader) (1976) 'Consideration of possibilities of co-ordination and of requirements for future research'. *Criteria and methods for assessment of carcase and meat characteristics in beef production experiments.* C.E.C. Luxembourg (EUR 5489), 401-04.

95. de Boer, H. (1978) 'International aspects of beef carcase evaluation'. *Proc. 6th International Beef Symposium.* Dublin, April 1978.

96. de Boer, H. (1978) 'Extrapolated values, representing the relation between fleshiness and fatness on the one side, and carcase composition and carcase dimensions on the other side'. Mimeo.

97. de Boer, H., Bergstrom, P.L., Jansen, A.A.M. and Nijeboer, H. (1975) 'Carcase measurements and visual assessments as predictors of lean meat content, with reference to the E.E.C. classification and grading system'. *26th Annual Meeting of the European Association for Animal Production.* Warsaw, 1975.

98. de Boer, H., Dumont, B.L., Pomeroy, R.W. and Weniger, J.H. (1974) 'Manual on E.A.A.P. reference methods for the assessment of carcase characteristics in cattle'. *Livest. Prod. Sci.* **1**, 151-64.

99. de Boer, H., Jansen, A.A.M., Nijeboer, H. and Pedersen, O.K. (1978) 'Classificatieproef met Deense K.S.A.-meter (Model II) in de Exportslachterij Vos te Lichtenvoorde'. *Proefrapport* I.V.O. 'Schoonord'.

100. Dennes, D.J., Parsons, S.A. and Campbell, D.J. (1975) 'Objective measurement of fat cover on hot unquartered beef carcases'. *Quart. Rev. Agric. Econ.* **28**, no. 1, Jan. 1975, 25-37.

101. Desmoulin, B. (1981) 'Absence de critères de qualité des viandes et classement des carcasses de porcs'. *32nd Annual Meeting of the European Association for Animal Production.* Zagreb, 1981.

102. Dinkel, C.A., Wilson, L.L., Tuma, H.J. and Minyard, J.A. (1965) 'Ratios and percents as measures of carcase traits'. *J. Anim. Sci.* **24**, 425-9.

103. Dowell, A.A., Engelman, G., Ferrin, E.F. and Anderson, P.A. (1949) 'Marketing slaughter cattle by carcase weight and grade'. *Tech. Bull. Minn. Agric. Exp. Sta.* no. 181.

104. Dumont. B.L. (1958) 'Méthodes indirectes de mésure de la graisse corporelle des mammifères'. *Ann. Nutr. Alim.* **12**, 95-158.

105. Dumont, B.L. (1967) *Étude sur les qualités des carcases de bovins en France.* Office Statistique des Communautés Européennes, Bruxelles.

106. Dumont, B.L. (1978) 'Variation and impact of muscle thickness'. In de Boer, H. and Martin J. eds. *Patterns of growth and development in cattle.* Current Topics in Vet. Med., Volume 2, Martinus Nijhoff, The Hague/Boston/London.

107. Dumont, B.L. and Boccard, R. (1981) 'Carcase characteristics of cull cows and systems of carcase description'. *The cull cow as a beef producer.* C.E.C. Luxembourg (EUR 7326), 120-36.

108. Dumont, B.L. and Destandau, S. (1964) 'Comparison de quatre méthodes de mesure de l'épaisseur des tissus adipeux sous-cutanés chez le porc vivant'. *Annls. Zootech.* **13**, 213-16.

109. Duniec, H., Kielanowski, J. and Osińska, Z. (1961) 'Heritability of chemical fat content in the loin muscle of baconers'. *Anim. Prod.* **3**, 195-8.

110. East of Scotland College of Agriculture (1976) 'Condition scoring of cattle'. *E.S.C.A. Bulletin* no. 6, Edinburgh.

111. Edwards, R.L., Smith, G.C., Cross, H.R. and Carpenter, Z.L. (1981) 'Estimating lean in pork carcases differing in back fat thickness'. *J. Anim. Sci.* **52**, 703-09.

112. Eikelenboom, G., Minkema, D., Van Eldik, P. and Sybesma, W. (1978) 'Production characteristics of Dutch Landrace and Dutch Yorkshire pigs as related to their susceptibility for the halothane-induced malignant hyperthermia syndrome'. *Livest. Prod. Sci.* **5**, 277-84.

113. Engelman, G. (1952) 'Objective carcase grade standards for slaughter hogs'. *Bull. Minn. Agric. Exp. Sta.* no. 414.

114. European Association for Animal Production (1976) 'Beef carcases — methods of dressing, measuring, jointing and tissue separation'. *E.A.A.P. Publication.* no. 18, Meat Research Institute, Bristol.

115. Evans, D.G., Kempster, A.J. and Steane, D.E. (1978) 'Meat quality of British crossbred pigs'. *Livest. Prod. Sci.* **5**, 265-75.

116. Evans, D.G. and Kempster, A.J. (1979) 'A comparison of different predictors of the lean content of pig carcases. 2. Predictors for use in population studies and experiments'. *Anim. Prod.* **28**, 97-108.

117. Evans, D.G. and Kempster, A.J. (1982) 'A multivariate study of pig carcase growth and composition. 1. Tissue weights and other carcase parts'. *J. Agric. Sci. Camb.* (in press).

118. Everitt, G.C. and Jury, K.E. (1964) 'Implantation of oestrogenic hormones in beef cattle. IV. Effects of oestradiol benzoate plus progesterone on carcase composition and a comparison of methods of carcase evaluation'. *N.Z. J. Agric. Res.* **7**, 158-73.

119. Falconer, D.S. (1960) *Introduction to quantitative genetics.* Oliver and Boyd, Edinburgh.

120. Février, R. and Zert, P. (1970) 'Appréciation du porc charcutier'. Le Centre Technique de la Salaison de la Charcuterie et des Conserves des Viandes, Paris.

121. Field, R.A., Kemp, J.D. and Varney, W.Y. (1963) 'Indices of lamb carcase composition'. *J. Anim. Sci.* **22**, 218-21.

122. Field, R.A. and Riley, M.L. (1968) 'Use of the carcase fat probe'. *Bull. Wyo. Agric. Exp. Sta.* no. 19.

123. Fisher, A.V. (1975) 'The profile area of beef carcases and its relationship to carcase composition'. *Anim. Prod.* **20**, 355-61.

124. Fisher, A.V. (1976) 'Live animal measurements as a means of evaluating animals in beef production experiments'. *Criteria and methods for assessment of carcase and meat characteristics in beef production experiments* C.E.C., Luxembourg (EUR 5489), 43-55.

125. Fitzhugh, H.A. (1975) 'Alternative measures of growth in relation to feed efficiency and shape of growth curve'. *A new look at growth.* Beef Improvement Symposium, Des Moines, Ia.

126. Fitzhugh, H.A. and Taylor, St. C.S. (1971) 'Genetic analysis of degree of maturity'. *J. Anim. Sci.* **33**, 717-25.

127. Food and Agricultural Organisation (1958) *Pig breeding, recording and progeny testing in European countries.* F.A.O., Rome.

128. Fortin, A. (1980) 'Fat thickness measured with three ultrasonic instruments on live ram lambs as predictors of cutability'. *Can. J. Anim. Sci.* **60**, 857-67.

129. Fortin, A., Sim, D.W. and Talbot, S. (1980) 'Ultrasonic measurements of back fat thickness at different locations and positions on the warm pork carcase and comparisons of ruler and ultrasonic procedures'. *Can. J. Anim. Sci.* **60**, 635-41.

130. Fowler, V.R. (1976) 'The nutritional control of growth'. In Lister, D., Rhodes, D.N., Fowler, V.R. and Fuller, M.F. *eds. Meat animals, growth and productivity* Plenum Press, New York and London, 285-99.

131. Fowler, V.R., Bichard, M. and Pease, A. (1976) 'Objectives in pig breeding'. *Anim. Prod.* **23**, 365-87.

132. Frahm, R.R., Walters, L.E. and McLellan, Jr., C.R. (1971) 'Evaluation of K^{40} count as a predictor of muscle in yearling beef bulls'. *J. Anim. Sci.* **32**, 463-9.

133. Frazer, A.E. (1976) 'New Zealand sheep meat grading'. *Proc. of the Carcase Classification Symposium.* Adelaide, May 1976, Australian Meat Board.

134. Fredeen, H.T. (1965) 'Pig breeding in Canada'. *Wld. Rev. Anim. Prod.* **2**, 87-98.

135. Fredeen, H. (1978) 'Revised index grid will be monitored by producers'. *Alberta Hog Journal.* Winter 1978, 12-13.

136. Fredeen, H.T., Martin, A.H. and Sather, A.P. (1979) 'Evaluation of an electronic technique for measuring lean content of the live pig'. *J. Anim. Sci.* **48**, 536-40.

137. Fredeen, H.T. and Weiss, G.M. (1970) 'Some characteristics of commercial beef carcases in Canada'. *Can. J. Anim. Sci.* **50**, 227-34.

138. Fredeen, H.T. and Weiss, G.M. (1981) 'Comparison of techniques for evaluating lean content of hog carcases'. *Can. J. Anim. Sci.* **61**, 319-33.

139. Garrett, W.N. (1968) 'Experiences in the use of body density as an estimator of body composition of animals'. *Body composition of animals and man*. National Academy of Sciences, Washington.

140. Gatherum, D.P., Harrington, G. and Pomeroy, R.W. (1961) 'Visual judgements of quality in meat. III. Assessment of bacon qualities by naive and experienced judges using photographic reference standards'. *J. Agric. Sci., Camb.* **57**, 401-17.

141. Geay, Y. (1976) 'Weight determination of the carcase, including fifth quarter and empty body weight'. *Criteria and methods for assessment of carcase and meat characteristics in beef production experiments* C.E.C. Luxembourg (EUR 5489), 109-19.

142. Gillis, W.A., Burgess, T.D., Usborne, W.R., Greiger, H. and Talbot, S. (1973) 'A comparison of two ultrasonic techniques for the measurement of fat thickness and rib eye area in cattle'. *Can. J. Anim. Sci.* **53**, 13-19.

143. Gooden, J.M., Beach, A.D. and Purchas, R.W. (1980) 'Measurement of subcutaneous back fat depth in live lambs with an ultrasonic probe'. *N.Z.J. Agric. Res.* **23**, 161-5.

144. Green, W.W., Stevens, W.R. and Gauch, M.B. (1971) 'Use of body measurements to predict the weights of wholesale cuts of beef carcases: wholesale short loin of 900 pound steers'. *Univ. Md. Agric. Expt. Sta. Bull.* A 174.

145. Griffith, G.R. (1976) 'The benefits of a national pig carcase measurement and information service'. *Proc. Carcase Classification Symposium*, Adelaide, May 1976, 1-10.

146. Hallett, D. (1976) 'We share responsibility for product integrity'. *The National Provisioner*. 28 Feb., 65-70.

147. Hamelin, M. and Desmoulin, B. (1975) 'Anatomical composition of pork carcases in relation to commercial grading in France and the criteria of the E.E.C. grille'. *Paper to Commission on Pig Production, 26th Annual Meeting of the European Association for Animal Production*, Warsaw, 1975.

148. Hammond, J. (1933) 'The anatomy of pigs in relation to market requirements'. *Pig Breed. Annu.* **13**, 18-25.

149. Hankins, O.G. and Howe, P.E. (1946) 'Estimation of the composition of beef carcases and cuts'. *U.S.D.A. Tech. Bull.*, 926.

150. Hansson, I. (1980) 'Assessment of pig carcases by means of M.F.A. − recorder'. *26th Meeting of European Meat Research Workers*. Colorado Springs, 1980.

151. Hansson, I. and Lindhé, B. (1979) 'Performance testing of bulls for body composition in dual purpose cattle breeds'. *30th Annual Meeting of the European Association for Animal Production*. Harrogate, 1979.

152. Harries, J.M., Pomeroy, R.W. and Williams, D.R. (1974) 'Composition of beef carcases. III. The reliability and use of visual assessment'. *J. Agric. Sci. Camb.* **83**, 203-11.

153. Harries, J.M., Williams, D.R. and Pomeroy, R.W. (1975) 'Prediction of comparative retail value of beef carcases'. *Anim. Prod.* **21**, 127-37.

154. Harries, J.M., Williams, D.R. and Pomeroy, R.W. (1976) 'Comparative retail value of beef carcases from different groups of animals'. *Anim. Prod.* **23**, 349-56.

155. Harrington, G. (1958) 'Pig carcase evaluation'. *Tech. Commun. Bur. Anim. Breed. Genet., Edinb.* no. 12.

156. Harrington, G. (1963) 'The separation of technical errors and biological variation and other statistical problems arising in body composition studies'. *Ann. N. Y. Acad. Sci.* **110**, 642-53.

157. Harrington, G. (1969) 'Carcase classification in other countries'. *Institute of Meat Bulletin.* no. 64, 2-16, 29-31.

158. Harrington, G. (1972) 'The potential advantages of carcase classification'. Mimeo.

159. Harrington, G. (1972) 'Fat measurement and conformation in the classification and grading of British pigs'. Note prepared for a meeting of E.E.C. experts on pig grading. Mimeo.

160. Harrington, G. (1973) 'Some technical problems in developing a beef carcase classification system'. *Institute of Meat Bulletin* no. 80, 21-6.

161. Harrington, G. (1973) 'Classification developments in Britain and Europe'. *Proc. M.L.C. National Meat Conference.* Stratford, Nov. 1973.

162. Harrington, G. (1976) 'How far has the M.L.C. beef carcase classification scheme met its objectives?' *Proc. of the Carcase Classification Symposium*, May 1976, Adelaide, Australian Meat Board.

163. Harrington, G. (1978) 'Problems in devising a European beef carcase classification system'. *European Congress for improved beef productivity.* Elanco Products Ltd., Paris.

164. Harrington, G. and Kempster, A.J. (1977) 'Beef carcase yields'. *Institute of Meat Bulletin.* no. 95, 2-15.

165. Harrington, G. and King, J.W.B. (1963) 'A note on the prediction of muscular tissue weight in sides of beef'. *Anim. Prod.* **5**, 327-8.

166. Harrington, G. and Pomeroy, R.W. (1959) 'The yields of wholesale cuts from carcases of Aberdeen Angus crosses fattened on grass and in yards'. *J. Agric. Sci., Camb.* **53**, 64-7.

167. Harrington, G., Pomeroy, R.W. and Williams, D.R. (1961) 'Variations in the retail yield of carcases of Aberdeen Angus cross steers and heifers and their relation to conformation, bone content and finish'. *VIIth Meeting of European Meat Research Workers*, Warsaw, 1961.

168. Harris, D.L. (1970) 'Breeding for efficiency in livestock production: defining the economic objectives'. *J. Anim. Sci.* **30**, 860-5.

169. Hawrysh, Z.J. and Berg, R.T. (1976) 'Studies on beef eating quality in relation to the current Canada grade classifications'. *Can. J. Anim. Sci.* **56**, 383-91.

170. Hazel, L.N. (1943) 'The genetic basis for constructing selection indexes'. *Genetics* **28**, 476-90.

171. Hazel, L.N. and Kline, E.A. (1952) 'Mechanical measurement of fatness and carcase value of live hogs'. *J. Anim. Sci.* **11**, 313-18.

172. Hazel, L.N. and Kline, E.A. (1959) 'Ultrasonic measurement of fatness in swine'. *J. Anim. Sci.* **18**, 815-19.

173. Hedrick, H.B. (1968) 'Bovine growth and composition'. *Res. Bull. Univ. Mo Coll. Agric.* no. 928.

174. Her Majesty's Stationery Office (1967) *The Agriculture Act, 1967.* HMSO, London.

175. Hinks, C.E. and Prescott, J.H.D. (1974) 'A note on the prediction of

carcase composition in beef cattle'. *Anim. Prod.* **19**, 115-17.

176. Hirzel, R. (1976) 'Grading of meat in South Africa'. *Proc. of the Carcase Classification Symposium*, Adelaide, May 1976, Australian Meat Board.

177. Hohenboken, W.D. and Hillers, J.K. (1974) 'Phenotypic and genetic relationships among live animal and carcase traits'. In *Genetic Improvement of Carcase Merit in Sheep*. 44-54. *Bull New Mex. State Agric. Exp. Sta.* no. 616.

178. Horst, P. (1971) 'Erste Untersuchungsergebnisse über den Einsatz des 'Vidoson' Schnittbild-gerätes beim Schwein'. *Zuchtungeskunde* **43**, 208-18.

179. Houdinière, A. (1957) 'L'examen des profils musculaires dans l'appréciation de la qualité des viandes'. *Bull. Acad. Vet. France* **30**, 51-62.

180. Hytten, F.E., Taylor, K. and Taggart, N. (1966) 'Measurement of total body fat in man by absorption of ^{85}Kr'. *Clin. Sci.* **31**, 111-19.

181. Iler, D.C., Locking, G.L. and Usborne, W.R. (1971) 'A study of some methods of evaluating and handling beef carcases for the purposes of grading'. Project Report, 1971.

182. International Standards Organisation (1975) 'Meat and meat products standards. Sampling — Part 1: Taking primary samples'. ISO 3100/1. 'Determination of total fat content'. ISO 1443. 'Determination of nitrogen content'. ISO 937.

183. Isler, G.A. and Swiger, L.A. (1968) 'Ultrasonic prediction of lean cut percent in swine'. *J. Anim. Sci.* **27**, 377-82.

184. Jackson, T.H. and Mansour, Y.A. (1974) 'Differences between groups of lamb carcases chosen for good and poor conformation'. *Anim. Prod.* **19**, 93-105.

185. Jensen, P. and Andresen, E. (1980) 'Testing methods for P.S.E. syndrome: current research in Denmark'. *Livest. Prod. Sci.* **7**, 325-35.

186. Jeremiah, L.E. (1978) 'A review of factors affecting meat quality'. *Tech. Bull. Research Branch, Agriculture Canada*. no. 1.

187. Johnson, E.R. (1981) 'Carcase composition of double-muscled cattle'. *Anim. Prod.* **33**, 31-8.

188. Johnston, D.D. Tyler, W.E., Murphey, C.E., Kimbrell, E.F., Manns, D.F., Strong, C.L., Carpenter, Z.L. and King, G.T. (1967) 'Estimating yield of retail cuts from lamb carcases'. *Proc. Amer. Soc. Anim. Prod.* Aug. 1967.

189. Junta Nacional de Carnes (1962) *Official Argentine standards for grades of steer carcases*. Argentine Meat Board, London.

190. Kallweit, E. (1976) 'Visual assessments'. In *Criteria and methods for assessment of carcase and meat characteristics in beef production experiments* C.E.C., Luxembourg (EUR 5489), 81-9.

191. Kauffman, R.G., St. Clair, L.E. and Reber, R.J. (1963) 'Ovine myology'. *Bull, Ill. Agric. Exp. Sta.* no. 698.

192. Kauffman, R.G. and St. Clair, L.E. (1965) 'Porcine myology'. *Bull. Ill. Agric. Exp. Sta.* no. 715.

193. Kauffman, R.G., Van Ess, M.E., Long, R.A. and Schaefer, D.M. (1975) 'Marbling: its use in predicting beef carcase composition'. *J. Anim. Sci.* **40**, 235-41.

194. Kauffman, R.G., Van Ess, M.D. and Long, R.A. (1976) 'Bovine compositional interrelationships'. *J. Anim. Sci.* **43**, 102-07.

195. Kemp. J.D. and Barton, R.A. (1966) 'Composition of lamb carcases and

cuts of the New Zealand export grades'. *N.Z. J. Agric. Res.* **9**, 590-627.

196. Kempster, A.J. (1978) 'Bone growth and development with particular reference to breed differences in carcase shape and lean to bone ratio'. In de Boer, H. and Martin J. *eds., Patterns of growth and development in cattle. A seminar in the EEC programme of co-ordination of research of beef production*, Ghent, Oct. 1977, 149-66. Current Topics in Veterinary Medicine, Volume 2. Martinus Nyhoft, The Hague/Boston/London.

197. Kempster, A.J. (1979) 'Effect of breed improvement on (pig) meat quality'. *Institute of Meat Bulletin*. no. 103, 12-20.

198. Kempster, A.J. (1979) 'Variation in the carcase characteristics of commercial British sheep with particular reference to over-fatness'. *Meat Science* **3**, 199-208.

199. Kempster. A.J. (1980) 'Entire males for meat: how far has the industry come?' *Meat*. June 1980, 13-18.

200. Kempster, A.J. (1980) 'Holsteins for beef: how do they compare with Friesians?' *Meat*. July 1980, 51-3.

201. Kempster, A.J. (1981) 'Fat partition and distribution in the carcases of cattle, sheep and pigs: a review'. *Meat Science*, **5**, 83-98.

202. Kempster, A.J. (1981) 'Recent developments in measuring techniques for use in pig carcase classification and grading'. *Pig News & Information,* **2**, 145-8.

203. Kempster, A.J., Arnall, D., Alliston, J.C. and Barker, J.D. (1982) 'An evaluation of two ultrasonic machines (Scanogram and Danscanner) for predicting the body composition of live sheep'. *Anim. Prod.* (in press).

204. Kempster, A.J., Avis, P.R.D., Cuthbertson, A. and Harrington, G. (1976) 'Prediction of the lean content of lamb carcases of different breed types'. *J. Agric. Sci. Camb.* **86**, 23-34.

205. Kempster, A.J., Charles, D.D. and Cook, G.L. (1982) 'The effect of breed on fat partition and distribution in beef carcases'. *J. Agric. Sci. Camb.* (in press).

206. Kempster, A.J. and Chadwick, J.P. (1982) 'Prediction of beef carcase composition 2. From fat and muscle measurements taken on cut surfaces between the 6th and 13th ribs'. *J. Agric. Sci. Camb.* (in press).

207. Kempster, A.J., Chadwick, J.P., Jones, D.W. and Cuthbertson, A. (1982) 'An evaluation of the Hennessy and Chong fat depth indicator and the Ulster Probe for use in pig carcase classification and grading'. *Anim. Prod.* (in press).

208. Kempster, A.J., Cook, G.L. and Smith, R.J. (1980) 'The evaluation of a standardized commercial cutting technique for determining breed differences in carcase composition'. *J. Agric. Sci., Camb.* **95**, 431-40.

209. Kempster, A.J. and Cook, G.L. (1982) 'The relationship between saleable meat yield and carcase value for beef steers of different breeds and crosses'. *J. Agric. Sci., Camb.* (in press).

210. Kempster, A.J. Cook, G.L. and Southgate, J.R. (1982) 'A comparison of suckler-bred cattle of different breeds and crosses. 2 Carcase characteristics'. *Anim. Prod.* (in press).

211. Kempster, A.J., Cook, G.L. and Southgate, J.R. (1982) 'A comparison of the progeny of British Friesian dams and different sire breeds in 16 month and 24 month production systems. 2. Carcase characteristics,

and rate and efficiency of meat gain'. *Anim. Prod.* (in press).

212. Kempster, A.J., Croston, D. and Jones, D.W. (1981) 'Value of conformation as an indicator of sheep carcase composition within and between breeds'. *Anim. Prod.* **33**, 39-49.

213. Kempster, A.J. and Cuthbertson, A. (1977) 'A survey of the carcase characteristics of the main types of British lamb'. *Anim. Prod.* **25**, 165-79.

214. Kempster, A.J., Cuthbertson, A. and Harrington, G. (1976) 'Fat distribution in steer carcases of different breeds and crosses. 1. Distribution between depots'. *Anim. Prod.* **23**, 25-34.

215. Kempster, A.J., Cuthbertson, A. and Harrington, G. (1982) 'The relationships between conformation and the yield and distribution of lean meat in the carcases of British pigs, cattle and sheep: a review'. *Meat Science.* **6**, 37-53.

216. Kempster, A.J., Cuthbertson, A. and Jones, D.W. (1976) 'Prediction of the lean content of steer carcases of different breed types from the lean content of sample joints'. *Criteria and methods for assessment of carcase and meat characteristics in beef production experiments* C.E.C. Luxembourg (EUR 5489), 209-19.

217. Kempster, A.J., Cuthbertson, A., Jones, D.W. and Owen, M.G. (1981) 'Prediction of body composition of live cattle using two machines of differing complexity: a report of four separate trials'. *J. Agric. Sci., Camb.* **96**, 301-07.

218. Kempster, A.J., Cuthbertson, A., Owen, M.G. and Alliston, J.C. (1979) 'A comparison of four ultrasonic machines (Sonatest, Scanogram, Ilis Observer and Danscanner) for predicting the body composition of live pigs'. *Anim. Prod.* **29**, 485-91.

219. Kempster, A.J., Cuthbertson, A. and Smith, R.J. (1981) 'A national survey of the weight loss in pig carcases between slaughter and 24 hours post mortem'. *Meat Science.* **5**, 383-7.

220. Kempster, A.J. and Evans, D.G. (1979) 'A comparison of different predictors of the lean content of pig carcases. 1. Predictors for use in commercial classification and grading'. *Anim. Prod.* **28**, 87-96.

221. Kempster, A.J. and Evans, D.G. (1982) 'The value of shape as a predictor of carcase composition in the British pig population'. *Anim. Prod.* (in press).

222. Kempster, A.J. and Harrington, G. (1979) 'Variation in the carcase characteristics of commercial British cattle'. *Meat Science.* **3**, 53-62.

223. Kempster, A.J. and Harrington, G. (1980) 'The value of "fat-corrected" conformation as an indicator of beef carcase composition within and between breeds'. *Livest. Prod. Sci.* **7**, 361-72.

224. Kempster, A.J. and Jones, D.W. (1977) 'Relationships between the lean content of joints and overall lean content in steer carcases of different breeds and crosses'. *J. Agric. Sci., Camb.* **88**, 193-201.

225. Kempster, A.J., Jones, D.W. and Cuthbertson, A. (1979) 'A comparison of the Danish M.F.A., Ulster and optical probes for use in pig carcase classification and grading'. *Meat Science.* **3**, 109-20.

226. Kempster, A.J. and Owen, M.G. (1981) 'A note on the accuracy of an ultrasonic technique for selecting cattle of different breeds for slaughter at equal fatness'. *Anim. Prod.* **32**, 113-15.

227. Kiehl, E.R. and Rhodes, V.J. (1960) 'Historical development of beef quality and grading standards'. *Res. Bull. Mo Agric. Exp. Sta.* No. 728.

228. Kielanowski, J. (1968) 'The method of pig progeny testing applied in Poland. 1. General principles and physiological background'. *Proc. Sub-Commission on Pig Progeny Testing. 9th Study meeting of the European Association for Animal Production*, Dublin, 1968.

229. Kirton, A.H. (1966) 'Meat grading standards and market requirements'. *Proc. Ruakura Farmers' Conference Week*, 1966.

230. Kirton, A.H. and Colomer-Rocher, F. (1978) 'The New Zealand sheep and lamb export carcase classification system'. *Wld. Rev. Anim. Prod.* **14**, 33-41.

231. Kirton, A.H. and Johnson, D.L. (1979) 'Interrelationships between GR and other lamb carcase fatness measurements'. *Proc. N.Z. Soc. Anim. Prod.* **39**, 194-201.

232. Kirton, A.H., O'Hara, P.J., Cairney, I.M., Bishop, W.H. and Nottingham, P.M. (1975) 'Determination of age of lamb carcases from pelvic ossification'. *Anim. Prod.* **21**, 257-64.

233. Kirton, A.H., Sinclair, D.P. and Dobbie, J.L. (1978) 'Over-fat lambs, significance, GR measurement and measurement strategies'. *Farm Production & Practice*. no. 126.

234. Klosterman, E.W. (1972) 'Beef cattle size for maximum efficiency'. *J. Anim. Sci.* **34**, 875-80.

235. Koch, R.M., Dikeman, M.E., Allen, D.M., May, M., Crouse, J.D. and Campion, D.R. (1976) 'Characterization of biological types of cattle. III. Carcase composition, quality and palatability'. *J. Anim. Sci.* **43**, 48-62.

236. Koch, R.M., Dikeman, M.E., Lipsey, R.J., Allen, D.M. and Crouse, J.E. (1979) 'Characterisation of biological types of cattle — cyle II: III. Carcase composition, quality and palatability'. *J. Anim. Sci.* **49**, 448-60.

237. Koch, R.M., and Varnadore, W.L. (1976) 'Use of electronic meat measuring equipment to measure cutout yield of beef carcases'. *J. Anim. Sci.* **43**, 108-113.

238. Kødbranchens Faellesrad (1976) 'Danish beef'. A trade guide from the Danish Livestock and Meat Board, Copenhagen.

239. Kotarbinska, M. (1968) 'The chemical composition of the body in growing pigs'. *19th Annual Meeting of the European Association for Animal Production*. Dublin, 1968.

240. Kräusslich, H. *ed.* (1974) 'General recommendations on procedures for performance and progeny testing for beef characteristics'. *Livest. Prod. Sci.* **1**, 33-45.

241. Land, R.B. (1981) 'An alternative philosophy for livestock breeding'. *Livest. Prod. Sci.* **8**, 95-9.

242. Latham, S.D., Moody, W.G. and Kemp, J.D. (1966) 'Techniques for estimating lamb carcase composition'. *J. Anim. Sci.* **25**, 492-96.

243. Lawrie, R.A. (1979) *Meat Science*. 3rd edn. Pergamon Press, Oxford.

244. Ledger, H.P., Gilliver, B. and Robb, J.M. (1973) 'An examination of sample joint dissection and specific gravity techniques for assessing the carcase composition of steers slaughtered in commercial abattoirs'. *J. Agric. Sci. Camb.* **80**, 381-92.

245. Ledger, H.P. and Hutchinson, H.G. (1962) 'The value of the tenth rib as a sample joint for the estimation of lean, fat and bone in the carcases of East African Zebu cattle'. *J. Agric. Sci. Camb.* **58**, 81-90.

246. Legras, P., Dumont, B.L. and Roy, G. (1971) 'La grille I.T.O.V.I.C.' *Pâtre.* **183**, April-May, 26-40.

247. Lerner, I.M. (1950) *Population genetics and animal improvement.* Cambridge University Press.

248. Lewis, R.W., Brungardt, V.H. and Bray, R.W. (1964) 'Influence of subcutaneous fat contours in estimating trimmable fat and retail yield of heifer carcases'. *J. Anim. Sci.* **23**, 1203 (Abstr.).

249. Limousin and Simmental Tests Steering Committee (1976) 'Report of the evaluation of the first importation into Great Britain in 1970-71 of Limousin bulls from France and Simmental bulls from Germany and Switzerland'. H.M.S.O., London.

250. Lindhé, B. (1975) 'Genetic change of energy deposition in beef cattle'. *Wld. Rev. Anim. Prod.* **11**, 19-25.

251. Lindhé, B., Averdunk, G., Brascamp, E.W., Duniec, H., Gajic, A., Legault, C. and Steane, D.E. (1978) 'Estimation of breeding value in pigs'. Report of a working party, *29th Annual Meeting of the European Association for Animal Production.* Stockholm, 1978.

252. Lindhé, B. and Henningsson, T. (1968) 'Crossbreeding for beef with Swedish Red and White cattle. II. Growth and feed efficiency under standardised conditions with detailed carcase evaluation'. *Lantbr. Högsk Annb.* **34**, 517-50.

253. Lister, D. (1976) 'Effects of nutrition and genetics on the composition of the body'. *Proc. Nutr. Soc.* **35**, 351-56.

254. Lister, D. (1976) 'Hormonal influences on the growth, metabolism and body composition of pigs'. In Lister, D., Rhodes, D.N., Fowler, V.R. and Fuller, M.F. eds. *Meat animals, growth and productivity.* Plenum Press, New York and London, 355-71.

255. Lister, D. (1980) 'Endocrine control of pig growth'. *Proc. Nutr. Soc.* **39**, 161-8.

256. Locking, G.L. (1976) 'Canada's beef carcase grading system'. *Proc. of the Carcase Classification Symposium*, Adelaide, May 1976, Australian Meat Board.

257. Losada, H. and Perez, A. (1972) 'A note on the estimation of animal age from the physical appearance of carcase bone'. *Rev. Cubana Cienc. Agric.* **6**, 183-8.

258. Luckock, C.R. (1976) 'The development of an objective beef carcase classification system for Australia'. *Proc. of the Carcase Classification Symposium*, Adelaide, May 1976, Australian Meat Board.

259. Luckock, C.R. (1980) 'A test of three electronic fat probes for measuring the fat depth of hot unquartered beef carcases'. Report to the National Carcase Classification Steering Committee.

260. Lund, A.A. and Pedersen, O.K. (1967) 'Ein neues automatisches Instrument zur Messung unregel-mässiger Flachen ins besondere am Schweinekotelett'. *Die Fleischwirtschaft* **3**, 263-4.

261. Lundström, K. (1975) 'Genetic parameters estimated on data from the Swedish pig progeny testing with special emphasis on meat colour. *Swedish*

J. Agric. Res. **5**, 209-21.

262. MacIntyre, D., Oldfield, J.A. and Nicol, A.M. (1974) 'The meat export grades investigating committee'. *Report to the New Zealand Meat Producers' Board*, Wellington.

263. Malmfors, G. (1981) 'Pig carcase evaluation by use of an electronic scanning planimeter, E.S.P.'. Thesis, Swedish University of Agricultural Sciences, Uppsala.

264. Malmfors, B., Eriksson, J.A. and Lundstrom, K. (1979) 'Effects of including meat quality in a selection index for pigs'. *Meat and Fat Quality of Boars, Gilts and Castrates*. Report No. 32, Swedish University of Agricultural Sciences.

265. Malmfors, B. and Nilsson, R. (1979) 'Meat quality traits in Swedish Landrace and Yorkshire pigs with special emphasis on genetics'. *Acta. Agric. Scand.* Suppl. 21: Muscle Function and Porcine Meat Quality. N.J.F. Symposium, August 1977, 81-90.

266. Martin, A.H., Fredeen, H.T., Weiss, G.M., Fortin, A.R. and Sim, D. (1981) 'Yield of trimmed pork product in relation to weight and back fat thickness of the carcase'. *Can. J. Anim. Sci.* **61**, 299-310.

267. Maybee, H.J. (1955) 'Hog grading in Canada'. *Canada Dept. of Agric. Publ.* 961.

268. Maybee, H.J. (1964) 'Beef and veal grading in Canada'. *Publ. Canada Dept. Agric.* no. 962.

269. McClelland, T.H., Bonaiti, B. and Taylor, St. C.S. (1976) 'Breed differences in body composition of equally mature sheep'. *Anim. Prod.* **23**, 281-93.

270. McGloughlin, P. (1980) 'Genetic aspects of pigmeat quality'. *Pig News and Information* **1**, 5-9.

271. McMeekan, C.P. (1941) 'Growth and development in the pig, with special reference to carcase quality characters. IV. The use of sample joints and carcase measurements as indices of the composition of the bacon pig'. *J. Agric. Sci., Camb.* **31**, 1-49.

272. McPherson, W.K. and Dixon, L.V. (1966) 'A quantitative evaluation of the ability of individuals to grade live cattle'. *J. Farm. Econ.* **38**, 61-74.

273. Meat and Livestock Commission (1975) 'Progress on beef carcase classification'. *Marketing and Meat Trade Technical Bulletin*. no. 22, M.L.C., Bletchley.

274. Meat and Livestock Commission (1977) 'Selecting cattle for slaughter'. M.L.C., Bletchley.

275. Meat and Livestock Commission (1978) 'Young entire male pigs for bacon'. *M.L.C. Marketing Newsletter*. no. 14. M.L.C. Bletchley.

276. Meat and Livestock Commission (1981) 'Lamb carcase production: planning to meet your market'. M.L.C., Bletchley.

277. Meat and Livestock Commission (1980) *Commercial pig production yearbook 1980*. M.L.C., Bletchley, Bucks.

278. Meat and Livestock Commission (1980) 'Beef conformation – appealing to eye . . . or to pocket?' Leaflet.

279. Meat and Livestock Commission (1980) *Commercial pig evaluation, Management and procedures*, M.L.C., Bletchley.

280. Meat and Livestock Commission (1981) *Commercial beef production*

yearbook, M.L.C., Bletchley.

281. Miles, C.A. (1976). 'Chemical composition of carcases and sample joints: specific gravity determination.' In *Criteria and methods for assessment of carcase and meat characteristics in beef production experiments*, pp. 253-262. C.E.C., Luxembourg. (EUR 5489).

282. Miles, C.A. (1978). 'Note on recent advances in ultrasonic scanning of animals.' *Proc. 24th European Meat Research Workers' Congress*, Kulmbach, pp. W13.3-W13.6.

283. Miles, C.A. and Speight, B.S. (1975). 'Recording the shape of animals by a Moiré method.' *J. Phys. Scientific Instruments* 8, 1-4.

284. Miller, R.H. and Pearson, R.E. (1979). 'Economic aspects of selection.' *Anim. Breed. Abstr.* 47, 281-90.

285. Moulton, C.R., Trowbridge, P.R. and Haigh, L.D. (1922) 'Studies in animal nutrition. III. Changes in chemical composition on different planes of nutrition'. *Mo Agric. Exp. Sta. Res. Bull.* No. 3.

286. Moxham, R.W. and Brownlie, L.E. (1976) 'Sheep carcase grading and classification in Australia'. *Wool Tech. & Sheep Breeding.* 23, no. 11, 17-25.

287. Mumford, H.W. and Hall, L.D. (1910) 'Market classes and grades of meat'. *Bull. Ill. Agric. Exp. Sta.* no. 147.

288. Murphey, C.E., Hallett, D.K., Tyler, W.E. and Pierce, J.C. (1960) 'Estimating yields of retail cuts from beef carcases'. *Proc. Amer. Soc. Anim. Prod.* Chicago.

289. Naumann, H.D. (1952) 'A recommended procedure for measuring and grading beef for carcase evaluation'. *Proc. Reciprocal Meat. Conf.* 5, 108-13.

290. Nelson, K.E. (1977) 'Economic effects of the 1976 Beef grade changes'. *Tech. Bull. U.S.D.A. Econ. Res. Service.* no. 1570.

291. Nervik, O. and Paterson, D.G. (1951) 'Marketing lambs: Comparison of liveweight method and carcase weight and grade method'. *Bull. South Dak. Agric. Exp. Sta.* no. 416.

292. Nervik, O., Pierce, E.A. and Glover, J.H. (1952) 'The effect on carcase yield and grade of holding lambs in packers' yards'. *Tech. Bull. South Dak. Agric. Exp. Sta.* no. 12.

293. New Zealand Meat Producers' Board (1967) 'A history of New Zealand lamb'. Booklet.

294. New Zealand Meat Producers' Board (1979) 'An illustrated Guide to New Zealand lamb and other carcase meat and meat products'. Booklet.

295. New Zealand Meat Producers' Board (1980) *57th Annual Report and Statement of Accounts for Year Ended September 30, 1979.* Wellington.

296. Niebel, E., Rittler, A. and Fewson, D. (1972) *Die Leistungsmechmodelle beim Rind. Wirtschaft Wirtschaftliche Bedenkung und Selektionswürdigkeit.* Teil B, Hohenheim Arbeiten Heft 64; Verlang Enzen Ulmer, Stuttgart.

297. O'Connell, J., Dempsey, M. and Meenan, K. (1979) *The marketing of Irish beef in France with special reference to price/quality relationships.* University College, Department of Agricultural Economics, Dublin.

298. Office National Interprofessionnel du Bétail et des Viandes (1975) *Classification et marquage des bovins, Module 1.* O.N.I.B.E.V., Paris.

299. Office National Interprofessionel du Bétail et des Viandes (1976) *Catalogue de classement EUROPA (Moutons)*. O.N.I.B.E.V., Paris.

300. Oliver, W.M. (1967) 'A review: shape or weight in cattle for beef'. *Tex. Agric. Exp. Sta. Tech. Rep.* no. 6.

301. Oliver, W.M., Carpenter, Z.L., King, G.T. and Shelton, M. (1968) 'Predicting cutability of lamb carcases from carcase weights and measures'. *J. Anim. Sci.* **27**, 1254-60.

302. Ollivier, L., Sellier, P. and Monin, G. (1978) 'Frequency of the malignant hyperthermia syndrome in French pig populations: relationship with muscular development'. *Annales de Genetique et de selection Animale* **10**, 191-208.

303. Olson, L.W., Dickerson, G.E., Crouse, J.D. and Glimp, H.A. (1976) 'Selection criteria for intensive market lamb production: carcase and growth traits'. *J. Anim. Sci.* **43**, 90-101.

304. Organisation for Economic Cooperation and Development (1961). 'Meat grading in OEEC member countries.' *Documentation in Food and Agriculture.* No. 43.

305. Osinska, Z. (1975) 'Backfat thickness and carcase quality in pigs'. *Festskrift til Hjalmar Clausen.* Det Kgl. Danske Landhusholdningsselskab, 279-89.

306. Pálsson, H. (1955) 'Conformation and body composition'. *Progress in the physiology of farm animals.* Volume 2, Butterworths, London.

307. Pearson, A.M., Bratzler, L.J., Hoefer, J.A., Price, J.F., Magee, W.T. and Deans, R.J. (1956) 'The fat-lean ratio in the rough loin as a tool in evaluation of pork carcases'. *J. Anim. Sci.* **15**, 896-901.

308. Pedersen, O.K. (1975) 'The basis for comparison of carcase quality and grading in pigs'. *Festskrift til Hjalmar Clausen.* Det. Kgl. Danske Landhusholdningsselskab, 291-305.

309. Pedersen, O.K. (1979) 'Relationship between meat quality and meat quantity'. *Proc. E.A.A.P./M.L.C./A.B.R.O. Pig Testing Conference.* Harrogate, 1979.

310. Pedersen, O.K. (1979) 'Pig carcase evaluation, grading and payment in Denmark'. *Seminar on pig carcase evaluation, grading and payment.* March 1979, Uppsala, Sweden.

311. Pedersen, O.K. and Busk, H. (1981) 'Development of automatic equipment for grading of pig carcases in Denmark'. *Paper to Commission on Pig Production, 32nd Annual Meeting of the European Association for Animal Production.* Zagreb, 1981.

312. Pfleiderer, U-E. (1969) 'Die Genauigkeit der neuen Fettflächenbegrenzung am Kotelettschnitt und ihre Aussagefähigkeit über den Schlactkörper'. *Z. Tierzücht. ZüchtBiol.* **86**, 349-55.

313. Pomeroy, R.W. (1966) 'Problems in pig carcass research'. *Institute of Meat Bulletin.* no. 51, 23-32.

314. Pomeroy, R.W. and Williams, D.R. (1974) 'The partition of fat in the bovine carcase'. *Proc. Brit. Soc. Anim. Prod.* **3**, 85 (Abstr.).

315. Pomeroy, R.W., Williams, D.R., Harries, J.M. and Ryan, P.O. (1974) 'Composition of beef carcases. I. Material, measurements, jointing and tissue separation'. *J. Agric. Sci. Camb.* **83**, 67-77.

316. Pommeret, P., Felix, Ph. and Naveau, J. (1981) 'Mesure de l'épaisseur

de lard avec fat depth indicator (F.D.I.) comparison avec l'intrascope'. *Techni. Porc.* **4**, 7-13.

317. Powell, W.E. and Huffman, D.L. (1968) 'Evaluation of quantitative estimates of beef carcase composition'. *J. Anim. Sci.* **27**, 1554-8.

318. Power, P. (1976) 'Beef carcase classification in Ireland'. *Proc. 5th International Beef Symposium*. Dublin, April 1976.

319. Preston, T.R. and Willis, M.B. (1970) *Intensive beef production*. Pergammon Press, Oxford.

320. Price, J.F. and Schweigert, B.S. eds. (1971) *The science of meat and meat products*. Freeman, San Francisco.

321. Purcell, W.D. and Nelson, K.E. (1976) 'Recent changes in beef grades: issues and analysis of the yield grade requirement'. *Amer. J. Agric. Econ.* **58**, 475-84.

322. Ramsbottom, J.M. and Strandine, E.J. (1948) 'Comparative tenderness and identification of muscles in wholesale beef cuts'. *Food. Res.* **13**, 315-30.

323. Republic of South Africa (1981) 'Regulations relating to the classification, grading and marking of meat intended for sale in the Republic of South Africa'. *Government Gazette*. R. 1010, 8 May, 2-14.

324. Rhodes, V.J. (1960) 'How the marking of beef grades was obtained'. *J. Farm. Econ.* **42**, 133-49.

325. Rhodes, V.J. (1961) 'Acceptance and yield of choice and good beef: research results and implications'. *J. Farm. Econ.* **43**, 181-96.

326. Ringkob, T.P., Zobrisky, S.E., Ross, C.V. and Naumann, H.D. (1964) 'Measurements of muscle and retail cuts of lamb'. *Res. Bull. Univ. Mo. Coll. Agric.* no. 876.

327. Riordan, E.B. and Mellon, K. (1978) 'Beef carcase classification as an aid to prediction of carcase value'. *Ir. J. Agric. Econ. Rur. Sociol.* **7**, 9-32.

328. Robelin, J. (1976) 'Estimation of body composition in vivo by dilution techniques'. *Criteria and methods for assessment of carcase and meat quality characteristics in beef production experiments*. C.E.C. Luxembourg (EUR 5489), 91-102.

329. Robinson, T.J., Binet, F.E. and Doig, A.G. (1956) 'Fat lamb studies in Victoria. I. An assessment of the relative value of various external measurements for differentiating between various grades of export lamb carcases'. *Austr. J. Agric. Res.* **1**, 345-65.

330. Ryan, O. (1978) 'Classification and carcase value'. *Proc. 6th International Beef Symposium*. Dublin, April 1978.

331. Scandinavian Association of Agricultural Scientists (N.J.F.) (1979) 'Muscle function and porcine meat quality'. A symposium of N.J.F. *Acta Agric. Scand.* Suppl. 21.

332. Schön, I. (1973) 'Improvement of market transparency in meat trade' *Wld. Rev. Anim. Prod.* **9**, 34-47.

333. Schön, I. (1975) 'Lammfleisch, Hammelfleisch und Schaffleisch im markt. Fragen der Transparenz und des Angebotes'. *Die Fleischwirtschaft*. no. 9, 1170-72.

334. Schön, I. (1981) 'Anforderungen und Vergleich der Kriterien für die Intervention und Empfehlungen für eine allgemeine Klassifizierung der Schlachtkörper von Rindern in EG-Mitgliedsländen'. Report prepared

for the E.E.C., Jan. 1981, Kulmbach.

335. Schön, L. (1966) 'Handelsklassen für Schweinehälften'. A.I.D., Bonn-Bad Godesberg, no. 248.

336. Schön, L. (1971) 'Handelsklassen für Rindfleisch'. A.I.D., Bonn-Bad Godesberg, no. 299.

337. Schön, L. (1973) 'Handelsklassen für Schweinehälften'. A.I.D., Bonn-Bad Godesberg, no. 248 (revised).

338. Schön, L. (1976) 'Handelsklassen für Schaffleisch'. A.I.D., Bonn-Bad Godesberg, no. 325.

339. Schön, L., Niebel, E., Fewson, D. and Scholz, W. (1977) 'Die Wirtschaftlichkeitskoeffizienten der Leistungsmerkmale beim Schwein und deren Bedeutung für die Zuchtarbeit 3. Mitteilung: Abschätzung des Fleischanteils beim Schwein, auf Grund von Teilstücken und deren grobgeweblicher Zusammensetzung'. *Zuchtungskunde* **49**, 253-69.

340. Schön, L. and Pedersen, O.K. (1977) 'Determination of the proportion of lean meat in pig carcases using the Danish K.S.A. − equipment'. *Information on Agriculture Series*. no. 38. C.E.C. Brussels-Luxembourg.

341. Schön, L. and Sack, E. (1981) 'Versuche mit S.K.G. im Vergleich zu K.S.A. in der Bundesrepublik Deutschland'. *32nd Annual Meeting of the European Association for Animal Production*. Zagreb, 1981.

342. Seebeck, R.M. and Tulloh, N.M. (1968) 'Developmental growth and body weight loss of cattle. II. Dissected components of the commercially dressed and jointed carcase'. *Aust. J. Agric. Res.* **19**, 477-95.

343. Shelton, M., Smith, G.C. and Orts, F. (1977) 'Predicting carcase cutability of Rambouillet rams using live animal traits.' *J. Anim. Sci.* **44**, 333-7.

344. Sissons, S. and Grossman, J.D. (1975) *The anatomy of the domestic animals* (revised Getty, R.). W.B. Saunders, Philadelphia and London.

345. Skjervold, H., Gronseth, K., Vangen, O. and Evensen, A. (1981) 'In vivo estimation of body composition by computerised tomography'. *Z. Tierzücht. ZüchtBiol.* **98**, 77-9.

346. Slakteriföreningen Scan (1974) 'Kött Klassificering' (Sweden) Leaflet.

347. Smallfield, P.W. and Wright, A.C. (1965) 'Meat export grades investigation committee'. *Report to the New Zealand Meat Producers' Board*. Wellington.

348. Smith, D.H. (1978) 'Report on European pig production'. *29th Annual Meeting of the European Association for Animal Production*. Stockholm.

349. Smith, G.C. (1980) 'Grades for the future: what, why and how?' *Proc. 33rd Annual Recip. Meat Conf.* June 1980, 89-99.

350. Smith, G.C. and Carpenter, Z.L. (1973) 'Evaluation of factors associated with the composition of pork carcases'. *J. Anim. Sci.* **36**, 493-9.

351. Smith, G.C. and Carpenter, Z.L. (1976) 'Eating quality of meat animal products and their fat content'. *Fat content and composition of animal products*. Proc. of a Symposium, Washington, 1974, National Academy of Sciences.

352. Smith, P.B. (1976) 'Developments in beef carcase classification'. *Bur. Agric. Econ., Canberra, Beef Res. Report*. no. 19.

353. Sornay, J. (1981) 'Variation between carcases in economic terms, considering either the carcase composition or the market prices'. *E.E.C.*

Meeting on the retail value of beef carcases. June 1981, Langford.

354. Sornay, J. (1976) 'Relationship between visually and objectively assessed characteristics and sample joint dissection with carcase composition'. *Criteria and methods for assessment of carcase and meat characteristics in beef production experiments.* C.E.C. Luxembourg (EUR 5489), 193-201.

355. Standal, N. (1980) 'Hormonal responses in pigs selected for different traits'. *31st Meeting of the European Association for Animal Production,* Munich, 1980.

356. Staun, H. and Jensen, P. (1974) 'Genetic aspects of meat quality in pigs'. *1st World Congress on Genetics applied to Livestock Production.* Plenary Sessions, 885-92. Editorial Garsi, Madrid.

357. Steel, N.C., Frobish, L.T., Davey, R.J. and Keeney, M. (1972) 'Effect of selection for backfat thickness in swine on lipogenic enzyme levels'. *J. Anim. Sci.* **35**, 225 (Abstr.).

358. Stouffer, J.R., Wallentine, M.V., Wellington, G.H. and Diekmann, A. (1961) 'Development and application of ultrasonic methods for measuring fat thickness and rib-eye area in cattle and hogs'. *J. Anim. Sci.* **20**, 759-67.

359. Sundgren, P.E. (1973) 'Studies on pig performance testing'. *Dept. Anim. Breed., Agric. Coll., Uppsala, Sweden.* Report no. 2, S 750 07.

360. Tardivat, J.-C. (1976) 'The French carcase classification − basis for an E.E.C. classification'. *Proc. 5th International Beef Symposium.* Dublin, 1976.

361. Tarrant, P.V., Gallwey, W.J. and McGloughlin, P. (1979) 'Carcase pH values in Irish Landrace and Large White pigs'. *Irish J. Agric. Res.* **18**, 167-72.

362. Taylor, St. C.S. and Craig, J. (1965) 'Genetic correlations during growth of twin cattle'. *Anim. Prod.* **7**, 83-102.

363. Taylor, St. C.S. and Young, G.B. (1966) 'Variation in growth and efficiency in twin cattle with live weight and food intake controlled'. *J. Agric. Sci. Camb.* **66**, 67-85.

364. Thorbek, G. (1975) 'Studies on energy metabolism in growing pigs. II'. *Beretning Stat. Husdyrbrugsforsøg.* **424**, 93-126.

365. Timon, V.M. and Bichard, M. (1965) 'Quantitative estimates of lamb carcase composition. 3. Carcase measurements and a comparison of the predictive efficiency of sample joint composition, carcase specific gravity determinations and carcase measurements'. *Anim. Prod.* **7**, 189-201.

366. Todd. M.C. and Cowell, M.D. (1978) 'Issues in the evaluation of the proposed carcase classification schemes'. *Bur. of Agric. Econ. Canberra.* Occasional Paper no. 45.

367. Tucker, H.Q., Voegeli, M.M., Wellington, G.H. and Bratzler, L.J. (1952) *A cross sectional muscle nomenclature of the beef carcase.* Michigan State College Press.

368. Tulloh, N.M., Truscott, T.G. and Lang, C.P. (1973) *An evaluation of the Scanogram for predicting the carcase composition of live cattle.* A report submitted to the Australian Meat Board, School of Agriculture and Forestry, University of Melbourne.

369. United States Department of Agriculture (1956) 'The meat-type hog'.

U.S.D.A. Agricultural Research Service. Special Report, ARS 22-31.

370. United States Department of Agriculture (1965) 'Feeder grades for cattle'. Scale shown by D. Acker (1971) in *Animal Science and Industry*. Prentice-Hall, New Jersey, 135-9.

371. United States Department of Agriculture (1968, revised 1978) 'U.S.D.A. yield grades for beef'. *U.S.D.A. Marketing Bulletin*. no. 45.

372. United States Department of Agriculture (1970) 'U.S.D.A. Grades for pork carcases'. *U.S.D.A. Consumer & Marketing Services, Marketing Bulletin*. no. 49.

373. United States Department of Agriculture (1970) 'U.S.D.A. yield grades for lambs'. *U.S.D.A. Marketing Bulletin*. no. 52.

374. Vangen, O. (1977) 'Studies on a two trait selection experiment in pigs. 1. Growth, feed consumption and feed conversion ratio after 10 years of selection for growth rate and backfat thickness'. *Acta Agric. Scand.* **27**, 332-40.

375. Verdon Smith Committee (1964) *Report of a Committee of Inquiry into fatstock and carcase meat marketing and distribution.* H.M.S.O., London.

376. von Rümker (1967) 'Handelsklassen für Schlachtrinder und Kälber'. A.I.D., Bonn-Bad Godesberg, no. 129.

377. Wallace, M.A., Stouffer, J.R. and Westervelt, R.G. (1977) 'Relationships of ultrasonic and carcase measurements with retail yield in beef cattle'. *Livest. Prod. Sci.* **4**, 153-64.

378. Walstra, P., Minkema, D., Sybesma, W. and Van De Pas, J.G.C. (1971) 'Genetic aspects of meat quality and stress resistance in experiments with various breeds and crosses'. *Proc. E.A.A.P. Conf.* Paris, Mimeo.

379. Webb, A.J. (1980) 'The incidence of halothane sensitivity in British pigs'. *Anim. Prod.* **31**, 101-05.

380. Webb, A.J. and Jordan, C.H.C. (1978) 'Halothane sensitivity as a field test for stress-susceptibility in the pig'. *Anim. Prod.* **26**, 157-68.

381. Weniger, J.H., Dumont, B.L., de Boer, H., Bergström, P.L., Engelke, F. and Glodek, P. (1966). *Etude sur les qualités des carcasses de bovins et porcins dans les pays de la Communauté Economique Européenne.* Office Statistique des Communautés Européennes, Bruxelles.

382. Whittemore, C.T. (1980) 'The Edinburgh computer model pig'. *Pig News and Information* **1**, 343-6.

383. Williams, D.R. (1969) 'The visual description of carcases'. *J. Agric. Sci. Camb.* **73**, 495-9.

384. Williams, D.R. and Bergstrom, P.L. (1976). *Anatomical jointing, tissue separation and weight recording proposed as the E.E.C. standard method for beef.* C.E.C. Luxembourg (EUR 5720).

385. Williams, D.R., Pomeroy, R.W., Harries, J.M. and Ryan, P.O. (1974) 'Composition of beef carcases. II. The use of regression equations to estimate total tissue components from observations on intact and quartered sides and partial dissection data'. *J. Agric. Sci. Camb.* **83**, 79-85.

386. Williams, W.F. and Stout, T.T. (1964) *Economics of the livestock-meat industry.* Macmillan, New York.

387. Willis, M.B. and Preston, T.R. (1970) 'Carcase characteristics of various breeds of beef cattle in Cuba'. *Rev. Cubana Cienc. Agric.* **4**, 85-90.

388. Wilson, B.R., Berg, R.T. and Richmond, R.J. (1971) 'Hog grading. An

amended table of differentials based on payment for carcase muscle content'. *Univ. of Alberta, Dept. of Animal Science, 50th Annual Feeders' Day Report*. 40-42.

389. Wilson, B.R., Bryson, J., Dains, J.R., Gutteridge, J.S., Hughson, A.G., Macnamara, P. and Todd, A.C.E. (1979) 'The proposed National Pig Carcase Measurement and Information Service'. *Australian Pig Manual*. Australian Pig Industry Research Committee, 47-53.

390. Wilson, B.R. and Campbell, D.A. (1972) 'Feasibility of implementing a national pig carcase grading system in Australia'. *Study Group Report*. Australian Pig Industry Research Committee.

391. Wolf, B.T. and Smith, C. (1979) 'Heritability of liveweight growth and carcase composition in crossbred meat lambs'. *Brit. Soc. Anim. Prod.* Winter Meeting.

392. Wolf, B.T., Smith, C., King, J.W.B. and Nicholson, D. (1981) 'Genetic parameters of growth and carcase composition in crossbred lambs'. *Anim. Prod.* **32**, 1-7.

393. Wolf, B.T., Smith, C. and Sales, D.I. (1980) 'Growth and carcase composition in the crossbred progeny of six terminal sire breeds of sheep'. *Anim. Prod.* **31**, 307-13.

394. Wood, P.D.P. (1975) *Considerations for the design and interpretation of cattle experiments*. Proceedings of a Symposium on cattle experimentation. British Society of Animal Production.

395. Woods, M.O. (1981) 'Some studies of the transmission of ultrasound in mammalian tissues and the measurement of fatness in farm livestock'. Ph.D. thesis, University of Bristol.

396. Wright, M.A. (1978) 'R.T.A. of mutton carcase grade/weight data. A 'hands free' data capture concept'. *Automation and Control*. 78/5.

397. Yeates, N.T.M. (1952) 'The quantitative definition of cattle carcases'. *Aust. J. Agric. Res.* **3**, 68-94.

398. Yeates, N.T.M. (1960) 'Suggestions for a quantitative approach to commercial beef carcase grading'. *Proc. Aust. Soc. Anim. Prod.* **3**, 126-9.

399. Yeates, N.T.M. (1962) 'Grading and branding of beef'. *Meat Industry Bulletin*. October.

400. Zert, P. (1970) *Le porc d'abbattage. Appréciation classement*. Institut Technique du Porc, Paris.

Index

Accuracy of grading 172, 189
Accuracy of visual assessments of carcase
    fatness 79
  on beef carcases 96-103
  on sheep carcases 103-104
Age
  break joint in lamb carcases (U.S.A.) 154
  cartilage and bone indicators 18-19
  comparisons at same 33, 230, 241-2
  distinction between lambs and hoggets
    (G.B.) 159
  ossification in beef grading (West
    Germany) 186-8
  pelvic fusion in lamb carcases 150
  teeth indicators 21-3, 179, 181
  variation in cattle (G.B.) 192-3
Anal fold assessment 66
Argentina
  beef carcase grading 179-80
Australia
  beef carcase grading and classification
    175-7
  pig carcase grading 131-2
  sheep carcase grading and classification
    151-2
Authentication of carcase weights 198-9
Automation of measurements at abattoirs
  Australia 152, 177
  Denmark 139
  Great Britian 94-5, 144
  New Zealand 150

Back-fat thickness
  adjustment of measurements by eye
    judgments 125, 128
  carcase measurements 83, 91-5, 96-100,
    103-104
  measurement by probing (carcase) 82-3,
    91-5, 98, 104
  measurement by probing (live animals)
    74-5
  measurement by ultrasonics 66-74, 85
  stability of regressions involving 247-55,
    266-70
  use in grading and classification 5-6,

    124-202
  use in pig testing 219, 223-7
Base-line techniques
  alternative definitions, detail 26-9
  distinction from predicting measure-
    ments 26
  standardisation 29-30, 271-3
Beef carcase grading and classification
    163-202
Beef quality
  role in beef carcase grading (U.S.A.)
    164-72
  role in grading and classification 116
Beef traits, relative importance 207-209
'Bias' 51-4
  avoidance of 256-9
  definition of 246
  effect on estimates of breed value 6,
    266-70
  evidence for 247-55
  explanation of 266-70
  historical recognition of 6
  importance in E.E.C. pig carcase grading
    6, 144-5
Boars 219, 239
Body dimensions 62-3, 230
Bone
  anatomy, position of animal and carcase
    12-13
  distribution 37-40
  species differences 13
Brazil
  beef carcase grading 180
Break joint, as index of age 154
Breed, as indicator of carcase composition
  beef 109
  sheep 110-12
Breed comparisons
  biased estimates 247-55
  choice of method, end point 240-43
  E.A.A.P. recommendations for cattle 240
  explanation of bias 266-70
  need for comparative research 271
Breed differences
  adjustment to equal fatness 34

Clay Center data on beef breeds 34-6
in beef grading (U.S.A.) 162-4
in fat distribution 40-43
in growth and development 33-6
in lamb grading (N.Z.) 147
in muscle distribution 37-9, 90
in muscle to bone ratio 33-5
in saleable meat and lean % 88-90
Breed substitution 206
Breeding companies (pigs)
comparisons between 217, 226-7, 250-51
explanation of 'bias' between 266-70
export of blockier types 221
indicator of carcase composition 108
influence 206-207, 226
limited attention to carcase and meat
traits 218
Breeding programmes 206
Butterfield school
explanation of fat distribution differences 44
historical importance 4-5
influence on beef classification 176-7
results on muscle distribution 37, 90

Canada
beef carcase grading 172-5
pig carcase grading 128-31
pig testing methods 227
Canonical variates, breeding company
differences explained 269-71
Carcase composition
average values 18
weights v. percentages 29
Carcase dimensions 81-2
accuracy on beef carcases 96-103
accuracy on pig carcases 95-6
accuracy on sheep carcases 103-104
Carcase evaluation
choice of techniques 45-6
costs 59, 239
diversity of applications xi
need for common approach 272-3
strategy 265-73
Carcase length
in Australian beef carcase grading 175-6
in Australian sheep carcase classification
151
in British pig carcase grading 141
in Danish pig carcase grading 139
safeguard against variability 221
value as predictor 81-2
Carcase measurements 80-85
relative accuracy 91-104
Carcase weight
authentication (G.B.) 198-9
benefits of heavier weights 8
effect on joint size 8
fat trimming (émoussage) 24, 122
hot v. cold 24, 122

increase in improved pigs 131, 219
index of carcase composition 81
in grading schemes 119, 122, 129
in sheep carcase grading (N.Z.) 147-50
prediction of lamb carcase weights 61-2
standardisation 23-5
variations in pig carcases (G.B.) 8, 141
Charcutier, role in France 136
Charles method, beef carcase classification
176-7
Chemical analysis, whole carcase 28-9
Chemical composition 11-12
Classification, carcase (see also Grading and
Classification, and Operation)
alternative meanings 121
choice of elements in 193
defining grades by 178
distinction from grading 120
remit of M.L.C. 193
written definitions for 121
Colour, as index of P.S.E./D.F.D. 221
Combined testing (M.L.C. pig scheme)
218-21, 226-7
Compensation in grading 118-19, 164-8
Commercial cutting methods, see Saleable
Meat Yield
Conformation (or shape)
accuracy on beef carcases 108-110
accuracy on pig carcases 107-108
accuracy on sheep carcases 110-112
blockier pigs, advantage 221
conflict between traders and scientists
105
control of fatness in studies of 106-107
E.A.A.P. definitions 182
effect of carcase hanging method 13, 158
failure to identify breed differences
267-70
in Brazilian beef carcase grading 180
in British beef carcase classification 195
in British pig carcase grading 144
in British sheep carcase classification
159-62
in Canadian beef carcase grading 173-5
in E.E.C. beef carcase classification
199-202
in E.E.C. pig carcase grading 144
in French beef grading and classification
184-6
in French pig carcase grading and classification 136-7
in French sheep carcase classification
155-8
in German beef carcase grading 186-8
in German pig carcase grading 132-6
in German sheep carcase grading 155
in Irish beef classification 189-90
in New Zealand sheep carcase grading
147-9
in Rhodesian beef carcase grading 178-81

in South African beef carcase grading
   177-80
in U.S. beef carcase grading 165-8
in U.S. sheep carcase grading 154
indicator of carcase composition 105-12
in selecting live sheep 237-8
objective measurements of 106-107
relation to trade valuations 271
Constant time or feed tests 241-2
Consumer attitudes to beef grades (U.S.)
   164-72
'Continental' breeds
   superior conformation (beef) 33, 35-6,
      110
   superior conformation (pigs) 207, 133-6,
      144-5, 221-3, 247-8
   superior conformation (sheep) 158, 254-5
Correlation coefficient 48-51
   partial 54
Cost of carcase evaluation 59
   alternative predictors 102-103
   relative to production costs 239-40
Cost-benefit grading and classification 123
Cow beef
   relative importance (G.B.) 191-2
   relative value (France) 186
Cross-sectional areas of muscle 84
   accuracy on beef carcases 96-103
   accuracy on pig carcases 95-6
   accuracy on sheep carcases 103-104

Data banks, value of xii, 240, 273
'Days on feed' as a factor in grading 171-2
Demerits
   role in Canadian pig carcase grading
      129-30
Denmark
   beef carcase grading 190
   bull testing methods 230-33
   link between selection and grading 6
   pig carcase grading 138-41
   pig testing methods 225
Density (or specific gravity) of carcases 85-6
   accuracy in beef carcases 96-103
   accuracy on sheep carcases 103-104
Dilution techniques 75
Directional definitions 18, 22
Dissection
   base-line technique 26-30
   facilities 240
   residue or waste 18
   results for average carcases 20
   standardisation 29, 240
Distribution of fat (fat partition)
   breed differences 40-43
   cause of prediction 'bias' 252-3, 266-71
   importance in carcase evaluation 43-4
   importance in explaining differences
      between pig breeding companies
      266-71

importance in trade 9, 11
in British beef carcase classification 194
in E.E.C. beef carcase classification 202
selection for 215-16
sex differences 40
Distribution of muscle
   breed differences 37-40
   Butterfield school 4, 37, 90, 176-7
   dissection v. commerical cutting 89-90
   effect on economic evaluations 261
   importance of muscle thickness 11
   relative size of muscles 15-17
   relative values 9, 129
   selection for 214-15
   sex differences 39-40

E.A.A.P. recommendations/surveys
   definition of conformation etc. 105-106
   for beef breed comparisons 240
   for beef carcase descriptions 79,
      105-106, 182-4
   for beef carcase separation procedures
      28
   for bull performance testing 229-33
   for live cattle measurements 230
   for pig testing and carcase evaluation 30,
      224
   potential of carcase system for use by
      E.E.C. 183-4
Economic appraisal of variations 259-61
E.E.C.
   beef carcase classification 118, 182-4,
      199-202
   comparison of beef carcase evaluation
      techniques 27 30
   comparison of pig carcase evaluation and
      grading techniques 6, 30, 247-52
   pig carcase grading 118, 132-6, 137,
      144-5
Efficiency
   as index of composition 44-5
   in relation to size 212-13
E.M.M.E.
   use for carcase assessment 85
   use for live animal assessment 76
Émoussage 24, 122
End point choice
   in experiments and breed comparisons
      33, 240-43
   in progeny and performance tests 212,
      230-32
Equipment for carcase assessment
   comparisons 50, 273
   E.M.M.E. 85
   probes 82, 93-5
   ultrasonics 85
Equipment for live animal assessment
   E.M.M.E. 76
   K^{40} 76
   N.M.R. 77

tomography 77
ultrasonics 66-70
X-rays 77
Experiments
carcase evaluation in 239-61
design 240
economic appraisal 259-61
numbers required 244, 246
planning carcase evaluation requirements 239-44
presentation of results 259-61, 265
use of subsampling with regression 256-9
Exports, role of grading and classification 115, 116, 138, 146-7, 151, 175, 177, 188-9

F.A.O./W.H.O. international classification system 181
Fat, depots and definitions 17
Fat areas 84-5
'Fat-corrected' conformation
beef carcases 109-110
pig carcases 107-108
sheep carcases 110-112
Fat quality 11-12
Fat thickness measurements on quartered carcases 83-4
accuracy on beef carcases 96-103
accuracy on pig carcases 95-6
accuracy on sheep carcases 103-104
Fat thickness measurements by probe 82-3
accuracy on beef carcases 98-103
accuracy on pig carcases 91-3
accuracy on sheep carcases 104
comparison of probes 93-5
Fatness
comparisons at same 33, 240-43
effect on beef quality 9, 164-72, 194
waste 9
'Fleshiness' 105-106, 182-4
Fleshing index, use in grading
beef carcases 175-81
sheep carcases 151
France
beef carcase grading and classification 184-6
pig carcase grading 136-7
sheep carcase grading 155-8

GR measurement 104, 150
Grading (see also Operation)
'days on feed' as factor in 171-2
defects of grading systems 118
defined by classifications 178
distinction from classification 120
variability within grades 118
variations in British trade requirements 197
Grading and classification (general) (see also Operation and Classification)

controversy in Great Britain 192-3
cost-benefit calculations 123
importance in experiments 244
link with experimental data 272
opposition from meat trade 117-18, 127, 162, 197
Great Britain
beef carcase classification 191-9
bull testing methods 230-33
pig carcase grading and classification 141-4
pig testing methods 226-7
sheep carcase classification 158-62
Grids, fatness and conformation combinations 107, 133, 136, 144-5, 162, 186, 195, 202
Growth and development
as index of carcase composition 6, 44-5, 60-61
influence of nutrition on composition 36-7
key importance in prediction 7, 266
mature weight, rate of maturity 31-5
relative tissue development 31-4

Halothane gene 108, 222-4
Hammond school xiii, 4-5, 81, 92
Handling livestock to assess fatness
beef cattle 65-6
sheep 64-5
Holsteins, inferior conformation 110, 174, 192, 195, 206, 233, 272
Hot-boning 172
Hot v. cold carcase weight 24, 122

Index method of pig carcase grading 128-31
Interactions (treatment with end point) 243
Intervention buying (E.E.C.) 118, 199
Ireland
beef carcase grading and classification 188-90

K^{40} 76
Killing-out percentage 23-6, 182
KKCF weight as index of carcase composition 83
accuracy on beef carcases 96-103
accuracy on sheep carcases 103-104
in British beef carcase classification 193-6
in British sheep carcase classification 159
in U.S.A. beef carcase grading 164-9
in U.S.A. sheep carcase grading 153-4

Lean body mass 17
Lean (muscle) to bone ratio
beef breed differences 33-5
increasing importance with pigs 219
relation to conformation differences between breeds 268-70

selection for 214-15
Lean (muscle) to fat ratio
    minimum fatness requirements in pig
        carcases 219
    selection for 212-14, 219
Leanness, relation to efficiency and trade
    importance 9
Live animal evaluation 60-78
    value in experiments 240, 244-5
Live cattle grading, relation to carcase
    E.E.C. study 182
    France 184
    U.S.A. 165-6
Live weight
    as index of composition 60-62
    comparisons at same 33, 230, 241-2
    composition of non-carcase part 25
    standardisation 23-4

Marbling
    as predictor of composition 169
    importance in U.S. beef carcase grading
        164-72
Market requirements, influence on selection
    209
Market support schemes, role of grading in
    117, 118, 142-3, 197, 199
Marketing of livestock and meat, role of
    grading and classification 115-23
    beef carcases 164-72, 172-5, 184, 196-9
    pig carcases 124-7, 131, 132, 137-8,
        138-9, 141-4
    sheep carcases 146-50, 151, 154, 158-62
Maturity, mature size 31-45, 238, 241-2
Meat quality
    correlated response to selection 216-17
    importance in grading 115-19, 124, 145
    in relation to intramuscular fat 216
    in U.S. beef carcase grading 164-72
    in U.S. sheep carcase grading 153
    role in experiments 244
Model pig 272
Moiré measurements 63
Muscle, muscles; definition, anatomy,
    location 15-17
Muscle thickness measurements (see also
    cross-sectional areas) 83-4, 95, 139-40
Muscularity (or muscling)
    definitions 105-106, 182-4
    difficulties of assessment in live animal
        214, 229-30
    in U.S. pig carcase grading 125
    relation to P.S.E./D.F.D. in pig carcases
        222
    selection for, in dairy heifers 234

National Pig Carcase Measurement and
        Information Service (Australia) 132
Netherlands
    beef carcase classification 190

pig carcase grading 137-8
    pig testing methods 227
New Zealand
    beef carcase grading 177-8
    sheep carcase grading 146-50
N.M.R. imaging 77
Nutrition, effect on composition 36-7

O.E.C.D., international classification system
    181
Operation of grading and classification
        schemes
    accuracy of Irish beef carcase grading
        189-90
    accuracy of U.S. beef carcase grading
        172
    independent application 136, 143, 198
    lack of supervision (Australia) 151
    standardisation of British beef carcase
        classification 196
    standardisation of E.E.C. beef carcase
        classification 202
    supervisory graders (New Zealand) 146
Ossification, as index of age 18-19, 186-8

Pelvic fusion, as index of age 150
Pelvic hanging 13
Percentage of variation explained 48-51
Performance testing
    alternative methods 230-33
    recommendations for bull tests 229-30
    use with sheep 235-8
pH, as index of P.S.E./D.F.D. 221
Photographic reference scales
    for conformation 106, 182, 185, 189,
        202
    for fatness 79-80, 182, 189, 202
Physiological predictors 77-8, 271
Pig carcase grading and classification 107,
    124-45
Pig meat quality 221-3, 225
Population studies and experiments 239-61
Prediction
    choice of predictors for experiments
        246-61, 266
    of carcase composition of live animals
        60-78
    precision in relation to cost 102-103
    precision of carcase measurements
        91-104
    statistical methods 47-55
Price differentials
    between New Zealand lamb carcase
        grades 148
    between Rhodesian beef carcase grades
        178-81
    fixed 137
    payment according to index 128-31
    payment by increments of lean content
        140

relation to Irish beef classifications 190
Price – reporting, role of grading and
        classification in market 116, 118,
        132, 136, 144, 148, 155, 163-4, 177,
        199
Probes, for measuring carcase fatness
    accuracy on beef carcases 98-100
    accuracy on pig carcases 93-5
    accuracy on sheep carcases 104
    alternative positions 141-3
    in Australian beef carcase classification
        177
    in Australian lamb carcase classification
        151
    in British pig carcase grading 141-4
    in Danish pig carcase grading 139-41
    in New Zealand lamb carcase grading
        150
Producer reports of carcase quality 175
Profile areas 63
Profiles, muscular 185, 199-200
Progeny testing
    beef 232-4
    pigs 223-8
    sheep 235-8
Promotion, role of grading and classification
        115
P.S.E. and D.F.D. (pigs) 221-3

Regression
    bias 51-4
    comparison of regressions 51-4
    curvilinear 56
    linear 47-54
    multiple 54-6
    variation between groups 246-59
Relative growth rate, selection for 213-14
Residual standard deviation 49-51

Saleable meat yield (and Commerical
        cutting methods)
    adjustment to equal fatness 88-90
    composition 18, 45-6
    definition 18
    prediction in British beef carcase classifi-
        cation 196
    prediction in U.S. beef carcase grading
        166-9
    prediction in U.S. sheep carcase grading
        153-4
    relation to dissection 19, 87-90
    weighting with joint values 261
Sample joint dissection 86-7
    accuracy on beef carcases 96-103
    accuracy on pig carcases 95-6
    accuracy on sheep carcases 103-104
    combination with joint weight 100-102
    combination with measurements 96-7
    prediction bias, beef 252-4
    prediction bias, pigs 251-2

prediction bias, sheep 254-5
    use in British pig testing 226-7
    use in subsampling with regression 256-9
Scoring scales for visual assessment
    conformation 105-106
    fatness 79-80
Selection
    choice of feeding system for tests 220,
        232
    choice of traits, beef cattle 229-34
    choice of traits, pigs 221-8
    choice of traits, sheep 235-8
    correlated responses to 211-12
    effects on meat quality 216-17
    for beef traits in dairy cattle 233-4
    for efficiency of lean meat production
        220
    for growth rate, effect on size 45, 237-8
    heritabilities of beef traits 233
    heritabilities of sheep traits 237-8
    indices 211, 226
    monitoring change 216-17
    objectives 205-210
    principles 210-212
    relation to optimum production environ-
        ment 220
    response to 210-212, 219
    role of control herds 217, 219
Serial slaughter 240-43
Sex differences
    distribution of fat 40
    distribution of muscle 39-40
    growth 33
    muscle to bone ratio 35
Shape – historical importance 4
Sheep carcase grading and classification
        146-62
Show ring influences 205-206
South African, beef carcase grading and
        classification 177-80
Stability on prediction equations
    beef cattle 252-4
    explanation of breed differences 266-71
    pigs 247-52
    sheep 254-5
Standardisation
    base-line techniques 29-30, 271-3
    disadvantages 273
Stereophotogrammetry 63
Stress 221-2
Subsampling with regression 245, 247-59
Sweden
    beef carcase grading 190-91
    sheep carcase classification 158

'Target' carcase concept 198
Teeth development, as index of age 21-3,
        179, 181
Testing methods, *see* Performance, Progeny
        and Combined testing

Texture of meat, variations 11
Tomography 77
Traits
    choice in experiments 240, 243-4, 265
    difficulties of improvement of carcase
        209-210
    importance of defining overall optimum
        efficiency 239
    used in British beef testing 230-33
    used in British pig testing 226
    used in Danish beef testing 230-33
    used in Danish pig testing 225
    used in sheep testing 235-8
Trimming percentage (pig carcases) 218

Ultrasonic measurements
    carcase 85
    live animals 66-74
    role in slaughtering at equal fatness
        241-2
    use in beef performance testing 229-33
    use in British pig testing 226
    use in Canadian pig testing 227
    use in Danish beef performance testing
        230
    use in Danish pig testing 225
    use in pig performance testing 224
    use in selection 214
    use in sheep performance testing 236-8
United States
    beef carcase grading 164-72
    historical approach to carcase evaluation
        6
    pig carcase grading 124-7
    pig testing methods 227-8
    sheep carcase grading 152-4

Valuation of carcases from retail cuts 261
Velocity of ultrasound 74
Vertebrae and ribs 13-15
Video scanning of carcases 95
Visual assessment
    carcase fatness 79-80
    conformation 105-107

live animals 63-6
E.A.A.P. scales 79, 105-106, 182
in relation to objective definitions 194
use in British beef carcase classification
    193-4
use in British sheep carcase classification
    159-62
use in E.E.C. beef carcase classification
    199-202

Water-holding capacity 12, 221
West Germany
    beef carcase grading 186-8
    pig carcase grading 132-6
    sheep carcase grading 154-5
Wiltshire bacon
    development of British pig industry 141
    development of Danish pig industry
        138-9
    historical influence 5
    need for uniformity 138
Written definitions of classes 121
    use in E.E.C. beef carcase classification
        199-202
    use in French beef carcase classification
        185
    use in French sheep carcase grading
        155-8

X-rays 77

Yeates' approach to beef carcase grading
    175-6
Yield grading 119
    beef carcases 97, 164, 166-72, 173-5,
        176, 188-9
    pig carcases 124-7, 128-31, 133-7,
        139-41
    sheep carcases 153-4, 155

Zimbabwe
    beef carcase grading and classification
        178-81